3rd International Symposium on Transportation Studies for Developing Countries

IOP Conference Series: Earth and Environmental Science
Volume 1000

Depok and South Tanerang
4 - 6 November 2021

ISBN: 978-1-7138-5443-2
ISSN: 1755-1307

Printed from e-media with permission by:

Curran Associates, Inc.
57 Morehouse Lane
Red Hook, NY 12571

Some format issues inherent in the e-media version may also appear in this print version.

Additional copies of this publication are available from:

Curran Associates, Inc.
57 Morehouse Lane
Red Hook, NY 12571 USA
Phone: 845-758-0400
Fax: 845-758-2633
Email: curran@proceedings.com
Web: www.proceedings.com

TABLE OF CONTENTS

IOP Conf. Series: Earth and Environmental Science 1000 (2022) 011001 doi:10.1088/1755-1315/1000/1/011001

PREFACE

The 3rd International Symposium on Transport Studies in Developing Countries (ISTSDC) is a biannual international symposium hosted by Universitas Indonesia and Universitas Pembangunan Jaya. This year's edition was held on 5 November 2021 and raised "The Role of Transportation in Civilization and Sustainable Environment" as the theme. Due to unforeseen circumstances, the 3rd ISTSDC was held through a virtual meeting considering the COVID 19 pandemic. Additionally, the 1st and 2nd ISTSDC symposiums were held at Makassar and Kendari.

The 3rd ISTDC aims to outline the development of transport science in developing countries through various topics such as Intelligent Transport System, Land use and Transport Interaction (LUTI), sustainable transport, traffic safety and engineering, public transport, pavement design, and highway engineering. Furthermore, ISTSDC also aims to be the media for research, practice, industry, and government to discuss and share breakthrough ideas to solve the transport-related problem in developing countries.

This year, the ISTSDC organizing committee invited three Keynote Speakers, namely Prof. Ronghui Liu from the University of Leeds, Prof. Hanaoka Shinya from Tokyo Institute of Technology, and Prof. Sutanto Soehodho from Universitas Indonesia, to share their knowledge and experience about the current issues related with the transportation system in the world. The international symposium, attended by numerous speakers, successfully provided ideas about the world of transportation and various disciplines related to it. The selected papers are published in this volume of the IOP Conference Series: Earth and Environment Science.

As the closing statement, we want to deliver our gratitude to all sponsors who supported this event, including Universitas Indonesia, Pembangunan Jaya University, Bentley Systems, Inc., PT. Jasamarga, Tbk., and PT. Kereta Cepat Indonesia-China (High-Speed Railway Consortium). To all the speakers and participants who contributed to the discussions, it was our pleasure to hold a symposium with exceptional papers despite being presented through the online meeting. Finally, we would like to appreciate our local organizing committee, who made this symposium possible, including the FSTPT Scientific Committee, who supported the review process to ensure the scientific quality of the selected manuscript.

Looking forward to seeing you again at the 4th ISTSDC, hopefully, we can meet in person in the future very soon!

Ir. Tri Tjahjono, M.Sc., Ph.D.
(Chief of Symposium Local Committee)

IOP Conf. Series: Earth and Environmental Science 1000 (2022) 011002 doi:10.1088/1755-1315/1000/1/011002

Peer Review Declaration Form Guidance

On the following page you will find the declaration form.

- Please answer each question.
- You should submit the form along with the rest of your submission files.
- The deadline is the submission date written in your publishing agreement.

All conference organisers/editors are required to declare details about their peer review.

We will publish the information you provide as part of your proceedings.

IOP Conf. Series: Earth and Environmental Science 1000 (2022) 011002 doi:10.1088/1755-1315/1000/1/011002

Peer review declaration

All papers published in this volume of IOP Conference Series: Earth and Environmental Science have been peer reviewed through processes administered by the Editors. Reviews were conducted by expert referees to the professional and scientific standards expected of a proceedings journal published by IOP Publishing.

- Type of peer review: **~~Single-blind~~ / Double-blind / ~~Triple-blind / Open / Other~~**
- Conference submission management system: **https://smc2021.fstpt.info/login**

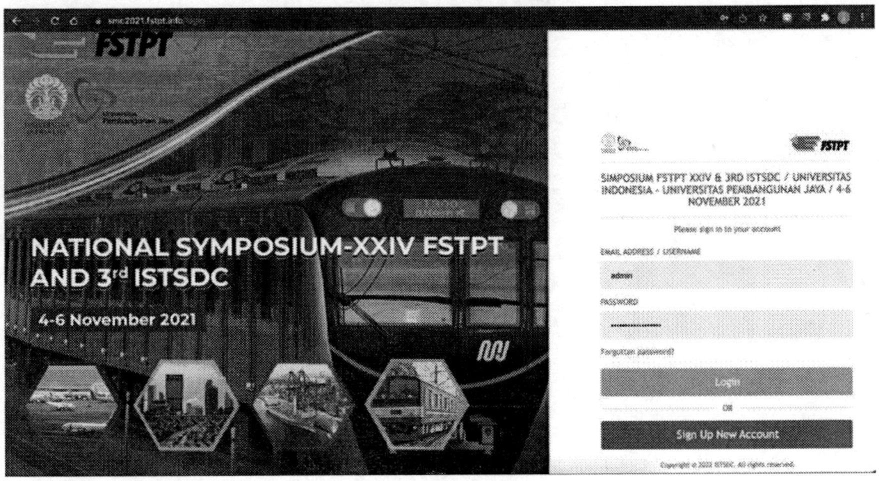

- Number of submissions received: **44 papers**
- Number of submissions sent for review: **44 papers**
- Number of submissions accepted: **32 papers**
- Acceptance Rate: **93% (for National and International Symposium), 73% (for International Symposium only).**
- Average number of reviews per paper: **two reviewers.**
- Total number of reviewers involved: **40**
- Any additional info on review process: **plagiarism checking with Turnitin**
- Contact person for queries:
  Name: ***Bagus Hario Setiadji, Ph.D.***
  Affiliation: ***Department of Civil Engineering, Diponegoro University, Indonesia***
  Email: ***bhsetiadji@ft.undip.ac.id***

IOP Conf. Series: Earth and Environmental Science 1000 (2022) 012001 doi:10.1088/1755-1315/1000/1/012001

Analysis of Exit Taxiway in the Northern Terminal of Jenderal Ahmad Yani International Airport Semarang

Ithmaanna S, Murwono D, Sartono W, and Muthohar I.

Gadjah Mada University, Depart. of Civil and Environmental Engineering, Yogyakarta, Indonesia

Corresponding author: shoffarisna@mail.ugm.ac.id

Abstract. The development of Jenderal Ahmad Yani International Airport is performed on the north side of the airport. From that, a new taxiway will be available to support the flight activities. This study aims to analyze the geometry of the exit taxiway on the north side of the airport following the requirement issued by ICAO and FAA. The analysis was based on the type of aircraft mainly operated at Jenderal Ahmad Yani International Airport. The geometry analysis was performed on ICAO Three Segment Method and Landing Length Requirement. The location of the existing exit taxiway has not obtained an excellent functional percentage. Seventy-seven point seven percent (77.7%) of the planes are required to turn around before entering the apron. Therefore, changing the location and type of exit taxiway is recommended to maximize the runway's performance in supporting the aircraft's operational activities.

1. Introduction

Transportation has become one of the most crucial aspects of city life. The national development relies on transportation, from strengthening the economy to uniting the nation. Hence, transportation has a significant and strategic position in the development of the nation. Through the Ministry of Transportation, the government is trying to develop the infrastructure and facilitate mobility in Indonesia. In line with that, the President of the Republic of Indonesia has issued Presidential Regulation Number 56 of 2018 on Acceleration of National Strategic Projects Implementation. One of the national strategic projects is the development of Jenderal Ahmad Yani International Airport.

The number of aircraft passengers is predicted to grow with the increase of low-cost carriers operating in Indonesia. The growth does not only occur in the movement of passengers, but also in the sector of goods and services. It is reinforced by the number of passengers using Jenderal Ahmad Yani international airport in 2017 with 4.4 million passengers and 17,630 tons cargo movement per year. The growth increased by 9.35 percent from 2011 until 2017. The data compiled from the Central Bureau of Statistics of Central Java stated that Jenderal Ahmad Yani International Airport had 22,800 flights in 2011, which increased to 38,600 flights in 2017. Meanwhile, the old terminal of Jenderal Ahmad Yani International Airport can only accommodate 800,000 passengers per year.

The old terminal of Jendral Ahmad Yani Airport is deemed unable to meet the needs of the aircraft transportation flow that increases every year. The lack of the passenger capacity available at the terminal can reduce safety, comfort, security, and service at the airport. It can also increase the potential for flight delays. The new Jenderal Ahmad Yani International Airport located on the north side of the runway is one of the government's efforts in solving these problems. The construction of the new terminal is intended to increase the passenger capacity by nine times with 6.5 million passengers per year as well as the ability of the aircraft movement.

Meanwhile, the apron constructed is as wide as 72,522 m^2, more expansive than the existing airport with 29,032 m^2 wide. It can accommodate 13 narrow-body planes or a configuration of 10 narrow-body aircrafts and two wide-body cargo planes. The parking lot in the new terminal is almost four times wider than the previous, which is 43,633 m^2, and can accommodate 1,200 cars.

With this planning, Jenderal Ahmad Yani International Airport is expected to meet the needs of aircraft transportation in the future. Meanwhile, several researches have been conducted to examine airport airside geometry [1-5]. Therefore, this study aims to analyze the exit taxiway of the northern terminal of Jenderal Ahmad Yani International Airport, precisely to determine the geometry of the exit taxiway for the type of aircraft served and to assess the effectiveness of the performance of the existing exit taxiway. The differences between prior studies and this investigation lie in the review, data, and aircraft type used in the analysis. This exit taxiway research needs to be explored for various cases in Indonesia to support the optimization of runway performance in airport development activities.

2. Theoretical background

2.1. Aircraft weight components

Several types of aircraft weight related to aircraft operations are as follows [6].

1. The operating weight empty or OWE is the aircraft's baseload, including crew and all equipment required for flight, excluding cargo and fuel.
2. Cargo (load) is the total revenues including the weight of passengers and baggage, mail, express, and cargo.
3. The zero-fuel weight or ZFW is the aircraft's empty operating weight (OWE) plus payload.
4. The maximum taxi weight or MTW is the maximum load to perform a movement or walk from the aircraft park to the base of the runway.
5. The maximum gross take-off weight is the maximum load allowed to take-off.
6. The maximum structural take-off weight or MSTOW is the maximum gross take-off weight for aircraft operating at sea level at 59° F (15° C).
7. The maximum structural landing weight or MLW is the structural capability of the aircraft or the maximum load when the aircraft wheels touch the hard layer (landing).

2.2. Airport classification

2.2.1. Classification of airports according to ICAO (International Civil Aviation Organization)

Classification of airports according to ICAO can be seen in Table 1. ICAO uses two elements of the Airport Reference Code called The Aerodrome Design Code.

Table 1. ICAO aerodrome reference code [7]

Code Number	Aeroplane reference field length (ARFL)	Code Letter	Wingspan	Outer Main Gear Wheel Span
1	<800 m	A	< 15 m	< 4.5 m
2	800 m - > 1200 m	B	15m - < 24 m	4,5m - < 6m
3	1200 m - <1800 m	C	24 m - < 36 m	6 m - < 9 m
4	>= 1800 m	D	36 m - < 52 m	9 m - < 14 m
		E	52 m - < 65 m	9 m - < 14 m
		F	65 m - < 80 m	14 m < 16 m

2.2.2. Classification of airports according to FAA (Federal Aviation Administration)

In determining the Airport Reference Code, FAA made a classification based on three categories as follows.

1. Categories by Aircraft Approach Category are based on aircraft speed when landing.

Table 2. Aircraft approach category [8]

Category	Approach Speed (Knot)
A	<91
B	91-120
C	121-140
D	140-166
E	>166

2. Categories by Airplane Design Group are based on the tail height and wingspan of the aircraft.

Table 3. Airplane design group [8]

Group Number	Tail Height	Wingspan
I	< 6m	< 15 m
II	6 m - < 9 m	15m - < 24 m
III	9 m - < 13,5 m	24 m - < 36 m
IV	13,5 m - < 18,5 m	36 m - < 52 m
V	18,5 m - < 20 m	52 m - < 65 m
VI	20 m - < 24.5 m	65 m - < 80 m

3. Categories by Taxiway Design Group are based on the aircraft wheelbase with the distance of the cockpit to the aircraft wheels.

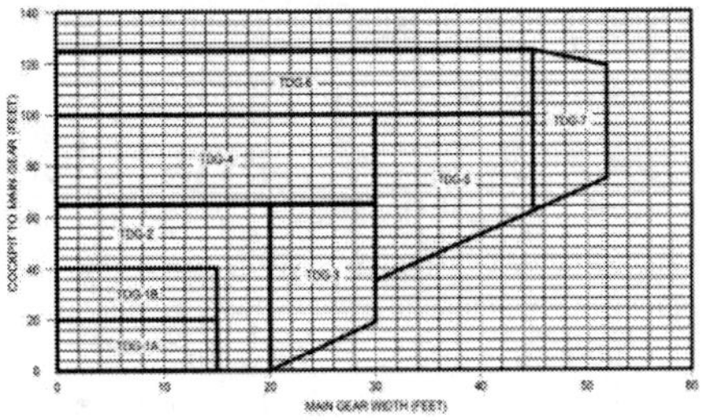

Figure 1. Taxiway design group (TDGs) [8]

2.3. Exit taxiway geometry

2.3.1. Exit taxiway geometry according to ICAO (International Civil Aviation Organization)
In determining the exit taxiway, ICAO developed the Three Segment Method considering each class of aircraft having its speed in passing the threshold to the intersection point of the runway and the exit taxiway. The segment is divided into flare segment, transition segment, and breaking segment. The division of these segments can be seen in Figure 2.

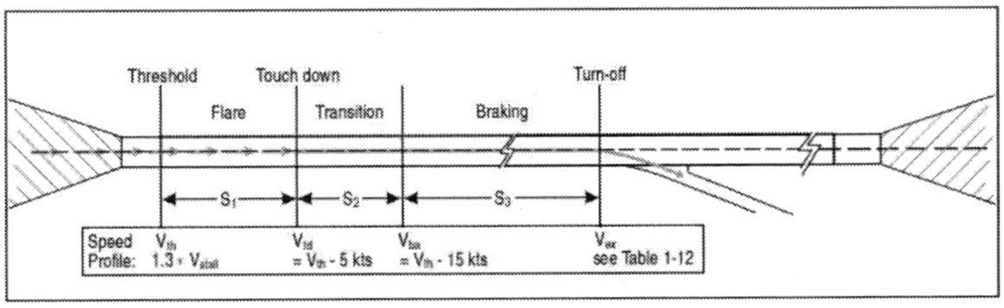

Figure 2. Three Segment Method [7]

1. Flare segment (S1) is a condition when the aircraft wheel touches the pavement surface. For aircraft categories A and B, S1 is 250 m. For aircraft categories C and B, S1 is 450 m.

2. The transition segment (S2) is a condition when the aircraft moves after touchdown while adjusting the speed and has not hit the brakes. The following equation calculates S2.

$$S2 = 5 \times (Vth-10)$$

With Vth = 0.95 x approach speed (knots).

3. Breaking segment (S3) is the segment when the aircraft starts the final braking. The following equation calculates S3.

$$S3 = \frac{(Vth-15)^2 - Vex}{8a}$$

With Vex is exit speed, and the value of the deceleration is 1.5 m/s^2.

For aircraft with codes 1 and 2, the Vex value is 15 knots. For aircraft with codes 3 and 4, the Vex value is 30 knots.

2.3.2. Exit taxiway geometry according to FAA (Federal Aviation Administration)
With the FAA method, the exit taxiway location is obtained by reading the graph between the Maximum Landing Weight and the runway length required for the aircraft to land. The graph is obtained from the Aircraft Characteristic Manual published by each aircraft manufacturer. There are two recommendations for exit taxiway locations for Boeing-type aircraft, including wet runway conditions and dry runway conditions, while for Airbus-type, there is only one recommendation. For other types of aircraft, the wet runway length is 115% of the dry runway length.

3. Method

There were several steps in conducting this study. Firstly, secondary data were retrieved from PT. Angkasa Pura 1 Jenderal Ahmad Yani Airport, such as the information on the location of Jenderal Ahmad Yani International Airport seen in Figure 3. Subsequently, the specifications of Jenderal Ahmad Yani International Airport are presented in Table 4. Secondly, analysis was carried out based on the obtained data covering airport layouts, aerodrome manuals, and aircraft movement using the ICAO Aerodrome Design Manual and FAA 150/5300-13. The exit taxiway was calculated using the ICAO Three Segment Method and the FAA Runway Landing Field Length method. With the ICAO method, the location of the rapid exit taxiway could be identified. With the FAA method, the exit taxiway location was obtained by reading the graph between the Maximum Landing Weight and the runway length required for the aircraft to land.

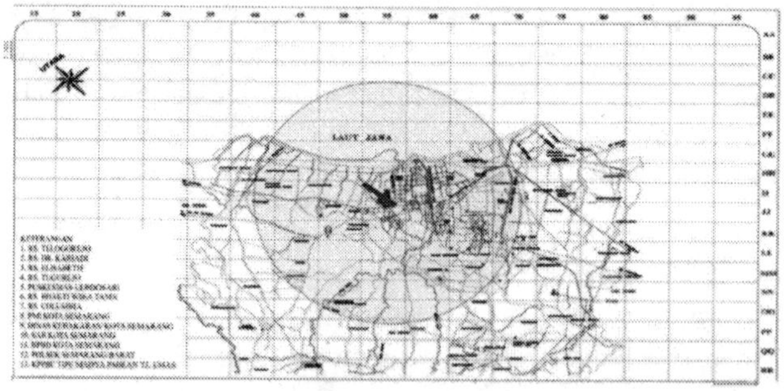

Figure 3. Jenderal Ahmad Yani International Airport network map up to a radius of 5 miles (±8 km) from the airport reference point [9]

Table 4. Jenderal Ahmad Yani International Airport Specifications [9]

No	Items	Description
1	Name	Jenderal Ahmad Yani International Airport
2	Location	Semarang City, Central Java Province
3	Coordinate	06°58′25″ S and 110°22′38″ E
4	Elevation	11 ft
5	Reference Temperature	33°C
6	Runway Dimension	2,560 x 45 m
7	Taxiway Dimension	TXW F: 261.5 x 23 m TXW G: 261.5 x 23 m

4. Analysis

4.1. Analysis of aircraft movements and determination of aircraft plans

The air traffic data of Jenderal Ahmad Yani International Airport for the last five years (2011-2017) were analyzed to determine the traffic frequency in each type of plane and the percentage of the movements at the location. The analysis of flight traffic of each plane type can be seen in Table 5. The exit taxiway site was examined in each kind of aircraft carrying out civil aviation activities at Jenderal Ahmad Yani International Airport. This analysis was performed to obtain an efficient exit taxiway location to reduce the time used by aircraft when landing on the runway (runway occupancy time). Each aircraft movement was analyzed for each runway direction, namely runway 13 and runway 31.

Table 5. The number of civil aviation movements in 2015-2020 [10-15]

No	Aircraft Type	Year						Total	Percentage (%)
		2015	2016	2017	2018	2019	2020		
1	A319	95	30	5	-	-	-	130	0.1
2	A320	1,787	3,135	3,699	5,793	5,490	2,406	22,310	22.2
3	AS330	-	11	10	-	-	-	21	0.0
4	AS36	-	-	-	-	-	8	8	0.0
5	AS56	-	-	-	5	-	-	5	0.0
6	ATR42	-	-	-	-	-	19	19	0.0
7	ATR72	3,138	3,754	3,436	4,550	3,967	2,019	20,864	20.7
8	B732	12	-	-	-	-	-	12	0.0
9	B733	233	296	401	612	641	349	2,532	2.5
10	B734	390	403	400	139	-	-	1,332	1.3
11	B735	1,326	1,078	1,277	1,699	998	107	6,485	6.4
12	B738	4,834	4,939	5,701	6,057	4,505	2,069	28,105	27.9
13	B739	2,716	2,378	2,204	2,169	1,684	1,176	12,327	12.3
14	CRJ1000	693	729	757	728	725	209	3,841	3.8
15	E135	-	-	15	6	-	5	26	0.0
16	E195	245	414	282	-	-	-	941	0.9
17	Other	384	350	318	255	193	164	1,664	1.6
			TOTAL					**100,622**	**100.0**

4.2. Exit taxiway analysis

The following is an analysis example for an A319 type aircraft.

4.2.1. ICAO method

Approach speed (V_{app}) = 130 knots
Threshold speed (V_{th}) = 0.95 x V_{app}
= 0.95 x 130 knots
= 123.5 knots
Exit speed (V_{ex}) = 30 knots (code number 4)

Average deceleration (a) = 1.5 m/s^2

Segment calculation:
S1 = 450 m (code letter C)
S2 = 5 x (V_{th} – 10)
= 5 x (130 – 10) = 568 m
S3 = ((V_{th} – 15)^2 - V_{ex}^2) / (8 x a)
= ((123.5 – 15)^2 – 30^2) / (8 x 1.5) = 906 m
S = $S_1 + S_2 + S_3$
= 450 + 568 + 906 m = 1,924 m

4.2.2. FAA method (runway landing field length)

Graphic readings for the A319 can be seen in Figure 4. The results of actual A319 runway length analysis can be seen in Table 6, while Table 7 shows the overall results of the analysis.

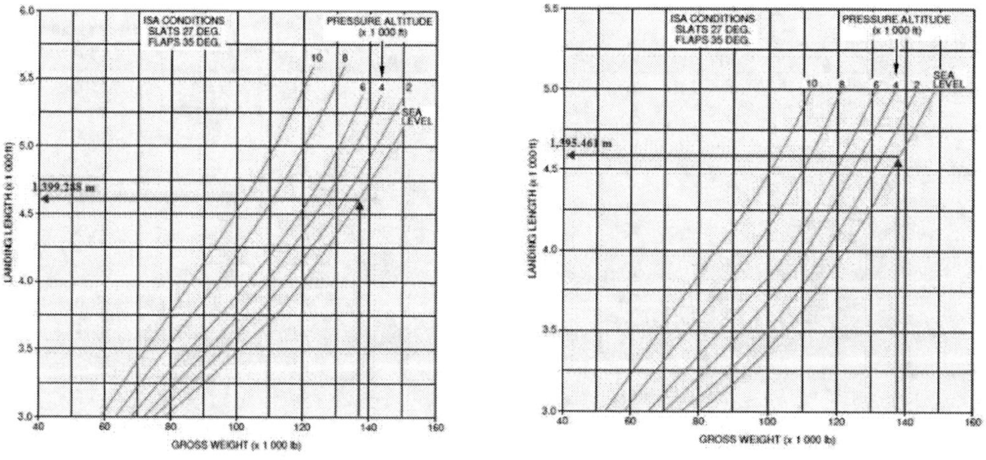

(a) **(b)**

Figure 4. Landing field length for aircraft A319 engine type CFM56-5A (a) and aircraft A319 engine type IAE-V2500 (b) [16]

Table 6. A319 landing runway length.

Engine Type	MLW (kg)	Basic Landing Field Length (m)	Runway Length Actual (m)
CFM56-5A	62,500	1,399.228	1,657
IAE V2500	62,500	1,395.461	1,653

IOP Conf. Series: Earth and Environmental Science 1000 (2022) 012001 doi:10.1088/1755-1315/1000/1/012001

Table 7. Exit taxiway calculation result

No	Aircraft Type	Engine Type	Flaps	ICAO Method (m)	FAA Method (m) Dry Runway	Wet Runway	Percentage (%)
1	A319	GE CFM56-5A	-	1,924	1,657		0.1
		IAE V2500	-		1,653		
2	A320	GE CFM56-5	-	2,058	1,795		22.2
		IAE V2500	-		1,767		
3	ATR72	PW100	-	1,592	1,083	1,245	20.7
4	B737-300	GE CFM56-3B2	15	2,035	1,674	1,907	2.5
			40		1,942	2,233	
5	B737-400	GE CFM56-3B1	15	2,127	2,200	2,515	1.3
			30		1,935	2,232	
			40		1,829	2,125	
6	B737-500	GE CFM56-3B1	15	1,880	1,849	2,098	6.4
			30		1,671	1,914	
			40		1,610	1,838	
7	B737-800	GE CFM56-7	30	2,198	2,087	2,408	28.0
8	B737-900ER	GE CFM56-7	30	2,174	2,025	2,319	12.3
9	CRJ1000	GE CF34-8C5A	30	1,816	2,055	2,362	3.8
10	E195	CF34-10E	30	2,035	1,509	1,735	1.0
11	A330-300	PW 4000	-	2,081	2,057		-
		RR TRENT 700	-		2,066		
		GE CF6-80E1	-		2,082		

The landing length requirement for each type of aircraft was analyzed to determine the functional percentage level of the existing exit taxiway. The landing length requirements of each aircraft were compared to the distance of the exit taxiway as seen from the landing direction of runway 13 and runway 31. The following is an example of a functional calculation of the exit taxiway from the landing direction of runway 13 in dry runway conditions.

From Figure 5, it was identified that the aircraft possible to use exit taxiway F is ATR72 with a traffic frequency of 20.7%. As for other types, they are required to turn around and use taxiway G. Thus, the functional percentage value of taxiway G for runway 13 in dry runway conditions is 0%. The amount of landing traffic required to make a turnaround is 77.6%. More detailed calculations are described below.

Functional percentage of TXW F dry runway = 20.7%
Planes which turn around = (0.1+22.2+2.5+1.3+6.4+28.0+12.3+3.8+1)% = 77.6%

Similarly, calculations were made for runway 31 on the dry runway and wet runway conditions. The results of the analysis can be seen in Table 8 and Table 9.

IOP Conf. Series: Earth and Environmental Science 1000 (2022) 012001 doi:10.1088/1755-1315/1000/1/012001

Figure 5. The existing location of the exit taxiway to runway 13 using the FAA (dry runway) method

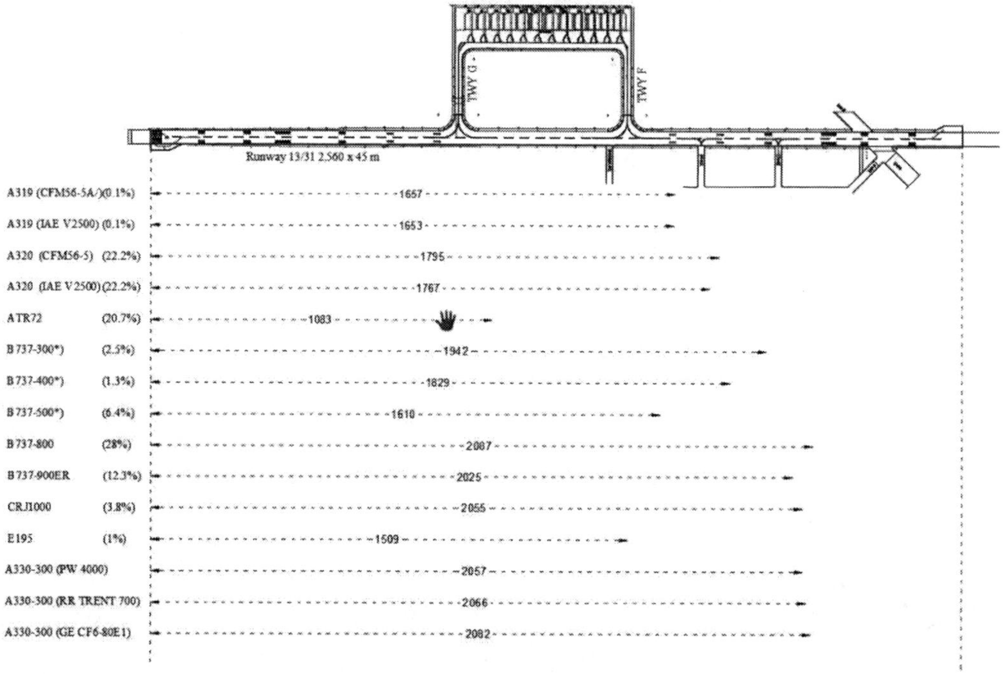

Table 8. Functional percentage of exit taxiway location to runway 13.

No	Exit Taxiway	ICAO Method (%) Rapid Exit Taxiway	FAA Method (%)	
			Dry Runway	Wet Runway
1	TXW F	-	20.7	20.7
2	TXW G	-	0	0
3	Turn around	-	77.6	77.6

Tabel 9. Functional percentage of exit taxiway location to runway 31.

No	Exit Taxiway	ICAO Method (%) Rapid Exit Taxiway	FAA Method (%)	
			Dry Runway	Wet Runway
1	TXW F	-	0	0
2	TXW G	-	21.7	20.7
3	Turn around	-	76.6	77.6

The results of the functional percentage analysis of the location of exit taxiways F and G showed insignificant results. It is necessary to consider the location and placement of an effective exit taxiway or the addition of a rapid exit taxiway to minimize the occupancy time of each aircraft. Recommendations for changing the exit taxiway can be seen in Figure 6. Meanwhile, the change of exit taxiway's functionality percentage can be seen in Table 10. and Table 11.

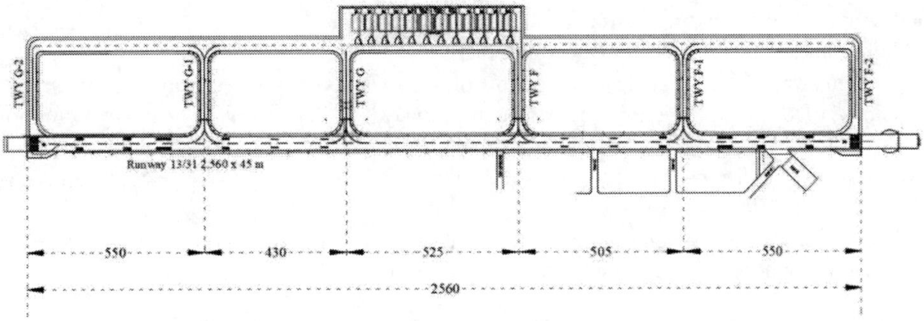

Figure 6. Recommendation for new exit taxiway location

Table 10. Percentage of exit taxiway to runway 13

Exit Taxiway	ICAO Method (%)	FAA Method (%)	
	Rapid Exit Taxiway	Dry Runway	Wet Runway
TXW F-1	-	54,2	50,4
TXW F-2	-	44,1	47,9
TXW G-1	-	-	-
TXW G-2	-	-	-

Table 11. Percentage of exit taxiway to runway 31

Exit Taxiway	ICAO Method (%)	FAA Method (%)	
	Rapid Exit Taxiway	Dry Runway	Wet Runway
TXW F-1	-	-	-
TXW F-2	-	-	-
TXW G-1	-	54.2	50.4
TXW G-2	-	44.1	47.9

5. Conclusion and suggestion

5.1. Conclusion

Based on the analysis and discussion of the exit taxiway geometry of Jenderal Ahmad Yani International Airport, it can be concluded as follows.

a. Based on the calculation of the exit taxiway location on runway 13 and runway 31 with the CIAO method, the functional exit taxiway percentage found is 0%. The CIAO method can only calculate the location of the rapid exit taxiway. Meanwhile, Jenderal Ahmad Yani International Airport only has a regular exit taxiway.

b. Based on the calculation of the location of the exit taxiway to runway 13, taxiway G has a percentage of 0% due to most aircraft landing through runway 13 making turnarounds on runway 31, which is 77.6%. The functionality rate of taxiway F is 20.7%.

c. Based on the calculation of the location of the exit taxiway to runway 31, taxiway F has a percentage of 0% since most of the aircrafts that land through runway 31 make turnarounds on runway 13 by 76.7% in dry runway conditions and 77.6% in wet runways. The functional percentage of taxiway G is 21.7% in dry runway conditions and 20.7% in wet runway conditions.

d. From the calculation of the change in the location of the exit taxiway on runway 13 and runway 31, it can be identified that based on the ICAO method, the number of functional exit taxiway percentages is 0%. This is because the method can only calculate the location of rapid exit taxiways. Meanwhile, Jenderal Ahmad Yani International Airport only has a regular exit taxiway.

e. From calculating the change in the location of the exit taxiway to runway 13, taxiway G has a total percentage of 0%. Taxiway G has a percentage amount of 0%. The functional rate of exit taxiway F is 20.7% on the dry runway and wet runway conditions. The rate for F-1 is 33.5% in dry runway conditions and 29.7% in wet runway conditions. The rate of F-2 exit taxiway is 44.1% in dry runway conditions and 47.9% in wet runway conditions.

f. From calculating the change in the location of the exit taxiway to runway 31, taxiway F has a percentage of 0%. The functional rate of exit taxiway G is 21.7% in dry runway conditions and 20.7% in the wet runway. The functional rate of G-1 is 32.5% in dry runway conditions and 29.7% in wet runway conditions. The functional percentage of exit taxiway G-2 is 44.1.4% in dry runway conditions and 47.9% in wet ones.
g. Rapid exit taxiway is not selected since if an intersection angle is used between 25 degrees to 45 degrees, there will be an overlap between the exit taxiways which causes conflict.

5.2. Suggestion

Suggestions for further research are as follows.

a. The payload value determined by each airline is required so the payload calculation for each stage can be carried out as closely as possible with conditions in the field.
b. Data on flight traffic movements should be accompanied by data on the direction of runway use for each aircraft, along with the airline and the type of aircraft used.
c. Further research can consider the decrease in flight traffic due to factors other than technical factors.
d. Further research can create programs to facilitate airport airside geometry analysis and efficient placement of exit taxiways by existing aviation traffic.

5.3. References

[1] Dewi N. Analisis Geometrik Runway, Taxiway, dan Apron Bandar Udara Internasional Ahmad Yani Semarang [Undergraduate]. Gadjah Mada University; 2012.
[2] Nugraha F. Analisis Geometri Runway, Taxiway, dan Apron Bagian Utara Bandar Udara Internasional Soekarno-Hatta Tangerang Banten [Undergraduate]. Gadjah Mada University; 2016.
[3] Dwihartadi R. Analisis Geometri Runway, Taxiway, dan Apron New Yogyakarta International Airport [Undergraduate]. Gadjah Mada University; 2017.
[4] Doda Y. Perencanaan Runway, Taxiway, dan Apron Bandar Udara Jalaludin Gorontalo [Undergraduate]. Universitas Negeri Gorontalo; 2015.
[5] Harris W. Analisis Geometrik Runway dan Exit Taxiway Bandar Udara Internasional Adi Soemarmo Surakarta [Undergraduate]. Gadjah Mada University; 2020.
[6] Horonjeff R. Planning and design of airports. 5th ed. New York: McGraw-Hill; 2010.
[7] Aerodrome design manual part 1 : runways. Montreal: International Civil Aviation Organization; 2020.
[8] Advisory Circular No. 150/5300-13A. Washington D.C.: Federal Aviation Administration; 2014.
[9] PT. Angkasa Pura I. Layout Runway, Taxiway, dan Apron Bandar Udara Internasional Jenderal Ahmad Yani. Semarang: PT. Angkasa Pura I; 2019.
[10] PT. Angkasa Pura I. Arus Pergerakan Lalu Lintas Angkutan Udara Berdasar Type Bandara: Achmad Yani Tahun 2015. Semarang: PT. Angkasa Pura I; 2019.
[11] PT. Angkasa Pura I. Arus Pergerakan Lalu Lintas Angkutan Udara Berdasar Type Bandara: Achmad Yani Tahun 2016. Semarang: PT. Angkasa Pura I; 2019.
[12] PT. Angkasa Pura I. Arus Pergerakan Lalu Lintas Angkutan Udara Berdasar Type Bandara: Achmad Yani Tahun 2017. Semarang: PT. Angkasa Pura I; 2019.
[13] PT. Angkasa Pura I. Arus Pergerakan Lalu Lintas Angkutan Udara Berdasar Type Bandara: Achmad Yani Tahun 2018. Semarang: PT. Angkasa Pura I; 2019.
[14] PT. Angkasa Pura I. Arus Pergerakan Lalu Lintas Angkutan Udara Berdasar Type Bandara: Achmad Yani Tahun 2019. Semarang: PT. Angkasa Pura I; 2019.
[15] PT. Angkasa Pura I. Arus Pergerakan Lalu Lintas Angkutan Udara Berdasar Type Bandara: Achmad Yani Tahun 2020. Semarang: PT. Angkasa Pura I; 2019.
[16] AIRBUS. Aircraft Characteristics Airport And Maintenance Planning. France: AIRBUS; 2020.

Design and Levitation Performance above A Permanent Magnet in Maglev Train Prototype

Natriya Faisal Rachman[1], Willy Artha Wirawan[1], Andri Pradipta[1], Didik Agus Setiawan[1]

[1]Indonesian Railway Polytechnic, Indonesia

Email: natriya@pengajar.ppi.ac.id, willy@pengajar.ppi.ac.id

Abstract. Maglev trains have a working system that will later be used to move the train. Magnetic Levitation (maglev) working system uses the principle of attractive or repulsive force generated by magnets. In its development, there are several systems used on maglev trains. This article describes how to design the strength of the magnetic field in the maglev prototype. Tests using a magnet based on the distance and diameter of the magnet. The results of measuring the magnetic field on a permanent magnet by varying the space to determine the position of the largest magnetic field, where the largest magnetic field is found in 2 magnetic pieces with a diameter of 15 mm with a value of 50.7 gauss. In the coil magnet, manual calculations are carried out, to produce a magnetic field equal to 2 pieces of 15 mm diameter magnet requires a current of 10 amperes
Keywords: Maglev, Magnetic Performance, Prototype

1. Introduction

Maglev trains have a working system that is used to drive trains. Magnetic Levitation (maglev) working system uses the principle of attractive or repulsive force generated by magnets. In its development, several systems are used on maglev trains, as in figure 1, including 1. Electromagnetic Suspension (EMS) is a working code is to utilize the attractive force between the rails and the electromagnet. In this EMS system, the accuracy of the distance between the fence and the train is essential to maintain the balance of the train[1]. In EMS technology, the train floats on the rails after a magnetic field is generated by an electromagnet (the fence pushes the train up). The magnets are formed by coils energized along the walls of the guidelines and on the rails. The roll of the rail gap will repel the magnet (electromagnet) under the train, thus making the train float between 1-10 cm above the rail. As the train lifts, electric power is applied to the coils within the walls of the guide rail to create a magnetic field that attracts and pushes the train along the rails[2]. The electric current given to the coil is carried out alternately to change its polarity. The change in polarity causes the magnet in front of the train to attract the train, and the magnet behind the train adds thrust, as figure 1.

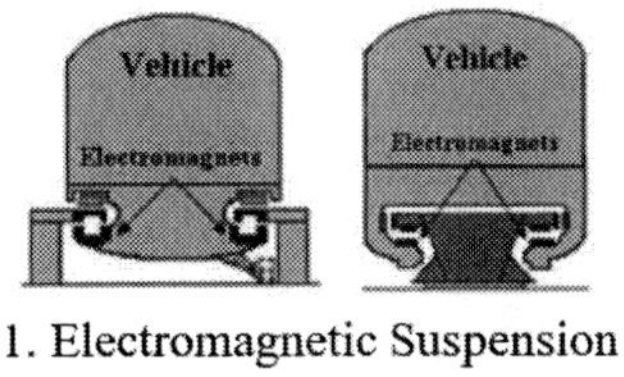

Figure 1. Electromagnetic Suspension (EMS)

The attractive and repulsive forces arising from the coil magnets on the track walls and the train walls in the maglev suspension system have the same strength. It is used to move the carriage and minimize the shaking or jerking caused when the polarity of the magnetic pole changes[3]. 2. Electrodynamic Suspension is to take advantage of the magnetic repulsion between the train and the rail. This system uses liquid nitrogen and superconducting materials that can be below critical temperatures[4]. Superconducting material is placed on the body of the train while the rail uses magnets. Superconducting material that has been given liquid nitrogen

and reaches a temperature below a critical point will produce a repulsive force with a magnet on the rail so that it can float[5]. On the track wall, a coil produces a repulsive force that can move the train. Electrodynamic Suspension has a drawback; namely, the system of natural repulsion will create magnetic fields at the front and rear of the train, which will provide resistance to the track to form obstacles[6]. This only happens at low speeds, while it has no impact on the train at high rates. 3. Inductrack system is the newest method of working the maglev train system by utilizing permanent magnets' repulsive force. The rail uses a permanent magnet that is elongated to support the train to be more economical. The train moves using the repulsive force generated by the electromagnet. There are two types of Inductrack designs, namely Inductrack I and Inductrack II. Inductrack I is made for high speed, while Inductrack II is for the low rate[7]. Inductrack can float ± 2.54 cm and has a better level of stability. Because of the considerable distance from the track, trains with the Inductrack system do not need a complicated system to keep the train stable. Previous studies of permanent magnets were not used because the researchers suspected that these magnets would not generate sufficient lift. An electromagnet is one whose magnetic field is made up of an electric current flowing[8]. The greater the current applied, the greater the magnetic field produced.
Induction magnets or electromagnets are made of a conducting material that carries an electric current. When a coil of wire is wrapped around a conductor (iron) and holds an electric current, magnetic lines of force will arise around the coil. The lines of magnetic force that arise are called Lorentz forces.
The Lorentz force that arises can be formulated as follows:

$$F = B \,.\, I \,.\, L \qquad (1)$$

And to calculate the strength of the magnetic field on the solenoid/coil using the following formula :

$$B = \frac{\mu 0 \,.I.N}{2 \,.\, a} \qquad (2)$$

Before calculating the length of the coil wire, you must calculate the number of turns used. The number of turns per layer can be calculated using the following equation:

$$n = \frac{l}{d} \qquad (3)$$

To calculate the total number of turns, the following equation can be used:

$$N = n \,.\, N_n \qquad (4)$$

Wire length

$$l_c = \pi(D_i + a_n \,.\, d_w)n \qquad (5)$$

In selecting the wire used, the specific resistance of each material must be considered and can be calculated using the following equation:

$$R_n = \frac{\rho \,.l_c}{A_w} \qquad (6)$$

The coil used must be able to generate torque. It can be estimated from the following equation :

$$\tau = B \,.\, I \,.\, A \,.\, N \qquad (7)$$

The following equation can calculate the solids pressure:

$$P = \frac{F}{A} \qquad (8)$$

Note :
F : Lorentz forces (N)
B : Magnetic field strength (T)
I : Strong currents (A)
L : Wire length (m)
a : solenoid radius (m)

$\mu 0$: Vacuum permeability = $4\pi \times 10^{-7}$ (Wb/A.m)
N : Number of turns

2. Infrastructure And Facilities Design of Maglev Train Prototype magnetic

The design of the maglev infrastructure was from the track construction, as figure 2. The structure of the maglev track at the bottom uses 3 layers of acrylic measuring 1200 x 90 mm, where the bottom layer is used as a base with a thickness of 2 mm. Then in the middle layer with a thickness of 4 mm, there are 400 holes of 8 mm on the sides and 40 holes of 15 mm in the middle where the hole is used to place a permanent magnet. Top layer with a thickness of 2 mm as a cover or permanent magnet clamp. The top layer has 7 holes on the right and left with a 100 x 3 mm size used to install the train guidelines. The guiding line serves to keep the train running straight. This section has a height of 40 mm and a thickness of 3 mm. Permanent magnets with a diameter of 8 mm are installed with the north poles facing upwards in sequence. As for permanent magnets with a diameter of 15 mm, they are installed with alternating north and south pole positions along the path.

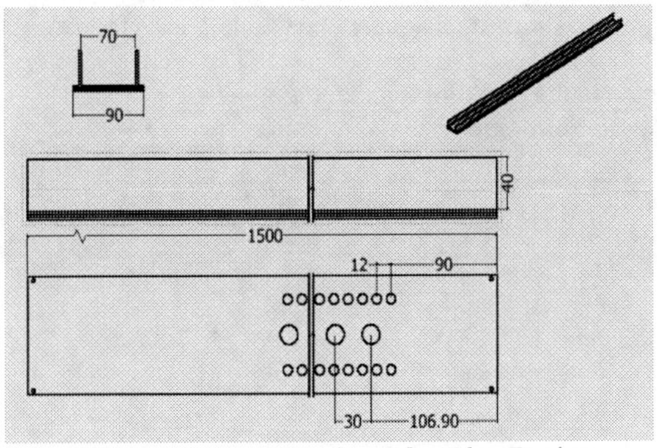

Figure 2 Maglev Jalur Line Design

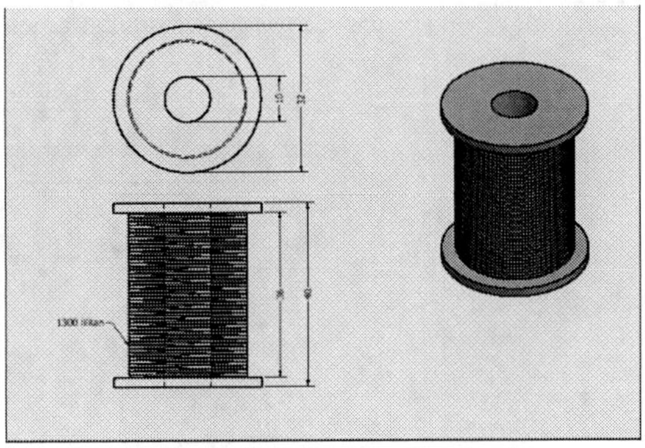
Figure 3 Coil Construction Design

The stages of facility design in making the design consist of:
1. Coil Construction Design
The coil construction will later be used to wind 0.8 mm copper wire and be placed inside the train, which functions as propulsion rather than the train to run, as figure 3. This design has a diameter of 32 mm with a length of 40 mm. There is a hole with a diameter of 10 mm in the middle as a place for an iron core that can conduct magnetic fields. There can be an interaction between an induced magnet and a permanent magnet with a diameter of 15 mm. The two ends of the coil are made a barrier with a thickness of 2 mm, which serves as a base for the coil to be placed inside the train. This construction can contain approximately 1300 turns of copper wire.
2. Train design
The train construction will have permanent magnets on the inside, coil magnets, and on the top of the train, there will be control equipment, as figure 4. The train structure has a size of 100 x 70 mm and a height of 55 mm, consisting of 4 mm thick acrylic on the bottom and 3 mm thick acrylic on the sides and top. The train base has 16 holes with a diameter of 8 mm located on the right and left sides. The hole serves to place a permanent magnet with a diameter of 8 mm and the direction of the north pole facing downwards. A magnetic position parallel between the track and the train can cause a repulsive force that can lift the train body. While in the center of the train base, there are 2 holes with a diameter of 10 mm with a distance between the holes of 45 mm, which serves to place M10 x 50 bolts and coil magnets. When the train is on track, the position of the front coil magnet is aligned with the permanent magnet of the way, and the rear coil magnet is located between the 2 coil magnets.

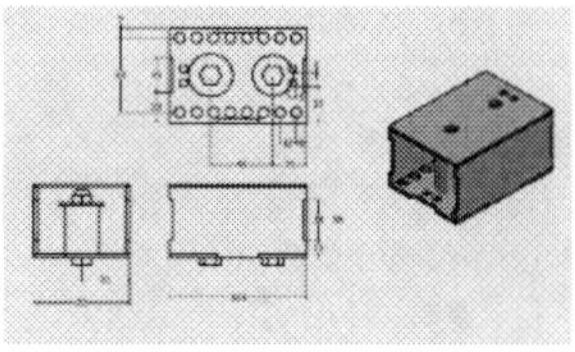

Figure 4. Train Design

3. Test of Magnetic Performance

Measuring the magnetic field is carried out on the magnets used to manufacture the maglev train prototype. This magnetic field measurement uses the gauss meter measuring tool application found on the Xiaomi redmi 5 cellphones. Magnetic strength measurements are carried out at a certain distance between 0 - 4 cm with a measurement variation of 0.5 cm at each measure from the tip of the magnetic chip.

3.1 Measurement Results of Permanent Magnets Diameter 8 mm.

The following is the measurement data for permanent magnets with a diameter of 8 mm and a thickness of 2 mm with a gauss meter measuring instrument with variations in distance. Data table 1 is as follows.

Table 1 Measurement results of 8 mm diameter magnets

	Magnetic field *(gauss)*	
Distance	1 piece	2 piece
0 cm	26	44
0.5 cm	11.4	26
1 cm	7	14.2
1.5 cm	4.3	9.2
2 cm	3.1	6.3
2.5 cm	2.2	4.4
3 cm	1.8	3.5
3.5 cm	1.6	2.8
4 cm	1.4	2.3

The data measurement results can be described through a graph of the strength of a permanent magnet, as shown in Figure 5.

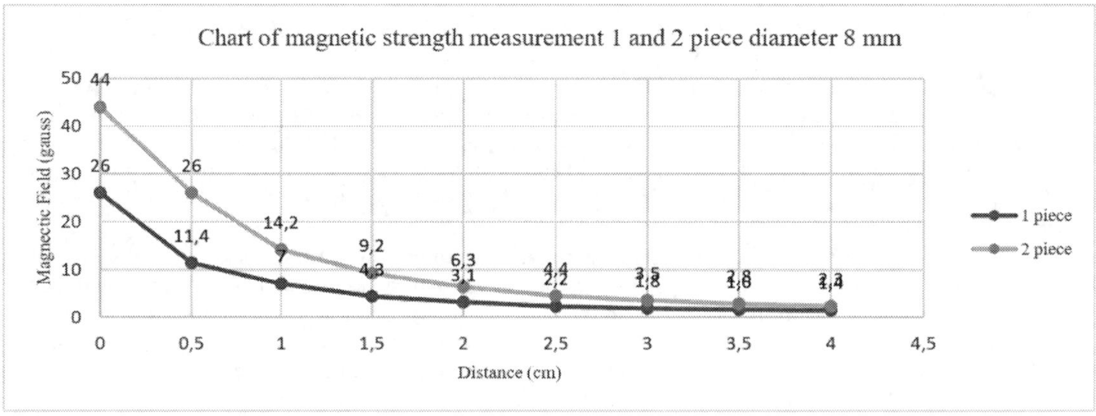

Figure 5. Graph of magnetic strength measurement 1 and 2 piece diameter 8 mm

3.2 Measurement results of permanent magnets (neodymium) with a diameter of 15 mm.

The following is the measurement data for permanent magnets with a diameter of 15 mm and a thickness of 2 mm with variations in distance. Data table 2 is as follows.

Table 2. Measurement results of 15mm. diameter magnets

	Magnetic field *(gauss)*	
Distance	1 piece	2 piece
0 cm	41.3	50.7
0.5 cm	35.3	49.1
1 cm	19.8	40.7
1.5 cm	15.2	33.4
2 cm	10.1	20.3
2.5 cm	8.2	14.2
3 cm	7.2	11.2
3.5 cm	6.7	8.8
4 cm	6.4	7.5

The data measurement results can be described through a graph of the strength of a permanent magnet, as shown in Figure 6.

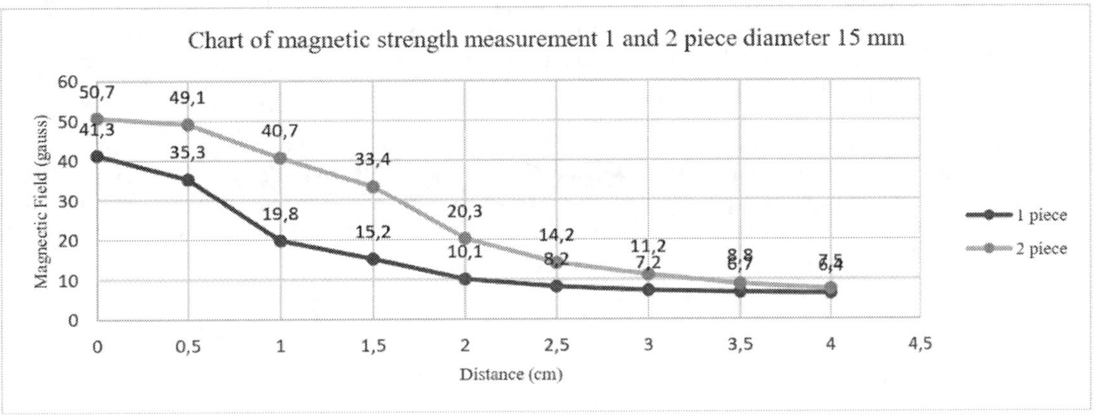

Figure 6. Graph of magnetic strength measurement 1 and 2 piece diameter 15 mm

3.3 Coil Magnetic Strength Measurement Results

The coil magnet is made by winding a copper wire on an acrylic coil with 1300 turns. In the middle of the coil, a bolt functions to drain the magnetic field generated by the winding after it is energized with 10 amperes of electric current. The gauss meter measuring instrument is measured on the Xiaomi redmi 5 mobile phones. Data table 3 is as follows.

Table 3. Measurement results of coil magnet

Distance	**0 cm**	**0.5 cm**	**1 cm**	**1.5 cm**	**2 cm**	**2.5 cm**	**3 cm**	**3.5 cm**	**4 cm**
Magnet Field (*gauss*)	51.1	47.3	41.5	40.4	38.3	26.7	19.4	15.2	11.3

The data measurement results can be described through a graph of the strength of a permanent magnet, as shown in Figure 7.

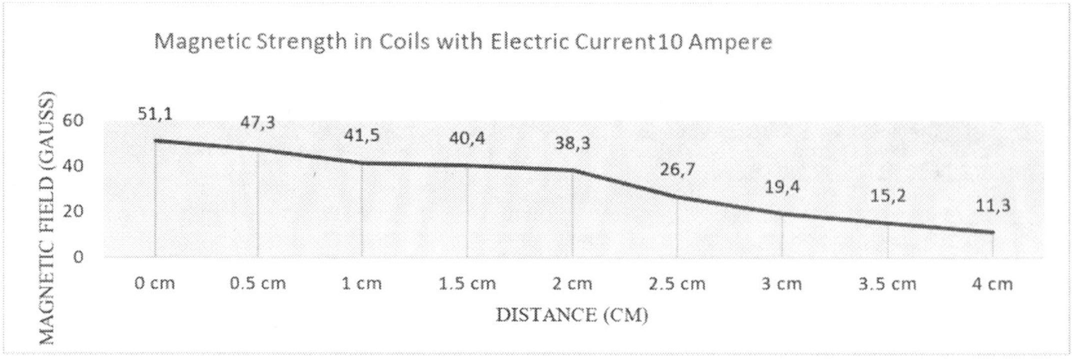

Figure 7. Graph of the measurement of the magnetic strength of the coil with an electric current flow of 10 amperes

Figure 7. graph of magnetic field measurements above are carried out at a distance of 0 - 4 cm with a measurement range of 0.5 cm from each end of the magnet. The resulting magnetic field is the largest at 0 cm or the closest position to each end of the magnet and the smallest at a distance of 4 cm or the furthest part from each end of the magnet.

3.4 Floating Train Calculation

In designing a maglev train prototype, pressure or lift is needed that makes the train float. This train weighs 600 grams or 0.6 kg. Using permanent magnets with a diameter of 8 mm and a thickness of 2 mm has a tensile strength of 0.1 kilograms per seed. To find out the amount of lift required, it can be calculated using the pressure formula below:

1. Calculation of the pressure needed to make the train float.

$P = \frac{F}{A}$

To find out F can be calculated using the following equation:

$W = m \cdot g$
$= 0,6 \times 9,8$
$= 5,9\ kg/m^2$ atau $5,9\ gram/cm^2$

The area of the permanent magnet base is calculated using the following equation.

$A = \pi \cdot r^2$
$= 3,14 \times 0,8^2$
$= 3,14 \times 0,64$
$= 2\ cm^2$

The amount of pressure that occurs in the prototype can be calculated by the following equation:

$P = \frac{F}{A}$
$= \frac{5,9}{2}$
$= 2,95\ gram/cm^2$, The lifting force required to lift a 600-gram cart is $2,95\ gram/cm^2$.

2. Calculation of the number of magnets needed to lift the train.

The number of magnets needed to lift a train weighing 600 grams or 0.6 kg can be calculated using the following equation.

$$n = \frac{\text{Weight of Train}}{\text{magnetic attraction strength per pcs}}$$

$$= \frac{0,6}{0,1}$$

$= 6$ pcs

Lifting or levitating a 600-gram train requires 6 permanent magnets with a diameter of 8 mm. To maintain the stability of the train while running, the installation of permanent magnets is made as tight as possible to minimize swaying when the train is running.

3.5 Coil Magnetic Field Calculation

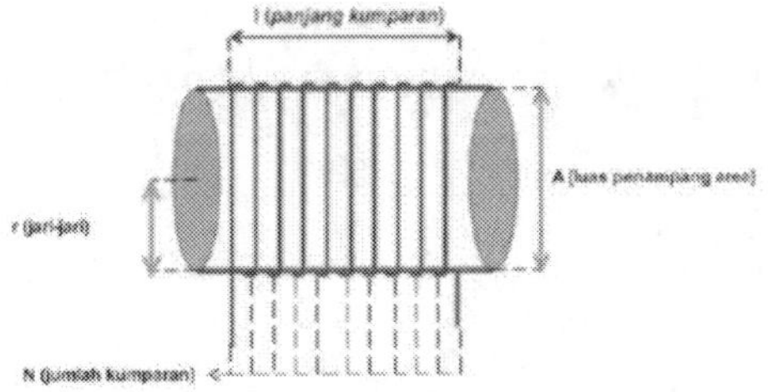

Figure 8. Coil/Solenoid Image

Calculation of coil/solenoid specifications as figure 8 is as follows:

a. Copper wire diameter = 0,8 mm.
b. Coil/solenoid diameter = 32 mm = 0,032 m dengan r = 0,016 m.
c. Coil/solenoid length = 36 mm = 0,036 m.
d. Number of turns = 1300
e. $\mu 0 = 4\pi \text{ x } 10^{-7}$ (Wb/A.m)
f. Copper wire type resistance = $1{,}68 \text{ x } 10^{-8}\ \Omega$ m

- Coil circumference/solenoid
  $\Theta = 2 \text{ x } \pi \text{ x r}$
  $= 2 \text{ x } 3{,}14 \text{ x } 0{,}016$
  $= 0{,}1$ m
- Coil/solenoid cross-sectional area
  $A = \pi . r^2$
  $= 3{,}14 \text{ x } 0{,}016^2$
  $= 3{,}14 \text{ x } 0{,}000256$
  $= 0.00080384 \text{ m}^2$
- The cross-sectional area of the wire
  $A = \pi . r^2$
  $= 3{,}14 \text{ x } 0{,}0004^2$
  $= 3{,}14 \text{ x } 0{,}00000016$
  $= 0{,}0000005 \text{ m}^2$

1) Number of turns required

   Number of turns per layer
   $n = \frac{l}{d}$
   $= \frac{36}{0{,}8} = 45$ turns per layer

   Total number of turns
   $N = n . N_n$
   $= 45 \text{ x } 29$
   $= 1305$ turns, the total number of turns in the manufacture of the coil is 1300 turns.

2) Calculation of the current required to produce a magnetic field of 50.7 gauss in the coil/solenoid

   $B = \frac{\mu 0 .I.N}{2 . a}$
   $= \frac{4\pi \text{ x } 10^{-7} \text{x } 10 \text{ x } 1300}{2 \text{ x } 0{,}016}$
   $= \frac{4 \text{ x } 3{,}14 \text{ x } 10^{-7} \text{x } 10 \text{ x } 1300}{2 \text{ x } 0{,}016}$

$= \frac{12,56 \times 10^{-7} \times 10 \times 1300}{2 \times 0,016}$

$= \frac{163280 \times 10^{-7}}{0,032}$

$= 51025 \times 10^{-7}$

$= 0,0051025$ T

$= 51,025 = 51$ *gauss*

Table 4. Table for calculating variations in electric current to magnetic fields

Electric current	Number of turns	Coil diameter	Magnet Field (*gauss*)
1 ampere	1300	0.032 m	5.1
2 ampere	1300	0.032 m	10.2
3 ampere	1300	0.032 m	15.2
4 ampere	1300	0.032 m	20.4
5 ampere	1300	0.032 m	25.5
6 ampere	1300	0.032 m	30.6
7 ampere	1300	0.032 m	35.7
8 ampere	1300	0.032 m	40.8
9 ampere	1300	0.032 m	45.9
10 ampere	1300	0.032 m	51

The electric current calculation table 4 above shows that a magnetic field of 50.7 gauss requires an electric current of 10 amperes.

3) The length of the wire required in the manufacture of the coil/solenoid can be calculated as follows

$l_c = \pi(D_i + a_n . d_w)n$

$= 3,14 (10 + 29 \times 0,8) 1300$

$= 3,14 (10 + 23,2) 1300$

$= 3,14 (33,2) 1300$

$= 3,14 (43160)$

$= 135522.4$ mm

$= 135$ m, the manufacture of one coil requires a copper wire of length is 135 m.

4) Calculation of resistance that occurs in the copper wire is as follows:

$R_n = \frac{\rho . l_c}{A_w}$

$= \frac{1,68 \times 10^{-8} \times 135}{0,0000005}$

$= \frac{2,268 \times 10^{-8}}{0,0000005}$

$= 4,536 = 4,5\ \Omega$, the resistance in each coil is 4,5 Ω.

5) Calculation of torque generated by the coil.

$\tau = B . I . A . N$

$= 0,0051025 \times 10 \times 0.00080384 \times 1300$

$= 0,053$ N/m, the torque produced by each coil is 0,053 N/m.

6) Lorentz force exerted on the coil.

$F = B . I. L$

$= 0,0051025 \times 10 \times 135$

$= 6,9$ N, the Lorentz force generated from the bait is 6,9 N.

The magnetic field measurement using a gauss meter and the calculation of the current required to determine the magnetic field can be concluded in Figure 12 below.

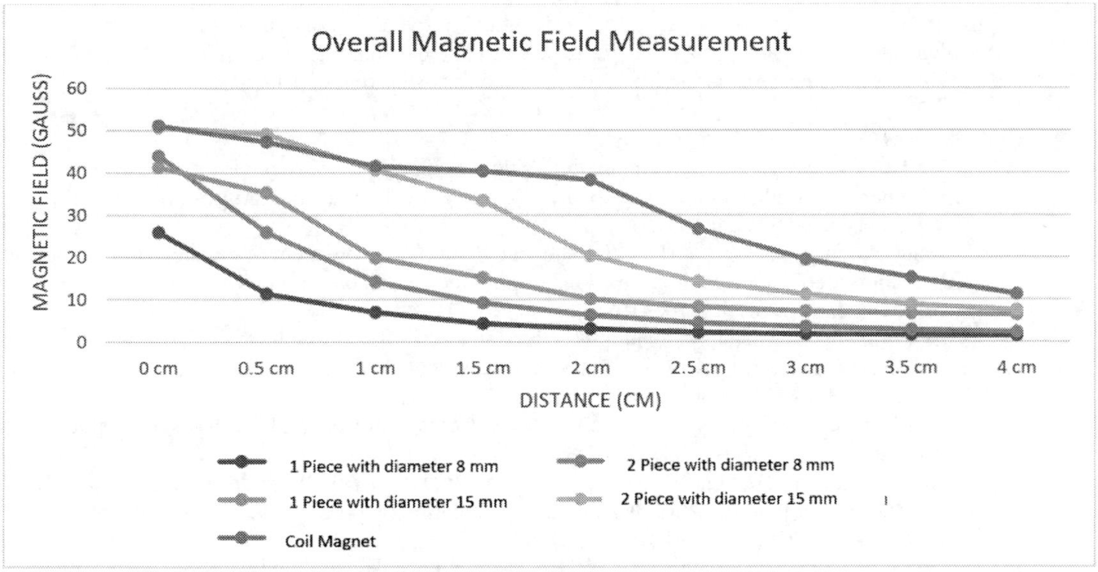

Figure 9. Magnetic Measurement Chart

Figure 9. magnetic measurement chart above results from measurements of all the magnets used to manufacture the maglev train prototype and various effects. The dark blue line shows the measurement results of the coil magnet, where at position 0 cm is the most significant magnetic field value with a value of 51.1 gauss. The yellow line shows the measurement results of 2 magnetic pieces with a diameter of 15 mm, where 0 cm is the most significant value with 50.7 gauss. The grey line shows the measurement results of 1 piece of the magnet with a diameter of 15 mm, where 0 cm is the most significant value with 41.3 gauss. The brown line shows the measurement results of 2 magnetic pieces with a diameter of 8 mm, where the 0 cm position is the most significant value with a value of 44 gauss. The light blue line shows the measurement results of 1 piece of the magnet with a diameter of 8 mm, where the 0 cm position is the most significant value with a value of 26 gauss. From the graph above, it can be concluded that the largest magnetic field is obtained from a coil magnet and 2 pieces of magnets with a diameter of 15 mm, both of which function as train drivers. The repulsive and attractive forces produced by the two magnets can cause the train to move. The interaction process of the coil magnet and 2 pieces of 15 mm diameter magnets can be seen in the following figure 10.

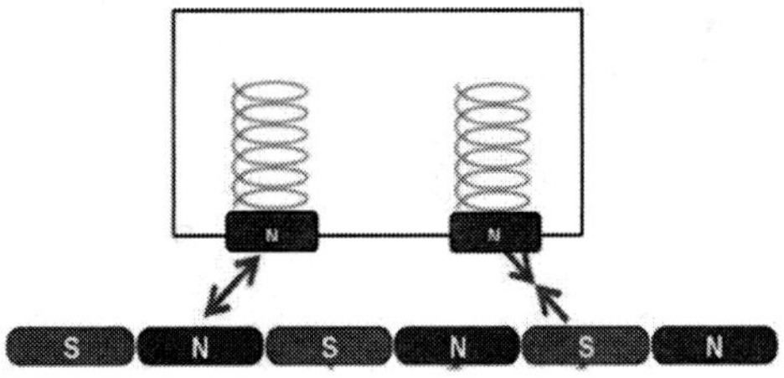

Figure 10. The position of the train with respect to the track

Installation of permanent magnets on the path is carried out alternately between the north and south poles. The interaction process between the two magnets occurs when the coil magnet is electrified. This will turn on the sensor which will detect the magnetic poles on the track. The magnetic poles on the coil will change to the same as the magnetic poles in the path. This process causes the magnet in front of the train to attract the train and the magnet behind the train to push the train to run.

4. Conclusion

To determine the magnetic field needed for the maglev train prototype, it consists of several stages, namely measuring the magnetic field on a permanent magnet by varying the distance to determine the position of the largest magnetic field, where the largest magnetic field is found in 2 magnetic pieces with a diameter of 15 mm with a value of 50,7 gauss. In the coil magnet, manual calculations are carried out to produce a magnetic field equal to 2 magnets with a diameter of 15 mm requires a current of 10 amperes.

5. References

[1] P. Wen *et al.*, "Design and Implementation of auto-filling liquid nitrogen for HTS maglev vehicles based on Kalman filter algorithm," *Cryogenics (Guildf).*, vol. 111, no. August, p. 103167, 2020, doi: 10.1016/j.cryogenics.2020.103167.
[2] F. Dong, Z. Huang, X. Xu, L. Hao, N. Shao, and Z. Jin, "Improvement of magnetic and cryogenic energy preservation performances in a feeding-power-free superconducting magnet system for maglevs," *Energy*, vol. 190, 2020, doi: 10.1016/j.energy.2019.116403.
[3] S. Si, J. Zheng, B. Zheng, Y. Zhang, N. Qian, and Z. Deng, "Levitation performance of different bulk YBaCuO arrays above a permanent magnet guideway for HTS maglev systems," *J. Alloys Compd.*, vol. 705, pp. 301–308, 2017, doi: 10.1016/j.jallcom.2017.02.105.
[4] Y. J. Li *et al.*, "Design and analysis of an electromagnetic turnout for the superconducting Maglev system," *Phys. C Supercond. its Appl.*, vol. 528, pp. 84–89, 2016, doi: 10.1016/j.physc.2016.07.021.
[5] L. Zhang and J. Y. Huang, "Dynamic interaction analysis of the high-speed maglev vehicle/guideway system based on a field measurement and model updating method," *Eng. Struct.*, vol. 180, no. September 2018, pp. 1–17, 2019, doi: 10.1016/j.engstruct.2018.11.031.
[6] J. Kim, G. B. King, C. H. Kim, and C. W. Ha, "Modeling and designing levitation, roll and pitch controller for high accuracy maglev tray system," *Mechatronics*, vol. 53, no. May, pp. 181–191, 2018, doi: 10.1016/j.mechatronics.2018.06.011.
[7] Q. Lai, J. Liu, A. Haghani, L. Meng, and Y. Wang, "Energy-efficient speed profile optimization for medium-speed maglev trains," *Transp. Res. Part E Logist. Transp. Rev.*, vol. 141, no. 3, p. 102007, 2020, doi: 10.1016/j.tre.2020.102007.
[8] M. Morishita, T. Azukizawa, S. Kanda, N. Tamura, and T. Yokoyama, "A New Maglev System for Magnetically Levitated Carrier System," *IEEE Trans. Veh. Technol.*, vol. 38, no. 4, pp. 230–236, 1989, doi: 10.1109/25.45486.

IOP Conf. Series: Earth and Environmental Science 1000 (2022) 012003 doi:10.1088/1755-1315/1000/1/012003

Home Delivery Trip Generation Model

Andika Fadhlansyah[1], Nahry[2]

Departemen Teknik Sipil, Fakultas Teknik, Universitas Indonesia, Kampus Baru UI Depok, 16424, Indonesia

Andikafadhlansyah02@gmail.com [1], Nahry@eng.ui.ac.id [2]

Abstract. As a result of online shopping's rapid development, more goods and services are being delivered directly into residences. The number of people who shop online using e-commerce platforms also increases with the Covid-19 pandemic and causes an increase in freight trip generation. This research aims to analyze the factors that affect freight trip generation and develop a freight trip generation model for home deliveries. Data collection is done using questionnaires with 273 people who reside in Jabodetabek as samples to understand the individual characteristics, household characteristics, and the number of freight trips generated by each residential unit. Collected data is analyzed using the multiple linear regression method into a multiple linear regression model. The result shows on multiple linear regression modeling only the home type, household income, and the number of vehicles have significance towards the model. This research can be used by city transportation authorities as a reference to predict the impact of urban area's development on freight trip generation.

1. Introduction

Since ancient times, buying and selling activities have existed where sellers and buyers engage with each other at a certain location to make a transaction. As technology develops, this buying and selling activity grows easier to do. Sellers and buyers can communicate and interact online on a website or application only. Thus, the buying and selling process can be done at home without traveling out of the house. The US Census Bureau defines e-commerce as the sale of goods and services for which buyers place orders, or prices and terms of sale are negotiated via electronic data interchange, the Internet, or other online systems. Payments can be made online or not (Moriset, 2020).

Trends in the use of e-commerce in Indonesia are predicted to increase every year until the next decade (Joewono et al., 2020). The number of e-commerce users in Indonesia in 2017 reached 139 million users, then soared 10.8% to 154.1 million users last year. This year, it is projected to reach 168.3 million users and 212.2 million by 2023 (Statista, 2019). The development of e-commerce has influenced consumer shopping behavior from traditional shopping to online shopping (Visser et al., 2014). This change of behavior also affects the resulting trip generation. According to (Tamin, 2000) Trip generation is a modeling stage that estimates the number of movements originating from a zone or land use and the number of movements attracted to land use or zone.

Previously, a buyer had to travel from home to a store to purchase an item. Meanwhile, nowadays, buyers can purchase goods online, which will then be sent directly to the buyer's door. Meaning that people's trips out of the house are replaced by courier trips to their homes in the context of shopping (Visser et al., 2014). Therefore, the house that was originally a source of trip production has turned into a trip attraction.

Research on trip generation in residential areas is still very limited. With the growth of residential areas, understanding the resulting trip generation patterns is needed (Wang & Zhou, 2015). In recent years, the increasing use of e-commerce has increasingly encouraged the importance of research on trip generation caused by residential areas. This research can be used by urban transportation planning as a reference for estimating the impact of residential area development on trip generation in the vicinity. In addition, this research can be useful for home delivery services to plan an effective and efficient delivery trip. By knowing the number of trips generated, this data can be used as a starting point for analyzing the impact on the environment due to vehicles.

2. Literature Review

Home delivery is the delivery of goods to houses from a store or retail (Visser et al., 2014). However, nowadays, home delivery can also occur from house to house. The development of home delivery since the presence of e-commerce is growing rapidly. A study conducted by (Xi et al., 2020) stated that same-day delivery online shopping replaced local shopping in China. Even though there is a change from conventional shopping to online shopping, it will not reduce trip generation. It may add trip generation itself. A study conducted by (Hidayatno et al., 2019) states that in urban areas in developing countries, around 40%-50% of commercial goods move to the city center, 20-25% move outside the city, and 25-40% move within the city. In Indonesia, the increase in e-commerce users was expected to reach 39.9 million users by 2020 (Hidayatno et al., 2019). Research by (Russo & Comi 2012) found that goods purchased through e-commerce tend to be sent in small volumes, causing high-frequency deliveries.

A study conducted by (Bjerkan et al., 2020) states that consumers who often use online shopping as a shopping method are people with a high level of education, usually live in crowded areas, and live in apartments or one-family houses. More than 60% of e-commerce users are families with children, with more than three people per family on average. This statement is in line with the research results conducted by (Wang & Zhou, 2015), where it is stated that the frequency of web use and high levels of education show a strong positive correlation with the tendency to shop online. A female, young, healthy, self-employed, with a high family income, living in a small household, and having children also positively correlates with the tendency to use e-commerce.

3. Research Data

The study was conducted from January 29, 2021, to March 9, 2021, on 273 respondents who live in Jabodetabek and have shopped online. The data was collected in the form of individual characteristics, household characteristics, and the average number of home deliveries during the week. Individual characteristics include age, gender, occupation, latest education, and internet use. Household characteristics include the type of residence, number of children, monthly family income, number of family members, number of vehicles. The survey results are presented in Table 1 and Table 2.

Table 1. Results of Questionnaire Survey, Part 1

		Family Members (X2)	Number of Vehicles (X10)	Number of Goods Deliveries (Y1)
N	Valid	273	273	273
	Missing	0	0	0
Mean		4,56	2,59	6,48
Median		4,00	2,00	5,00
Mode		4	2	10

IOP Conf. Series: Earth and Environmental Science 1000 (2022) 012003 doi:10.1088/1755-1315/1000/1/012003

Std. Deviation	1,744	1,625	5,595

Table 2. Results of Questionnaire Survey, Part 2

Variable Names	Description	Variable Symbol	Frequency	Percentage
Type of residency (X1)	Residential home	X1-1	263	96,3
	Boarding home	X1-2	8	2,9
	Apartment	X1-3	2	,7
	Total		273	100,0
Number of Children (X3)	0		152	55,7
	1		65	23,8
	2		47	17,2
	3		9	3,3
	Total		273	100,0
Age (X4)	18-20		45	16,5
	21-25		62	22,7
	26-39		38	13,9
	40-55		98	35,9
	>55		30	11,0
	Total		273	100,0
Gender (X5)	Male		104	38,1
	Female		169	61,9
	Total		273	100,0
Occupation (X6)	Students	X6-1	94	34,4
	Private employees	X6-2	82	30,0
	Housewife	X6-3	34	12,5
	Civil Servant	X6-4	26	9,5
	Unemployed	X6-5	22	8,1
	Entrepreneur	X-6-6	15	5,5
	Total		273	100,0
Family's Monthly Income (X7)	< Rp. 2.000.000	X7-1	14	5,1
	Rp. 2.000.000 - Rp. 5.000.000	X7-2	49	17,9
	Rp. 5.000.000 - Rp. 10.000.000	X7-3	56	20,5
	Rp. 10.000.000 - Rp. 20.000.000	X7-4	66	24,2
	Rp. 20.000.000 - Rp. 50.000.000	X7-5	59	21,6
	> Rp. 50.000.000	X7-6	29	10,6
	Total		273	100,0
Latest Education (X8)	High School/Equivalent/Below	X8-1	35	12,8
	Diploma/Equivalent	X8-2	12	4,4
	Undergraduate	X8-3	191	70,0
	Postgraduate	X8-4	33	12,1
	S3	X8-5	2	,7
	Total		273	100,0
Usage of Internet (X9)	Rarely (<2 a week)	X9-1	22	8,1
	Rather Often (2-3 a week)	X9-2	31	11,4
	Often (4-5 a week)	X9-3	32	11,7
	Very Often (every day a week)	X9-4	188	68,9
	Total		273	100,0

Before the data is tested for multiple linear regression, it is necessary to identify outliers in the Y1 variable. The outlier determination method used the boxplot method with the help of the SPSS application. Table 3 presents the comparison of outliers not being removed and outliers being removed.

Table 3. Comparisons of outliers not being removed and outliers being removed on Y1 variable

		Outlier not being removed	*Outlier* being removed
N	Valid	273	253
	Missing	0	0
Mean		6,48	6,47
Median		5	5
Std. Deviation		5,595	4,324

4. Model Specifications

This study uses the correlation test method to determine the correlation between the independent variable of X and the dependent variable of Y, then performed multiple linear regression analysis as a method of analysis and modeling by focusing on the classical assumption test in the form of the dependent variable normality test, residual normality test, linearity test, multicollinearity test, heteroscedasticity test. The model of the multiple linear regression of this study will be in the form of:

$$Y_i = \beta_0 + \beta_1 X_{1i} + \beta_2 X_{2i} + \ldots + \beta_k X_{ki} + \varepsilon_i \tag{1}$$

Where
Yi = Respons for subject i
Xi = Predictor for subject i
εi = Error for subjecti

5. Result Analysis

The correlation test results using SPSS show that there are eight variables with a significant correlation to the Y1 variable, which is presented in Table 4. The Residential Variable (r = 0.177) has a positive correlation to the average number of arriving items to the house in a week (Y1), meaning that people who live in residential houses tend to generate delivery of goods to their homes compared to people who live in boarding houses (r = -0.161). The more the family members (r = 0.154), the more goods are sent to the house. Females (r = 0.165) tend to generate home delivery compared to the male gender. Families with an income of 20-50 million (r = 0.202) and above 50 million per month (r = 0.152) tend to generate home delivery of goods compared to an income of 2-5 million per month (r = -0.212). The more the number of vehicles owned, the more likely it is to generate home delivery.

Table 4. Correlation Test Results

Correlation between variable Y and X	Average Number of Arriving Packages to The House During the Week	
	Y1	
	R value	positive/negative correlation

IOP Conf. Series: Earth and Environmental Science 1000 (2022) 012003 doi:10.1088/1755-1315/1000/1/012003

Residential House	X1-1	0,177	+
Boarding House	X1-2	-0,161	-
Family Member	X2	0,154	+
Gender	X5	0,165	+
2 - 5 million rupiah per month	X7-2	-0,212	-
20-50 million rupiah per month	X7-5	0,202	+
> 50 million rupiah per month	X7-6	0,152	+
Number of Vehicles	X10	0,253	+

The variables of Residential Houses and Boarding Houses have a high correlation with an R-value of 0,891. Thus, these two variables cannot be used in multiple linear regression analysis to avoid multicollinearity. There is an assumption that the Family's Monthly Income variable has a high correlation with the Number of vehicles variable, but after analyzing the correlation using SPSS, the r-value is 0.192 between X7-2 and X10, and 0.164 between X7-5 and X10. Then these variables are considered not have a high correlation with each other so they are still used in the analysis. That is, the variable X1-1. X2, X5, X7-2, X7-5. X7-6 and X10 will be used in the next analysis.

After the dependent normality test was performed, it turns out the Y1 variable was not normally distributed. Therefore, a transformation of the Y1 form was carried out to be in the form of Log (Y1); thus, the variable was more normally distributed. The Log variable (Y1) from now on will be called the Y2 variable.

Variable Y2 performed multiple linear regression analysis with a combination of the seven variables. Variable elimination was based on variables with a low correlation with Y2. Then, one by one was removed until only one variable. The best model was the model with the highest coefficient of determination (R^2) value, the most variable, the smallest constant, and the mathematic sign according to expectations. The results of multiple linear regression analysis can be observed in Table 5.

Based on Table 5, Model 1 is the best current model because its because it fulfills 3 of 4 best model conditions that are highest R^2 value, most variable, and the mathematic sign according to expectations. However, it is necessary to perform a T-Test to determine each variable with a significant effect on the model equation. The results of the T-Test in Table 6 show that Model 11 with variables X1-1, X7-2, X7-5, and X10 has all the variable coefficients significantly to the model. That is, Model 11 is the best model. In addition to the T-Test, an F-test was also conducted to determine the significance from all variables of Model 11 on the model simultaneously. The result of the F-test is 10.279, which is greater than the F table (2,504), meaning that all Model 11 variables are significant to the model simultaneously.

Table 5. Multiple linear regression model on the variable number of goods sent home in a week in logarithmic (Y2)

Variable	Expected sign	parameter	Model 1	2	3	4	5	6	7
Constant		c	0,194	0,186	0,247	0,45	0,585	0,607	0,558
Residential Houses	+	X1-1	0,196	0,203	0,224				
Family Member	+	X2	0,021	0,021					
Gender	+/-	X5	0,177	0,178	0,177	0,185			

Income of 2 mio-5million rupiah	+/-	X7-2	-0,117	-0,128	-0,116	-0,199	-0,138	-0,166	
Income of 20 mio-50 million rupiah	+	X7-5	0,168	0,151	0,152	0,164	0,144		
Income above 50 million rupiah	+	X7-6	0,100						
Number of Vehicles	+	X10	0,033	0,038	0,044	0,046	0,045	0,48	0,56
		R^2	0,228	0,222	0,21	0,193	0,125	0,106	0,071

Table 6. T-Test Results of Multiple Linear Regression Model

	Model 8		Model 9		Model 10		Model 11	
Variable	t	Sig	t	Sig	t	Sig	t	Sig
Constant	2,752	,006	2,682	,008	2,409	,001	3,376	,001
X1-1	2,299	,022	2,374	,018	2,357	,013	2,575	,011
X2	1,799	,073	1,823	,069	1,511	,024		
X7-2	-2,465	,014	-2,703	,007			-2,502	,013
X7-5	2,397	,017	2,101	,037	3,079	,016	2,133	,034
X7-6	1,414	,159			1,788	,150		
X10	2,303	,022	2,799	,006	2,609	,006	3,317	,001
R^2	0,166		0,159		0,155		0,148	

Model 11 is the best model with a coefficient of determination of 0.148 with the equation:

$$Y = 0{,}345 + 0{,}259(X1\text{-}1) - 0{,}134\,(X7\text{-}2) + 0{,}103\,(\text{X7-5}) + 0{,}042\,(\text{X10}) \qquad (2)$$

Based on the trip generation model in equation (2), people who live in residential homes will increase goods delivered to their homes by $10^{0,259}$ or 1,81 compared to those who do not live in residential homes. Families with an income of 2 to 5 million per month will reduce the trip generation to the homes by $10^{0,134}$ or 1,36 goods. Meanwhile, families with an income of 20 to 50 million per month increase a trip generation to homes by $10^{0,103}$ or 1,26 goods. Each number of vehicles owned by families will generate a home delivery of $10^{0,042}$ or 1.1 goods. It should be noted that this model only has a coefficient of determination of 0.148.

The Family's Monthly Income of 2-5 million and 20-50 million has a difference of 2.62 goods delivered in a week. This means, with an increase in income of 18-45 million, an increase in goods shipments is only 2.62, this effect is quite minimal. For the Number of Vehicles variable, each vehicle owned will increase the delivery of goods to homes by 1.1 goods per week. The thing to note is that the type of vehicle does not count, people who have 1 motorbike and people who have 1 car will produce the same number of shipments of goods every week.

6. Conclusions

This study analyses the factors that influence trips generation of home delivery and modeling the generation of home delivery trips with multiple linear regression methods on data collected through a questionnaire survey.

Factors that influence trips generation of home-delivery in e-commerce are the type of residential houses, gender, total family income, and the number of vehicles.

The best multiple linear regression model for predicting the trip generation of home delivery uses five variables, i.e. the number of arriving packages to the house in a week in logarithmic (Y2), type of residence (X1-1), a total income of 2 million to 5 million rupiahs per month (X7 -2), a total income of 20 million to 50 million rupiahs per month (X7-5), and the number of vehicles (X10). The equation of this model is Y = 0.345 + 0.259 (X1-1) - 0.134 (X7-2) + 0.103 (X7-5) + 0.042 (X10) with a coefficient of determination (R^2) of 0.148. Meaning that the variable X1-1. X7-2, X7-5, and X10 collectively affect the Y variable by 14.8%. This effect can be stated to be very little.

Based on the whole series of research that has been done, for future research, it is recommended to increase the number of samples that will be used for linear regression modeling so that the distribution of the data is more normally distributed and will have an impact on the strength of the model on the actual conditions. This study only focuses on developing a linear regression model, variables that are not normally distributed in future studies can be analyzed by another regression analysis method. In addition, it is necessary to conduct research on the trip generation model after the pandemic condition ends. In these extreme conditions, people's online shopping patterns are boldly unstable. This future research is expected to get results with higher variable correlations.

References

[1] Bjerkan K Y, Bjørgen A, and Hjelkrem O A 2020 *E-commerce and prevalence of last mile practices* Transportation Research Procedia 46(2019) **293–300** https://doi.org/10.1016/j.trpro.2020.03.193

[2] Hidayatno A, Destyanto A R, and Fadhil M 2019 *Model conceptualization on e-commerce growth impact to emissions generated from urban logistics transportation: A case study of Jakarta* Energy Procedia 156 (September 2018) **144–148.** https://doi.org/10.1016/j.egypro.2018.11.119

[3] Joewono T B, Rizki M, Belgiawan P F, and Irawan M Z 2020 *Why do shoppers keep making online shopping trips? Learning from evidence in Bandung, Indonesia* Asian Transport Studies, 6(July), 100016. https://doi.org/10.1016/j.eastsj.2020.100016

[4] Moriset B 2020 *e-Business and e-Commerce* International Encyclopedia of Human Geography (Second Edi, Vol. **4**). Elsevier. https://doi.org/10.1016/b978-0-08-102295-5.10044-7

[5] Russo F, and Comi A 2012 *City Characteristics and Urban Goods Movements: A Way to Environmental Transportation System in a Sustainable City* Procedia Social and Behavioral Sciences 39 **61–73.**

[6] Tamin O Z 2000 *Perencanaan dan pemodelan transportasi.*

[7] Visser J, Nemoto T, and Browne M 2014 *Home Delivery and the Impacts on Urban Freight Transport: A Review* Procedia Social and Behavioral Sciences 125 **15–27** https://doi.org/10.1016/j.sbspro.2014.01.1452

[8] Wang X C, and Zhou Y 2015 *Deliveries to residential units: A rising form of freight transportation in the U.S* Transportation Research Part C: Emerging Technologies 58 **46–55** https://doi.org/10.1016/j.trc.2015.07.004

[9] Xi G, Cao X, and Zhen F 2020 *The impacts of same day delivery online shopping on local store shopping in Nanjing, China* Transportation Research Part A: Policy and Practice, 136(February) **35–47**

An overview of inland freight transportation in Indonesia based on vehicle operating cost

Ridwan Anas[1]*, Medis S Surbakti[1], and Ika Puji Hastuty[1]

[1]Department of Civil Engineering, Faculty of Engineering, Universitas Sumatera Utara, Medan

*Email: ridwan.anas@usu.ac.id

Abstract. From an economic point of view, the high cost of freight transportation is indicated to increase the production of cost and weaken the industrial sector's competitiveness. Indonesia's logistic cost is the highest in Southeast Asia, which has absorbed more than 26% of the Gross Domestic Product (GDP). The operational costs of truck transportation, as the major freight transportation in Indonesia, is the highest compared to the operational cost of trucks in Vietnam, Thailand, Malaysia, and China. This paper introduces the issues related to the costs of inland freight transportation in Indonesia. The results show that high operational costs are caused by geographic, trip length, congestion, imbalance of freight movement, waiting time and the disutility of truck. Meanwhile, fuel consumption is a major component of the high transportation costs.

Keywords: freight transportation, inland freight transportation, transport cost, logistic system

1. Introduction

Freight transportation refers to the delivering products from the specific location to the another and allows the product to be obtained by the customer [1]. Its performance depends on the terms such as delivery schedules, the quality product, delivery service, and often disregarded as a source of competitive advantage [2]. The logistic cost is usually defined as cost that are related to the distribution of goods and costs related to the warehouse [3], which include four components of cost: transportation, inventory, storage and administration fee [4]. Transport costs are defined as a monetary value or expenses which are calculated by the flow of goods during the process of production (Taking Raw Material; manufacture to consumer).

Transporting the goods may be carried out not only through land, but also through rail, sea, inland waterway and air. The cost of each type of transportation varies and detailed, as transportation is the major component of logistics cost, reduction in transport costs will have a great impact to the total cost of logistics cost [5]. At the aggregate level, efficient transportation reduces costs in many economic sectors, historical data underlines that increasing transport costs by 10% reduces trade volume by more than 20% [6].

Although transportation is derived demand, the need for transportation cannot be separated from the regional economy, and must provide access to people and as a logistical function. On that subject, the debate on the contribution of transportation to the economic sector is not new matter [7], the high cost

IOP Conf. Series: Earth and Environmental Science 1000 (2022) 012004 doi:10.1088/1755-1315/1000/1/012004

of inland freight transport in Indonesia is indicated to cause increase in the costs of production thereforeit can reduce the competitiveness of the industrial sector [8].

Considering the cost of transportation has always been important in the industrial sector. The objective of the research was to identify the inland freight transport cost in Indonesia, the means used for moving the goods is a vehicle or a truck-trailer. The first issue is to determine the cost of the transportation in inland freight service which is considered as a part of the industrial sector. The second issue is the description of the inland freight transportation cost in Indonesia. The starting point of this paper is the concept of the cost of transportation, which provides a scientific description of an empirical study for inland freight transportation services in Indonesia.

2. Measuring the costs of transportation

There are many disparities of transportation costs for inland freight services between countries. For example; average costs for transporting a 20-foot container costs approximately $450 in Singapore and Malaysia however exceeding $5500 in Chad and the Central African Republic [9].

The cost of truck transportation service, as the main type of freight transportation services in Indonesia, costs US 34 cents per mile. These costs are higher than the average costs in other South Asian countries, such as Vietnam, Thailand, Malaysia, and China, which costs only US 22 cents per mile [8]. This paper explains the detail of the cost included in transportation service both fixed and variable cost. Other costs, such as the value of time, warehouse and terminal handling are not included.

2.1. Inland Vehicle Operating Costs Structure

Indeed, there isn't any clear consensus or concept, in particular the accurate measurement of transportation costs [10]. In this study, the costs of transportation are considered only from the truck transportation service point of view. From this point of view, there are two components of transportation cost, fixed costs, and variable costs [11].

The trucks used in the inland freight transportation service can either be owned by a party in the production department or can be rented from the third party that arranges the delivery of good, by delivering the cargo from the production sector to the consumer. The fixed costs included in the transportation service are time-related. Investment, insurance, administration, driver salary, and additional costs are included under fixed costs. The costs vary in transportation service are operational costs such as the cost of fuel and lubricant, maintenance cost, tires, loading, and unloading personnel cost, and other operating costs. The relationship between fixed costs and variable costs can be seen in the following figure [12].

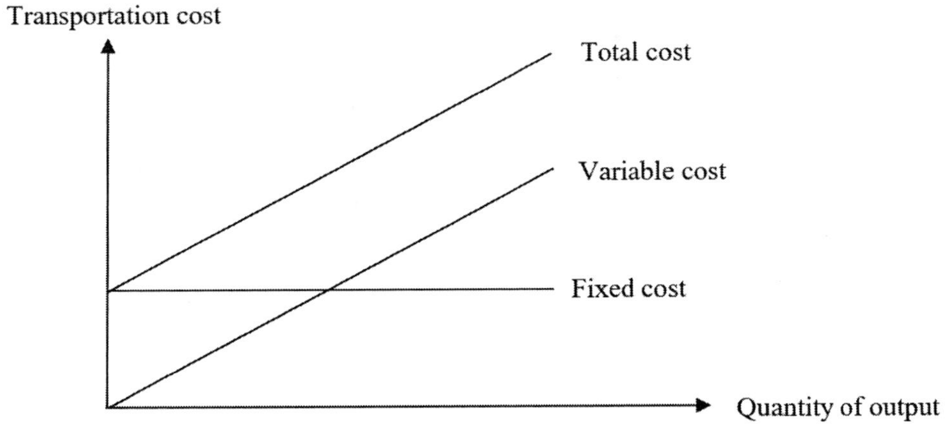

Figure 1. Transport cost and quantity.

There main factor that affect transportation costs are [13], mentioned below:

- Geography
  The distance and accessibility are the two main factors that are related to geographical conditions. Distance is the main factor that affects the costs of freight transportation services. It can be detailed in terms of the distance of the trip, travel time, and operational costs.
- The type of product
  The type of goods distributed will affect the costs, related to size, packaging, and the risk of damage. Insurance costs are also considered as a function of the value to the ratio of weight and the risk related with the transportation.
- Economies of scale
  Other conditions that affect transportation costs are related to economies of scale are the amount transported, to acquire lower unit of the transportation costs if transported in large quantities. For instance, larger container ships involve lower unit costs.
- Energy
  Transportation is a sector that consumes a large amount of energy, mainly fuel. Approximately 60% of the entire global fuel consumption is related to the transportation activities. For transportation costs, usually approximately + 25% of the entire operational costs are costs for consuming energy.
- Trade imbalances
  The trade imbalances will affect the transport of goods and the cost of transportation. As an example, it occurs when import exceed export, the container transportation service will suffer a deficit due to the trade imbalances.
- Infrastructure
  Transport infrastructure directly affects the speed of freight movement, as well as the efficiency of handling and transport processes in terms of their performance.
- Mode
  Different types of transport modes will have different transportation costs because each has its capacity limitations and operational conditions.
- Competition and regulation
  Transportation services that occur in highly competitive systems tend to be lower than systems which have limited competition (oligopolies or monopolies). In developing countries, the costs set due to regulations will impose additional transport costs.
- Surcharges
  Regarding the temporary conditions that may affect costs assumed by the transporting services, usually additional fuel costs, security costs, geopolitical risk premiums, and additional baggage fees.

2.2. Transport Cost involved in the industrial sector

An Inclusive and a sustainable industrialization is essential to achieve a sustainable development, among reducing the logistic cost and allow the efficient use of resources. Logistics is one of the non-core activities frequently outsourced in various industries during the previous decades, and controlling the logistic cost will increase the competitive advantage of the firms [14].

Another important issue in logistics costs is the proportion of the price of a product. Logistic costs are a substantial proportion of the price of a product (fig. 2), which is important to calculate and reduce the logistic cost [15].

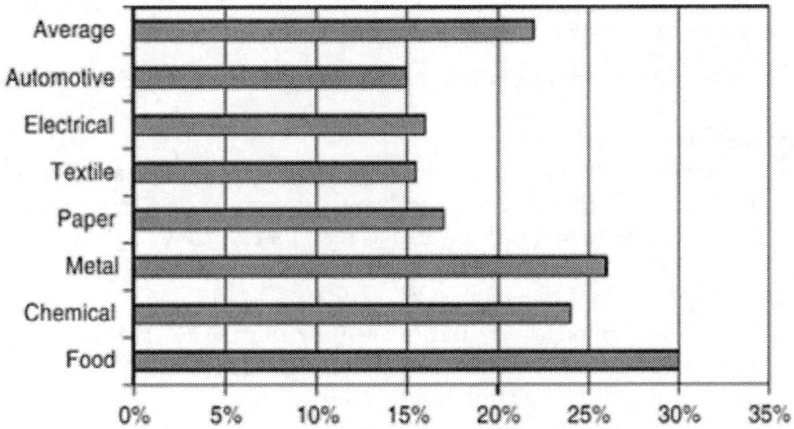

Figure 2. Logistics costs as a proportion of product prices [16].

The figure above illustrates the logistic costs of the European country. Indonesia's logistics costs are very high, in average approaching to 14.08% of production cost, compared to Japan's average logistic costs approximately 4.88% of the total production cost [17].

The contribution of the transport sector to the industrial sector is not only direct benefits, but also indirect benefits. Lower freight transport costs reduce logistic cost thereby increase the efficiency and reduce the prices of production inputs (fig 3).

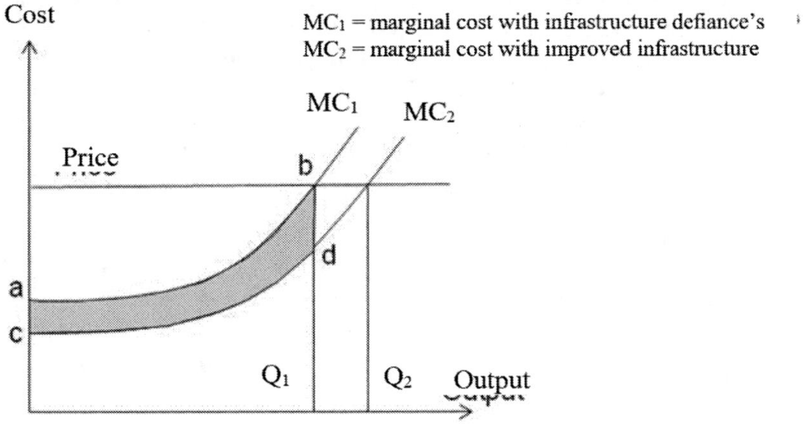

Figure 3. Transport cost and the efficiency of production [18].

Marginal costs (MC_1) at every level of production, and given the market price of their output, produce Q_1 units of output. As transport costs drop, the marginal cost curve shifts to a lower level (MC_2). Also, with efficient freight transportation, the company will be able to reach a more extensive market or expand the market range.

3. Methodology

3.1 Freight rate

freight rate is the price of transportation services paid by the user, as a monetary cost that is negotiated to move a unit of freight between two places (a specific origin and destination). It depends on the distance, delivery times, dimension or weight of the cargo.

The two elements to cost of transporting goods are vehicle operating costs and management fee, therefore the formulation of freight rate is illustrated as mentioned below:

Freight rate = Transportation Cost + Management Fee + Overhead Cost

3.2 Vehicle operating cost of truck

this study only considers vehicle operating costs to analyze the transportation costs of inland freight transport in Indonesia. The vehicle operating costs consist of fix costs and variable costs, whereas the formulation of vehicle operating costs is illustrated as mentioned below:

- Fuel consumption $= 0.284v^2 - 3.0644v = 141.68$
- Oil/lubricant consumption $= 0.00186v^2 - 0.22035v + 12.06486$
- Tyre wear $= .0015553v + 0.005933$
- Maintenance cost $= 0.01511v + 1.21$
- Depreciation $= {}^{1}/_{6v} + 300$
- Insurenace = annual interest of vehicle/average annual mileage

Where:

v = speed

4. Result and discussion

4.1. The cost of freight transportation in Indonesia

The geographical nature of Indonesia with its many islands is described as an uneven distribution of the population (56.9%) and GDP disparities (57.38%) which are concentrated in Java, and the conditions of transport infrastructure that differ between the western and eastern regions which pose major challenges in freight movement and further develop the regional economic disparities [17].

The total area of Indonesia is 7.8 million km^2 which consists of 5.9 million km^2 of sea area with a coastline length of 99,093 km and the land area of 1.9 million km^2. The domestic trade flows for Indonesia container see in following figure.

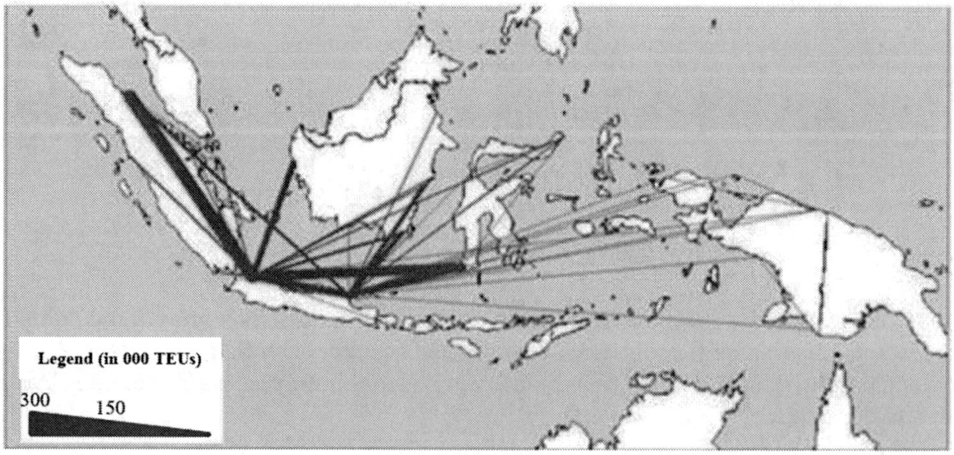

Figure 4. Domestic freight movement in Indonesia [19].

There is an imbalance in inter-island trade and competition in Indonesia as a result of high domestic logistics costs. Domestic freight movement is dominated by inland freight transportation [20]. Inland road transportation is estimated at 72.21%. higher compared to other services using railroad modes around 0.51%, and sea modes around 19.66% [21].

The national logistic cost amounts up to 25.03% of GDP, lower than the average amount of Indonesian logistics costs 27% of GDP. Indonesia logistic performance index and the rank its indicators in 2015 (table 1).

Table 1. Logistic performance index [21].

Country	Logistic Cost (% of GDP)	LPI Score	LPI Rank
United States	9.9	3,92	9
Japan	10.6	3,91	10
Singapore	8.0	4,00	5
Malaysia	13	3,59	25
Thailand	20	3,43	35
Vietnam	25	3,15	48
Indonesia	27	3,08	53

Indonesia rank rised from 75 to 53 in 2010-2014 period from 160 countries which have been surveyed. High logistics costs are a problem for any country's economy as it makes products and services which are less competitive. The logistic cost in Indonesia is the highest in the region compared to Singapore, Malaysia, Thailand and Vietnam. The highest cost component is the transportation cost compared to the costs of warehousing and administration fee [18].

Table 2. Freight transport cost per mode of transportation [21].

Year	Land	Water	Air	Rail
2008	78,13%	14,81%	1,58%	0,41%
2009	69,51%	22,59%	1,78%	0,58%
2010	70,96%	22,01%	2,31%	0,46%
2011	70,70%	22,04%	2,70%	0,51%
2012	72.21%	19.66%	2,20%	0,51%

Table 3 illustrates the freight movement, which comprises mostly which is more than 70% of the total freight transportation cost in Indonesia, but also the water/sea transport mode has a high share.

4.2. Inland freight transport cost in Indonesia

Indonesia is currently paying high transportation costs for the inter-island distribution of goods. Inefficiencies of inland freight transport result in disparities in the prices of commodities across regions. The cost details of inland freight transportation cost are obtained from literature review, interviews with trucking companies and simulation result.

Table 3. Cost component of truck.

Cost component	LPEM-UI [8]		LAPI (v=60 km/jam)		PT. A		PT. B	
	Rp/km	%	Rp/km	%	Rp/km	%	Rp/km	%
Fuel	1,370.46	39%	1,434.50	40%	1,030.00	31%	1,144.44	16%
Gasoline			581.70	16%	31.81	1%	82.33	1%
Tyre	456.82	13%	177.20	5%	241.87	7%	394.20	5%
Maintenance	140.56	4%	0.40	0%	42.33	1%	515.51	7%
Mechanic	105.42	3%	42.10	1%				
Drivers	386.54	11%	560.60	16%	181.41	5%	1,294.00	18%
Depreciation	175.70	5%	795.50	22%	1,425.00	43%	1,477.56	20%
Interest	351.40	10%						
Insurance					204.08	6%	234.00	3%
Tax					45.35	1%		
Administration					9.07	0.03%	2,128.35	29%
Others	527.10	15%			137.04	4%	33.80	0%

The table above illustrates that the fuel is the highest cost. The matters that affect fuel consumption are trip length, speed, geographical, and road conditions. Trucking of inter-island transportation is more preferred, although sea transportation is at least 30-40% cheaper. Flexibility and time are two key criteria for shippers/consignees for choosing the inland freight transport mode.

As a comparison, the average annual mileage of trucks in Indonesia is approximately 50,000 km, much lower than East Africa 's (100,000 km) or France 's (121,000 km), and Europe/IRU members (100,000 km). Additionally, the waiting time or immobilization before delivery in Indonesia could reach 18 hours compared to 12 hours average waiting time in East Africa and 1,6 hours in France [23].

In Jakarta, traffic congestion caused the transport cost from the industrial area (Cikarang) to Tanjung Priok Port ($13.54/km) is much higher compared to Malaysia ($7.9/km). For export-import activities at Tanjung Priok Port, the flow of containers dominated by single delivery trucks (90-94%), indicating the inefficiency of truck movements [24].

Reducing the high transportation cost which provides low profits, truck operators normally upgrades the size of truck cargo which is relatively more extensive (over dimension) to be able to carry more goods (overloaded trucks). In Indonesia, the percentage of overloaded trucks can reach more than 60% of the total number of trucks used for inland freight transportation [25].

5. Conclusion

This paper elaborates an overview of inland freight transportation costs in Indonesia as a part of the logistic system. An efficient logistics system is a crucial factor in the socio-economic development of Indonesia. Industrial policy has again become a major issue, Indonesia needs to develop a more integrated policy approach for transportation and in addition for supporting industrial development, by reducing the freight transport cost.

Inland freight transport is a preferred mode of inter-island transportation, although sea transportation is at least 30-40% cheaper. The transport cost is a major contributor to the overall cost of logistic. Our study discovered a disparity in population and GDP cause trade imbalances that becomes one of the factors causing high freight transportation cost in Indonesia.

For inland freight transportation, high operational costs are caused by geographic, trip length, congestion, waiting time and the disutility of truck. Meanwhile, fuel consumption is a major component of the high transportation costs. Dealing with the high transport cost, trucking companies usually transport the goods more than the maximum legal limit (overloaded and over capacity).

Acknowledgments
The authors gratefully acknowledge that the present research is supported by Ministry of Research and Technology. The support is under the research grant DRPM of the year 2020 Contract Number 11/AMD/E1/KP.PTNBH /2020.

References

[1] Parkhi, Shilpa, Jagadeesh D., Kumar, R. Arun 2014 *Journal of Supply Chain Management Systems* **3** 4 pp 31-38
[2] Tracey, M. 2004 *International Journal of Logistics Management* **15** 2 p 32
[3] Lambert, D. Grant, D. Stock, J., Ellram, L. 2006 *Fundamentals of Logistics Management, European Edition* McGraw-Hill Berkshire UK, p 57
[4] Zeng AZ, Rossetti, C. 2003 *Int J Phys Distrib Logist Manage* **33** 9 pp 785-803
[5] Muha Robert 2019 *Scientific Journal of Maritime Research* **33** p 102
[6] Rodrigue, Dr. Jean-Paul, Dr. Theo Notteboom 2009 *The Geography of Transport Systems 7th edition* Hofstra University New York, USA p 171
[7] Banister, David and Joseph Berechman 2000 *Transport Investment and Economic Development* UCL press pp 38-41
[8] LPEM-UI 2008 *Biaya Transportasi Barang Angkutan, Regulasi, dan Pungutan Jalan di Indonesia* The Asia Foundation pp34-52
[9] Behar, Alberto, and Venables, Anthony J. 2011 *A Handbook of Transport Economics* Edward Elgar Publishing UK chapter 5
[10] Estache , Antonio, Trujillo, Lourdes 2007 *European Conference Of Ministers of Transport* OECD Publishing pp 109-123
[11] Jacyna M., Wasiak M. 2015 *Combustion Engines* **162** 3 pp 85-90
[12] Martin, James R., Ph.D., CMA 1987 *Issues In Accounting Education* Spring pp 72-84
[13] Rodrigue, Jean-Paul 2013 *The Geography of Transport Systems Third edition* Routledge pp 236-239
[14] Bokor, Zoltán 2012 *Journal Traffic & Transportation* **24** 6 pp 515-524
[15] Farahani, Reza Zanjirani 2009 *Supply Chain and Logistics in National, International and Governmental Environment: Concepts and Models* Springer pp 57-59
[16] Amos P 2007 *Responding to global logistics trends with a National Logistics Strategy* World Bank
[17] Ministry of Transportation 2012 *Dukungan Sektor Transportasi Dalam Menunjang sistem logistik nasional* RAKORDATIN Kementerian Perhubungan pp 2-3
[18] Lakshmanan, T.R. 2011 *Journal of Transport Geography* **19** pp 1–12
[19] Indonesia Infrastructure Initiative 2010 *Academic Paper to Support National Port Master Plan* p 38
[20] Lubis et al (2005): Multimodal Transport In Indonesia: Recent Profile And Strategy Development, Proceedings of the Eastern Asia Society for Transportation Studies, Vol. 5, 46 – 64p
[21] World Bank 2013 *State of Logistic Indonesia* pp 21-23
[22] World Bank 2015 *State of Logistic Indonesia* 2015
[23] Raballand, Gaël, Macch, Patricia 2004 *The Need to Revisit Donors' Policies in Transport in Africa* World Bank reports p 5
[24] Anas, Ridwan, Sembiring, Irwan 2019 *7th International Conference on Euro Asia Civil Engineering Forum* 615 012126
[25] Jihanny, Jongga, Subagio, Bambang Sugeng and Hariyadi, Eri Susanto 2018 *MATEC Web of Conferences* **147** 5 p02006

THE EXTERNALITY OF PARCEL LOCKER SERVICE

Mia Meliaresti
Faculty of Engineering Universitas Indonesia
Depok, West Java
miameliaresti@hotmail.com

Nahry
Faculty of Engineering
Universitas Indonesia
Depok, West Java
nahry@eng.ui.ac.id

Abstract

A type of e-commerce which is growing rapidly is B2C (Business- to-Customer), thus, home delivery, the delivery service that supports this activity, is also developing. As the result, there is competition between home delivery services that causes last mile segment to become fragmented. Parcel locker exists to improve the operational effectiveness of home delivery. Additionally, planning for the delivery of goods has not considered the externalities that may arise from the delivery trips to the impactees. This study aims to analyse the effectiveness of the parcel locker to reduce the external costs due to the CO2 emissions produced by the delivery trips. The effectiveness is represented as a comparison between the external costs of the parcel locker and the one of home delivery service. The result showed that in term of externalities reduction due to CO2 emissions home delivery are three to seven times more effective than parcel locker. To increase the use of parcel locker, it is necessary to relax the delivery slot-time arrangement in order to reduce the externalities while maintaining good service to customers.

Keywords: B2C, home delivery, parcel locker, last-mile delivery, emission, externalities

INTRODUCTION

The growth of e-commerce in Indonesia is increasing year by year. It affects the proliferation of the B2C (Business-to-Consumers) business concept, which is a type of e-commerce business that markets goods and direct service from manufacturers to consumers. By the rapid growth of B2C business, the need of goods delivery also increases. The type of the goods delivery that specifically becomes the main support of e-commerce activities is home delivery system [1]. The increasing of this need causes the emergence of many goods' delivery services, which triggers a competitive market between them. This condition encourages consumers to use various delivery services that they consider being able to meet their needs. As a result, with the point of location of the consumers, which tends to be spread out, and the number of different delivery services used, the activities of goods delivery in the last segment from the overall logistics system – the last mile segment- becomes fragmented [2]. The fragmentation of delivery activities in this segment causes an increase in the number of kilometers of delivery trips. This is exacerbated by various technical problems that arise related to delivery, especially in the home delivery type. Therefore, the last mile segment is not efficient, most expensive, and most polluting segment [3] with various negative impacts, including noise, congestion, and increased air pollution [4]. To reduce the negative impact of delivery activities in the last mile segment, parcel locker is presented as an innovative product delivery system that is located near areas where the consumers live. In addition, parcel locker is also placed in central office areas, parking areas, shopping centers, and public transportation stops.

Parcel locker has the potential to reduce traffic congestion, increase cargo users by consolidating deliveries, and shorten the process of handling goods [5]. On the other hand, although various efforts have been made to improve the efficiency and effectiveness of delivery activities, the schematics of the delivery system still do not fully consider the negative impact on the environment [6]. This impact is classified as an impact caused by externalities, which is the aspect felt by those who are not directly involved in the goods delivery [7]. One aspect of externalities that has a significant role in the planning of the delivery system is air pollution. With the development of delivery activities that cause the adverse impacts, especially in the last mile segment, planning in the delivery system needs to involve aspects of externalities, one of which is air pollution. Regarding the parcel locker system as an innovative solution to reduce the number of unsuccessful delivery and the number of kilometers travelled, it is necessary to study the effectiveness of parcel locker in reducing the impact of air pollution to create a sustainable delivery transportation system that not only considers the economic aspects, but also the environmental aspect. The current study aims to analyse the effectiveness of the parcel locker, which is represented by the comparison between the external costs of home delivery system and the one of parcel locker.

LITERATURE REVIEW

The main problem of home delivery is the significant fragmentation of delivery due to the insistence of consumers who shop in small quantities and expect the orders to arrive in a short time [1]. In addition, the time of receipt of goods is uncertain, so consumers are forced to wait at home or, sometimes, when the goods arrive at their home or destination there are no consumers [8]. Security problem is also an obstacle because sometimes the goods do not arrive or the goods are damaged when the consumer receives them [9].

Parcel locker is a machine for delivery activities that is regularly placed in locations that are frequently visited, and is also monitored [1]. The location can be placed in the office center area, a parking area, a shopping centre, or a public transportation stop. There is a significant difference between the use of home delivery service and parcel locker, which is the use of a locker as a warehouse. In the use of a normal warehouse, more employees are needed, thereby reducing the efficiency of the warehouse function. Second, the locker system is equipped with technology that plays a role in increasing the efficiency of all delivery activities and the security of goods. Third, the parcel locker system provides convenience for the consumer with the estimated time presented in real-time so that they can more easily predict when the goods will arrive.

The goods delivery, both through home delivery and parcel locker, is clearly related to transportation planning. In general, transportation planning still focuses on improving operational efficiency and route optimization to obtain delivery methods with the most efficient operational costs (internal cost) without considering environmental impacts. In fact, the impact of transportation of goods related to air pollution appears very clear [10]. This impact is called an externality, in which parties are not directly involved in transportation activities also get the impact. One way of measuring it is by reviewing the variables of vehicle kilometers travelled (VKT), fuel consumption, and CO2 emission factors [11].

Externalities will increase due to the increasing number of delivery transportation activities, especially in land transportation modes. Thus, it is necessary to quantify the negative externalities that are generated by transportation activities by representing them as costs, which are called external costs.

RESEARCH METHOD

The effectiveness of the parcel locker delivery system is represented by a comparison between the external cost for each item of home delivery and the external cost for each item using parcel locker. This means that the parcel locker delivery system is considered to be more effective if the external cost of each items delivered is less than the external cost of each item in home delivery. Home delivery trip data were obtained from one operator of home delivery service as many as 50 trip data, while parcel locker trip data were obtained from one operator of parcel locker service totaling 540 data.

For home delivery, there are five warehouses for five municipalities in Jakarta, namely Sunter warehouse representing North Jakarta City, Pejati warehouse representing East Jakarta City, Cengkareng warehouse representing West Jakarta City, Kemayoran warehouse representing Central Jakarta City, and Pesanggrahan warehouse representing the South Jakarta city. The data obtained from home delivery operator are the location of the origin warehouse, the district of destination, the number of packages sent, the type of vehicle, and the type of gasoline. The lockers in delivery services provided by parcel locker operator act as a substitute for a hub or warehouse for home delivery. The parcel locker owned by the operator consists of three types, namely universal locker, operational locker and customer locker. However, currently, not all types of parcel lockers have been activated in the Jabotabek area. Operational lockers have been developed at several points in Jabotabek. Operational locker is used as a temporary storage place for goods before the goods are carried by the courier to the final destination, namely the consumer. This operational locker is located in the transit hub. This study focuses on seven transit hubs in the five municipalities in DKI Jakarta. Those are Bright Artha Gading Locker and Malacca Lockers in North Jakarta, Rawamangun locker in East Jakarta, Joglo Locker in West Jakarta, Bendungan Hilir Locker in Central Jakarta, and Lebak Bulus Locker and Bright Gandaria Locker (COCO) in South Jakarta. Data obtained from parcel locker operator include the location of locker, courier name, preferred delivery time, total delivery distance, number of delivery items, type of vehicles, and type of gasoline.

Externalities in the delivery of goods are aspects that are experienced by parties who are not directly involved in the activity of goods delivery, in positive or negative way [7]. This current study examines the externalities related to air pollution. There are six levels in the calculation of externalities based on the ease of the method and the accuracy level of the result [11] (Figure 1). This study used the third level model as shown on Figure 1 by taking into account measured activity data, assumptions of fuel consumption efficiency, and emission factors as main components of the calculation. The delivery activity was measured from vehicle kilometers travelled [12]. This study examined the externalities that are generated by each item of delivery. Equations 1 and 2 show the formulas to calculate the external cost of each item in a single delivery trip.

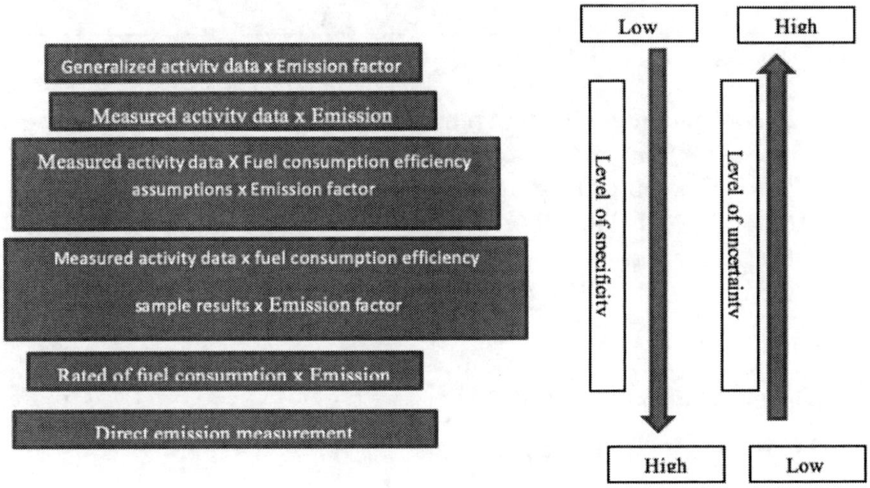

Figure 1. Methods of Externalities Calculation

$$Externalities\ per\ item = \frac{Vehicle\ Kilometers\ Traveled}{The\ number\ of\ items\ deliver}\ x\ Fuel\ consumption\ factor\ x\ Emission\ factor \quad (1)$$

$$External\ costs\ per\ item\ = Externalities\ per\ item\ x\ unit\ cost \quad (2)$$

VKT (Vehicle Kilometers Travelled) is the total distance of one delivery trip. In home delivery, the VKT is measured by the sum of the total stem mileage and the total drop mileage of the home delivery couriers. Stem mileage is the distance from the last warehouse to the delivery zone, or vice versa, while drop mileage is the distance between delivery points in a delivery zone [13]. In the parcel locker, the VKT is the total distance to deliver all the parcel by the parcel locker couriers.

The fuel consumption factor represents the amount of fuel needed by a vehicle to move one unit distance. In general, this factor is influenced by the type of vehicle (Table 1).

Table 1. The Fuel Consumption Factor

Transportation Modes	Fuel Consumption (km/liter)	Fuel Consumption (liter/km)
Car	12	0.0833
Motorcycle	43.85	0.285
Box (diesel)	10	0.1

source: [14]

The emission factor represents the amount of CO_2 emissions produced per one liter of fuel. This factor is influenced by the type of fuel used (Table 2).

Table 2. Carbon Emission

Types of Fuel	Carbon Emission (kgCO_2/liter fuel)
Diesel oil	2.2
Fuel oil	2.6

source: [15]

The external cost per delivered item represents the monetary value of the externality of CO2 emissions for every single item of goods delivered. The unit cost of CO2 emissions for Indonesia is €7.46 / ton CO2 [16]. According to Euro currency exchange rate on June 5, 2020 as IDR 15,889.81, thus, the external cost of CO2 emissions is IDR 118,239.78 / ton CO2. As it is converted to kilograms, the external cost of CO2 emissions is IDR 118/kg CO2.

RESULT AND DISCUSSION

External Cost per Item Home Delivery

- *Vehicle Kilometres Travelled (VKT) of Home Delivery*

In order to test the similarity of delivery activity patterns in each municipality, the VKT was tested by the Kruskal-Wallis test. The hypotheses are as follows:

H0: There is no difference in the average value of VKT in each hub location of home delivery.
H1: There is a difference in the average value of VKT in each hub location of home delivery.

The result of Kruskal-Wallis analysis showed a sigma of 0.003 ($p < 0.05$), which means that there is a significant difference in terms of VKT from each municipality. The result of Mann-Whitney analysis indicated the differences in VKT in North Jakarta and Central Jakarta, East Jakarta and Central Jakarta, West Jakarta and Central Jakarta, and South Jakarta and Central Jakarta. Central Jakarta shows relatively low VKT. The difference in characteristics in Central Jakarta is due to this area having a relatively small area (only 7% of the total area of DKI Jakarta) and it is dominated by office areas. The lesser residential areas in Central Jakarta may cause the activity of goods home delivery is low. In addition, it can be concluded that home delivery activity is still dominated by home destinations. The data also indicates that the North Jakarta, West Jakarta, East Jakarta and South Jakarta areas have high goods delivery activity, while the Central Jakarta areas show low delivery activity. For home delivery, the average VKT for high activity area is 175.4 km, whereas for low activity area is 73.3 km.

- *The Total Item of Home Delivery*

In order to test the similarity in the number of delivery items in each municipality, this variable was tested by the Kruskal-Wallis test. The hypotheses are as follows:

H0: There is no difference in the average number of delivery items at each hub location of home delivery.
H1: There is a difference in the average number of delivery items at each hub location of home delivery.

The result of Kruskal-Wallis test showed a sigma value of 0.352 ($p > 0.05$), which means that there is no significant difference in the total delivery items from each municipality. Thus, the post-hoc was not performed. This shows that there is no difference in the characteristics of consumer purchase of goods. The consumers tend to buy goods in the form of parcels which is in relatively small quantities. Overall, the mean total delivery items for home delivery for one round trip is 101 items with a standard deviation of 0.9 items.

- *External Cost per Item of Home Delivery*

In high goods delivery activity area, the average external costs per items for one round trip of home delivery is IDR 12.3 / item with a standard deviation of IDR 0.9 / item. For low delivery activity area, the average external costs per item is IDR 5. 13 / item, with a standard deviation of IDR 0.25 / item.

External Cost per Item Parcel Locker

Parcel locker operator serves the delivery of goods using locker by applying the concept of same day delivery, which means that the goods will reach the consumer in just one day. Delivery of goods is also classified based on time slot to simplify the delivery process.

- *Vehicle Kilometres Travelled of Parcel Locker*

To test the similarity of delivery activity patterns in each municipality, the VKT was tested by the Kruskal-Wallis test. The hypotheses are as follows.
H0: There is no difference in the average VKT in each hub location of parcel locker.
H1: There is a difference in the average VKT in each hub location of parcel locker.

The result of Kruskal-Wallis test shows a sigma value of 0,000 ($p<0.05$), which means that there are significant differences in the VKT from each municipality. The Mann-Whitney test results show that there is a difference in North Jakarta and Central Jakarta, East Jakarta and Central Jakarta, West Jakarta and Central Jakarta, as well as South Jakarta and Central Jakarta. Central Jakarta shows relatively low VKT. The difference in characteristic in Central Jakarta is due to this area having a relatively small area (only 7% of total area of DKI Jakarta) and it is dominated by office areas. The lack of residential areas causes the activity of home delivery low. Thus, it can be concluded that the North Jakarta, West Jakarta, East Jakarta and South Jakarta areas have high goods delivery activity, while the Central Jakarta areas has low delivery activity. In parcel locker service, the average vehicle kilometers travelled for high activity area is 19.4 km, whereas for low activity it is 14.5 km.

- *Total Delivery Items of Parcel Locker*

To test the similarity in the number of delivery items in each municipality, this variable was tested by the Kruskal-Wallis test. The hypotheses are as follows.

H0: There is no difference in the average number of delivery items at each hub location of parcel locker.
H1: There is a difference in the average number of delivery items at each hub location of parcel locker.

The result of Kruskal-Wallis test showed a sigma value of 0.279 ($p > 0.05$), which means that there is no significant difference in the total of delivery items of each municipality. Thus, the post-hoc was not performed. This shows that there is no difference in the characteristics of consumer purchase of goods. The consumers tend to buy goods in the form of parcels in relatively small quantities. Overall, the mean of the total delivery items for parcel locker for one round trip is 5.04 items with a standard deviation of 5.7 items.

- *External Cost per Item of Parcel Locker*

In high goods delivery activity area, the average external costs per items for one round trip of parcel locker service is IDR 36.3 / item with a standard deviation of IDR 19.7 / item. For low delivery activities area, the average external costs per item is IDR 34.7 / item with a standard deviation of IDR 23.9 / item.

The Effectiveness of Parcel Locker

Overall, in high delivery activity area, the average external cost for home delivery is IDR 12.3/ item, while the parcel locker service is IDR 36.3 / item. In low goods delivery activity area, the average external cost for home delivery is IDR 5.13 / item, while for the parcel locker it is IDR 34.7 / item. From these two categories, it can be concluded that home delivery system is more effective than parcel locker.

Both types of delivery service have similar characteristics in terms of the type of vehicle and the type of gasoline used, so the values of the fuel consumption factor and CO2 emission factor are the same. Thus, the factor that distinguishes the two services is the VKT per item. The VKT of home delivery have an average value of 175.4 km for high delivery activity area and 73.3 km for low delivery activity area, while parcel locker delivery has an average value of 19.4 km for high delivery activity and 14.5 km for low delivery activity. The VKT of home delivery is greater than the parcel locker. This is due to the location of the parcel locker hubs that are spread across the five municipalities, and they are located near to the offices and residential areas, thereby it increases the efficiency in terms of length of delivery trip. On the other hand, a home delivery warehouse is not designed to be located near an office or residential area.

However, the external cost per item of the parcel locker is greater than the external cost per item of home delivery. This is due to other factors, namely the total number of delivery items. The number of delivery items in home delivery reached an average value of 101 items, while the parcel locker only had an average value of 5 items. In other words, the total item of home delivery is 20 times higher than the parcel locker. It is due to the parcel locker has a time slot system so the couriers are required to adjust the number of delivery items with a certain slot. As a result, the total goods delivered was small. In contrast to home delivery, the home delivery operators can regulate the allocation of delivery items without being fixed by a certain time since the home delivery service does not consider time slot. It can increase the quantity of items delivered. Consequently, the vehicle kilometers travelled per item on home delivery system is smaller than parcel lockers. As the result, the external cost per item in the home delivery system is also smaller than parcel lockers. In other words, the home delivery system is more effective than parcel lockers in term of reduction of external cost.

CONCLUSION

Parcel Locker as an innovative delivery system is established to reduce the negative impact of home delivery services in the last mile segment. This research analyzed the effectiveness of parcel locker compared to home delivery in term of their externalities. Based on the travel diary of parcel locker operator and home delivery operator, it is concluded that for high delivery activities area the average external cost of home delivery is IDR 12.3 per item and IDR 36.3 per item for the parcel locker service. For low delivery activities area, the average external cost of home delivery is IDR 5.13 per item and IDR 34.7 per item for the parcel locker. The external costs of home delivery are three times smaller than the parcel locker in high delivery activities area and seven times smaller in low delivery activities area. It means that home delivery is more effective that parcel lockers in terms of reduction of externalities. This is due to the fact that the parcel locker applies a time slot system, which causes inexplicability in regulating delivery times, while the home delivery does not have such a system. In terms of service to customers, the time slot system is intended to guarantee the timeliness of receiving goods. Research on parcel locker [17] shows that punctuality of delivery time is the most important factor that influences consumers in choosing the delivery service. In order to maintain the existence of parcel locker as an innovative solution to reduce the number of unsuccessful delivery and the number of kilometers travelled, and to give more attention not only to the economic aspects, but also the environmental aspect it is important to be able to reduce externalities while maintaining service levels for parcel locker customers. Relaxation of time slot arrangements is needed as well as more efficient delivery of route arrangements. Increasing the number of deliveries is also expected to reduce the externalities per item of delivery.

ACKNOWLEDGMENTS

This research is supported by the Research Fund of PUTI (Publikasi Terindeks Internasional Prosiding) of Universitas Indonesia, 2020.

REFERENCES

Iwan, S., Kijewska, K., and Lemke, J., 2016, Analysis of Parcel Lockers' Efficiency as the Last Mile Delivery Solution - The Results of the Research in Poland (Tenerife, 17-19 June 2015).

Souza, R.D., Goh, M., Lau, H.C., Ng, W.S., and Tan, P.S., 2014, Collaborative Urban Logistics - Synchronizing the Last Mile: A Singapore Research Perspective (Bali, 17-19 June 2013).

Gevaers, R., Voorde, E.V., and Vanelslander, T., 2011, City Distribution and Urban Freight Transport, Cheltenham, Edward Elgar Publishing, page 60.

Pronello, C., Camusso, C., and Valentina, R., 2017, Last mile freight distribution and transport operators' needs: which targets and challenges? (Shanghai, 10-15 July 2016).

PT PaxelBox Digital Unggul, 2017, http://paxel.co

Bektas, T., Ehmke, J.F., Psaraftis, H.N., and Puchinger, J., 2019, The role of operational research in green freight transportation, European Journal of Operational Research, 274, page 804-823.

Demir, E., Huang, Y., Scholts, S., and Woensel, T.V., 2015, A selected review on the negative externalities of the freight transportation: Modelling and pricing, Transportation Research Part E, 77, page 95-114.

Visser, J., Nemoto, T., and Browne, M., 2014, Home Delivery and the Impacts on Urban Freight Transport: A review, Procedia - Social and Behavioural Sciences, 125, page 15-27.

van Duin, J.H.R., de Goffau, W., Wiegmans, B., Tavasszy, L.A., and Saes, M., 2016, Improving Home Delivery Efficiency by Using Principles of Address Intelligence for B2C Deliveries. Transportation Research Procedia, 12, page 14-25.

Hernandez, A.S., Alvarez, P., Lerga, L., Rubiano, L.R., and Faulin, J., 2016, Improving Home Delivery Efficiency by Using Principles of Address Intelligence for B2C Deliveries, Transportation Research Procedia, 12, page 14-25.

Williams, I., Kemp, S., Coello, J., Turner, D.A., and Wright, L.A., 2016, A beginner's guide to carbon foot printing. Carbon Management, 3, page 55-67.

Fenn, M., 1997, "Transportation Statistics Annual Report". United States Department of Transportation, Washington, U.S.A.

Rushton, A., Oxley, J., and Croucher, P., 1997, Transportation Statistics Annual Report, United States Department of Transportation, Washington, U.S.A.

Sukarno, I., Matsumoto, H., and Susanti, L., 2016, Transportation energy consumption and emissions - a view from city of Indonesia, 2.

Badan Perencanaan Pembangunan Nasional, 2014, Definition of Fuel Consumption, http://ranradgrk.bappenas.go.id/

OECD, 2019, Taxing Energy Use, http://oecd-ilibrary.org

Vilardi and Nahry, 2019, Consumer's point of view on parcel lockers in DKI Jakarta, MATEC Web of Conferences, 270.

Development of Land Used Intensity-Traffic Interaction Model for Bandar Lampung City, Indonesia

Muhammad Zainal Ibad[a], Reza Asriandi Ekaputra[b,c] , Arif Ramadhan[a], Rahayu Sulistyorini[d], Zenia F Saraswati[a], Muhammad Alfat Rizki Pratama[b], Salwa Nabilla Antiqasari[a]

[a]Departement of Urban and Regional Planning, Institut Teknologi Sumatera, Jalan Terusan Ryacudu Nomor 1, Kabupaten Lampung Selatan, Provinsi Lampung, Indonesia
[b]Departement of Civil Engineering, Institut Teknologi Sumatera, Jalan Terusan Ryacudu Nomor 1, Kabupaten Lampung Selatan, Provinsi Lampung, Indonesia
[c]Department of ICT Integrated Safe Ocean Smart Cities, Dong-A University, Busan, Republic of Korea
[d]Departement of Civil Engineering, Faculty of Engineering, Universitas Negeri Lampung, Jl. Prof. Soemantri Brojonegoro, No 1, Bandar Lampung
reza.asriandi@si.itera.ac.id

Abstract Social history has shown that a city plays an important role in meeting human needs such as housing, service facilities, entertainment areas, and transportation networks. Therefore, the interaction between demand and infrastructure creates a traffic flow. Previous studies show that traffic flow is strongly correlated with land use types' scale and operational characteristics. In addition, traffic volume can represent logistics distribution, which is one of the parameters to assess regional economic conditions. This condition prompted researchers to research to develop an interaction model between land-use intensity and traffic. The study was conducted in Bandar Lampung City, Indonesia, the economic center of Lampung Province, Indonesia. The methodology used in this study is the multiple linear regression analysis for the origin-destination matrix. This analysis was performed using 23 parameters that could influence the model, but we try to find the most significant influence variables in this study. The process of evaluating some statistical parameters is considered as decision parameters. Finally, the analysis results show a strong correlation between land use and traffic volume in Bandar Lampung, Indonesia. The best model $y = 62{,}3 + 2{,}275\ x_{16} + 1{,}348\ x_{20}$ with x_{16} is store building area, and x_{20} is the number of schools.

Keywords: Land Use, Interaction Model, O-D Matrix, Regression, Step Wise

1. Introduction

The city functions as a service system for divergent people need by providing housing, commercial and services areas, entertainment areas, and transport networks [1]. The components are interacting each other and finally develop a land use function. The quality of this land use function is different for every location and depend on the distribution of city density, land-use functions, traffic flow. This movement is influenced by the size and scale of activities that differ in each land use type or the intensity of land use [2]. Some research describes various kinds of activities, for example, settlements, industries, offices, and shopping centers as types of land/activities, with sizes namely: housing units, office units, office area, school area, number of workers and number of employees [3].

Bandar Lampung, Indonesia, has a vital role in the economy of Lampung Province, Indonesia. Based on BPS Bandar Lampung City data, Indonesia contributed 25.45% to the GRDP of Lampung Province, Indonesia in 2016, which occupies the 2nd position as the most significant contributor to GRDP in Lampung Province, Indonesia. In addition, Bandar Lampung, Indonesia, has the status of a National Activity Center (PKN) and is a metropolitan city, so that Bandar Lampung, Indonesia, has a high level of importance in Lampung Province, Indonesia.

Reliable economic conditions are ensured by the smooth distribution of products and the smooth activities of the population. However, land-use problems in Bandar Lampung City, Indonesia, especially for trading and services, tend to grow and develop following the main road network (located on the side of the main road), causing side barriers, decreased speed, increased vehicle volume and increased activity in and out of vehicles this results in reduced accessibility. This condition lead researcher to do a research related to the land use-traffic interaction.

A number of studies have been carried out related to landuse-traffic interaction to find the best mathematical relationship. Good prediction can reduce a number of problems derived from transportation such as:
1. Vehicle emission impact to the environment
2. Congestion impact to the economy
3. Change of consumer surplus

2. Research Methodology

In the research methodology chapter, we will explain the material of the research and how is the research conducted. This process must be carefully proceeded to provide a good quality research.

2.1. The Data Collection

In this study there are some of data which used for analysing. The data was categorized in primary data and secondary data that will be explains in the table below:

Table 1. The Data Collection

No	Data	Data Category	Source
1	Traffic Counting	Primary	Survey
2	The Number of Worker	Secondary	BPS, Dinas Ketenagakerjaan, Dinas Penduduk Catatan Sipil
3	The Number of District Population	Secondary	BPS
4	RTRW Document of Bandar Lampung City	Secondary	Bappeda
5	Number of Education Facilities	Secondary	BPS
6	Number of Health Facilities	Secondary	BPS
7	The Number of Student	Secondary	BPS
8	Number of Attraction	Secondary	Dinas Pariwisata

Source: Analysis Results, 2019

2.2. *Target 1: Identify the movement of Indonesia, Bandar Lampung city.*

This analysis was used to know the trip generation and trip attraction, the route, and the distribution in the zones. In discovering the movement that happened in the community, It needed theoretical analysis such as traffic flow analysis and O-D Matrix analysis. The analysis outcome will be used as the variable in the multiple regression analysis[4].

2.2.1. *Traffic Flow.*

In obtaining the flow in the format of pcu/hr, the Vehicle's total (in the same category of Vehicles) will be multiplied with the factor of passenger car equivalent (emp)[5].

$$Q_{pcu} = Q_{veh} \times pcu \tag{1}$$

With:
Q_{pcu} = Traffic Flow (pcu/hour)
Q_{veh} = Vehicle Volume (veh/hour)
pcu = Passenger car equivalence

The emp value depended on the road type, the total traffic flow in the lane, or the volume of traffic (veh/hr) and lane width (meters). The total vehicles formula in the lane was showed in the equation below:

$$\sum_{i=a}^{b} Q_{pcu}\, T_X\, i = Q_{pcu}\, T_X\, a + Q_{pcu}\, T_X\, b \tag{2}$$

With:
$Q_{pcu}\, T_x\, a$ = Traffic flow direction a at location T_x;
$Q_{pcu}\, T_x\, b$ = Traffic flow direction b at location T_x.

After that, the Traffic Flow (Q_{pcu}) will be used as input data in O-D Matrix Analysis.

2.2.2. *O-D Matrix.*

O-D Matrix was created by input the value of Traffic Flow in the observed zones. O-D Matrix was used for representing the movement pattern which was happened in the observed area[6]. The O-D matrix was created from two dimensions matrix, which consists of rows and columns that present O-D zones in the observed area. The substance of the matrix giving us the Interzone movement information.

$$O_i = \sum_{i}^{n} T_{id} \tag{3}$$

$$D_d = \sum_{d}^{n} T_{id} \tag{4}$$

$\sum_{d}^{n} T_{id}$ = Number of Generations of origin zone i to destination zone d in each row d
$\sum_{i}^{n} T_{id}$ = Number of Attractions of origin zone d from destination zone i in each column i

The Origin-Destination Matrix, to have reliability, must meet the following requirements:

$$T_{total} = \sum_{i=A}^{I} O_i = \sum_{d=A}^{I} D_d \tag{5}$$

$\sum_{i=A}^{I} O_i$ = Number of columns O_i (i = A - I)
$\sum_{d=A}^{I} D_d$ = Number of lines D_d (d = A - I)

After that, the outcomes from the matrix consisting of O_i and D_d will be used as the value of trip generation (origin) and trip attraction (destination) as 'y variable' in the multiple regression analysis.

2.3. *Target 2: Indonesia, Bandar Lampung City Movement Model Identification based on the Land-Use Intensity.*

Traffic interaction model development of Bandar Lampung, Indonesia, the multiple linear regression analysis would be involved. Which explained below:

This analysis aims to measure the influence of the independent variable on the dependent variable and predict the dependent variable using the independent variable [7]. There are two types of variables in this analysis: the independent variable (x) as the explanatory variable and the dependent variable (y) as the explained variable. Regression explains the relationship between the independent and dependent variables or states the size of the influence expressed in the following equation:

$$y = a + b_1x_1 + b_2x_2 + \dots + b_nx_n \tag{6}$$

Where:
y = Dependent variable
x_n = Independent variable
a = Constant / *intercept*
b_n = Coefficient
n = Number of samples
The value of constants and coefficients has obtained using the following equation:

$$b = \frac{N\sum_i^n(X_iY_i) - \sum_i^n(X_i)\sum_i^n(Y_i)}{\sum_i^n(x_i^2) - (\sum_i^n x_i)^2} \tag{7}$$

$$a = \bar{y} - b\bar{x} \tag{8}$$

$\bar{y}$ = Average value of y
$\bar{x}$ = Average value of x

The following criteria determine the good regression model:

a. The coefficient of determination (r^2) close to 1;
b. The sign (positive or negative) from the regression coefficient is corresponding with the theory;
c. The regression constant value (a) is close to 0; and
d. The number of independent variables (x_n) will be good if it is more and substantial.

3. Research Analysis & Result

3.1. *O-D Matrix Analysis*

Movement modelling in Bandar Lampung City, Indonesia uses a zone system. The zone used is based on the City Area Section. Therefore, in the subsequent analysis, nine zones will be found according to the number of BWK in Bandar Lampung City, Indonesia. Taking a zoning system based on administrative boundaries makes it easier to obtain socio-economic data needed for further analysis. Based on the traffic volume survey results, the number of movements in each zone is obtained. With the following data:

Table 2. Traffic Flow

No	Code		Direction ($i-d$)	Q (Pcu/Hour) am	Q (Pcu/Hour) pm	No	Code		Direction ($i-d$)	Q (Pcu/Hour) am	Q (Pcu/Hour) pm
1	T1	a	G-A	1159.4	1328.8	12	T12	a	F-B	613.4	553.8
		b	A-G	1869.6	1137.8			b	B-F	652.8	830
2	T2	a	A-B	2912	1659	13	T13	a	B-F	1209.2	1118.4
		b	B-A	1943.8	2237.4			b	F-B	2005.4	1158.2
3	T3	a	C-A	3410.2	2257.6	14	T14	a	C-E	789.4	960.6
		b	A-C	2179.4	3082.4			b	E-C	913.6	973.8
4	T4	a	A-I	380	853.8	15	T15	a	C-E	1456.4	1828
		b	I-A	641	622.6			b	E-C	1693.8	1572.8
5	T5	a	G-A	979	1376.6	16	T16	a	E-e4	954.6	768.6
		b	A-G	1507.8	680			b	e4-E	637.4	796
6	T6	a	G-A	1336.6	1373.2	17	T17	a	D-e3	3084.6	3160.2
		b	A-G	1869.6	1137.8			b	e3-D	2379.2	2244.8
7	T7	a	H-e1	396.8	456.4	18	T18	a	D-I	1949.2	1018
		b	e1-H	463.8	390.4			b	I-D	1106.2	883.2
8	T8	a	H-G	1269.2	1583.2	19	T19	a	I-e2	1498.6	1369
		b	G-H	495.2	814.4			b	e2-I	1475.4	818.6
9	T9	a	G-F	1165.6	1008.6	20	T20	a	D-I	1290.6	1129.6
		b	F-G	1019.8	1386.8			b	I-D	1019	1462
10	T10	a	e6-F	560	631.6	21	T21	a	D-I	1388.8	964.2

No	Code		Direction (i – d)	Q (Pcu/Hour) am	Q (Pcu/Hour) pm	No	Code		Direction (i – d)	Q (Pcu/Hour) am	Q (Pcu/Hour) pm
		b	F-e6	686.8	655.2			b	I-D	750	1237.2
11	T11	a	e5-F	1044.2	831.8	22	T22	a	C-D	2249.6	2961.4
		b	F-e5	686.8	1054.2			b	D-C	2845.6	2589.6
						23	T23	a	I-G	1169.2	796
								b	G-I	637.4	768.6

Source: Analysis Results, 2019

Table 3. O-D Matrix

O \ D	A	B	C	D	E	F	G	H	I
A	--	3295.4	3082.4	--	--	--	8401	--	3520.3
B	3970	--	633	--	--	1209.2	--	--	--
C	3410.2	633	--	2961.4	2788.6	--	--	--	1457.5
D	-	-	2845.6	-	1351	-	-	-	5359.6
E	-	-	2667.6	1514	-	-	-	-	-
F	-	2005.4	-	-	-	-	1386.8	-	-
G	7205.6	-	-	-	-	1165.6	-	1660.9	768.6
H	-	-	-	-	-	-	2429.7	-	-
I	3307.5	-	1457.5	4536.4	-	-	1169.2	-	-

Source: Analysis Results, 2019

After the O-D matrix has been obtained, the data will be used for calculating the total movement which happened in Bandar Lampung, Indonesia based on BWK with this formula:

$$Ttotal_i = O_i + D_d \tag{9}$$

After calculating the T_{totali} value, the data has been collected into the table below:

Table 4. Total Trip

BWK	Generation	Attraction	Total
A	18299.1	17893.3	36192.4
B	5812.2	5933.8	11746
C	11250.7	10686.1	21936.8
D	12716.4	11391	24107.4
E	5136.2	4935.6	10071.8
F	5133.2	4050.6	9183.8
G	10800.7	13386.7	24187.4
H	2998.7	2123.9	5122.6
I	11946	12581.4	24527.4

IOP Conf. Series: Earth and Environmental Science 1000 (2022) 012006 doi:10.1088/1755-1315/1000/1/012006

Source: Analysis Results, 2019

According to the data in the table, the flow is divided according to the source location and the destination location to form the desired line pattern leading to the points of the centroid area and has a line thickness based on the amount of movement between the centroid areas. It can be seen in Figure 1.

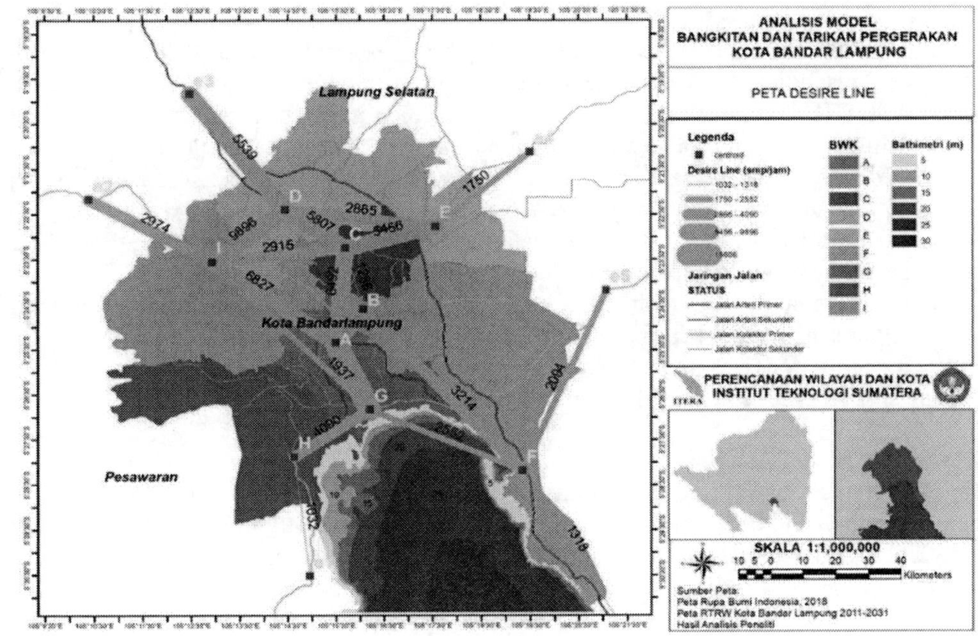

Figure 1. Desire Line Maps

From the Figure 1, sorted from the largest to the smallest, which has shown in the table below:

Table 5. Normality Test of Data

No.	Movement (pcu/Hour)	Desire Line
1	15606	A-G
2	9896	D-I
3	7265	A-B
4	6827	A-I
5	6492	A-C
6	5807	C-D
7	5456	C-E
8	4090	G-H
9	3218	B-F
10	2915	C-I
11	2865	D-E

No.	Movement (pcu/Hour)	Desire Line
12	2552	G-F
13	1937	G-I
14	1266	B-C

Source: Analysis Results, 2019

The movement pattern shows a large pattern of passenger movement between BWK G and BWK A with 15,606 pcu/hour. This indicates a very large movement between zones compared to movement between other zones. The BWK A zone is an area with land designation as a city center and a center for trade and services, while BWK G is a designated area for the city government center and provincial government. These two areas become the center for the movement of goods and people compared to other BWK. The second-largest movement is 9896 pcu/hour between BWK I and BWK D. It is an area for education and a residential area, making the relationship between the two zones intense. Meanwhile, areas with large movements between 5000-6000 pcu/hour are I-A, A-B, A-C, C-E, and C-D. The relationship between areas I, B, E with BWK A is the 3rd largest movement where zones I, B, E are designated as urban settlements, making this an important movement because people move from their homes to the city center for trade and services. The relationship between other zones such as H-G, G-F, G-I, B-C is the smallest movement in the city of Bandar Lampung, Indonesia.

3.2. Movement Model Analysis

In obtaining the Bandar Lampung City, Indonesia movement model, multiple linear regression analysis was carried out, which had initial assumptions before the study, namely the assumptions of normality, multicollinearities, and heteroskedasticity. For this reason, an assumption test was carried out to fulfil this.

3.2.1. *Normality Test of Data.* The first step is to perform a normality test to meet the assumption of multiple linear regression. Namely, the error value follows the normal distribution function. Therefore a normality test is carried out. Shapiro Wilks is used in this method because the number of n is nine (9) included in a small sample, the analysis using Shapiro Wilks. An error normality check was carried out in the SPSS output, which could be seen through Shapiro Wilks' hypothesis testing, suitable for the small sample type ($n<50$).

Normality hypothesis:
H_0: normally distributed error
H_1: not normally distribute the error

The number of research samples is nine samples, so it is included in the small sample, for that, the Shapiro Wilks method is used. The test criteria are to accept the null hypothesis if the p-value of Shapiro Wilks' test is greater than 5% (0.05).

Table 6. Normality Test of Data

	Kolmogorov-Smirnov[a]			Shapiro-Wilk		
	Statistic	df	Sig.	Statistic	Df	Sig.
Total of Movement	0.204	9	.200*	0.935	9	0.533
Number of Traditional Market	0.196	9	.200*	0.891	9	0.203
Number of Mall	0.182	9	.200*	0.904	9	0.276

	Kolmogorov-Smirnov[a]			Shapiro-Wilk		
	Statistic	df	Sig.	Statistic	Df	Sig.
Number of Industry	0.284	9	0.035	0.766	9	0.008
Number of Attractions	0.239	9	0.146	0.81	9	0.027
Number of Schools	0.148	9	.200*	0.952	9	0.717
Service Trade Area	0.214	9	.200*	0.888	9	0.191
Office Area	0.397	9	0	0.554	9	0
Settlement Area	0.18	9	.200*	0.944	9	0.623
Industry Area	0.364	9	0.001	0.5	9	0
Attraction Area	0.279	9	0.042	0.676	9	0.001
Public Service Facility Area	0.167	9	.200*	0.904	9	0.274
Store Building Area	0.266	9	0.066	0.847	9	0.07
Office Building Area	0.421	9	0	0.541	9	0
Housing Area	0.163	9	.200*	0.96	9	0.797
Industrial Building Area	0.372	9	0.001	0.491	9	0
School Building Area	0.286	9	0.032	0.796	9	0.018
Attraction Building Area	0.263	9	0.073	0.81	9	0.027
Number of Students	0.182	9	.200*	0.907	9	0.298
Number of Industrial Worker	0.396	9	0	0.489	9	0
Number of Government Employee	0.354	9	0.002	0.665	9	0.001
Number of Population	0.121	9	.200*	0.972	9	0.908

*. This is a lower bound of the true significance.

a. Lilliefors Significance Correction

Source: Analysis Results, 2019

After the normality test and data transformation were carried out, the number of research samples was nine samples, so it was included in the small sample, for that the Shapiro Wilks method was used. The test criteria are to accept the null hypothesis if the p-value¬ of Shapiro Wilks' test is greater than 5% (0.05)

Based on the SPSS output table, it is known that Shapiro Wilks' p-value for all variables studied is more than 0.05. so it can be said that the hypothesis H0 is accepted. That is, the error follows a normal distribution.

3.2.2. *Correlation Test of Data.*

Correlation test was conducted between the independent variable and the dependent variable using Bivariate Pearson Product Moment using SPSS with the following results:

Table 7. The Correlation of dependent Variable with Independent Variable

Code	Variable	Pearson Correlation	Sig. (2-tailed)	N	Correlation	*p-value*
x_{16}	Store Building Area	0.848	0.004	9	Very Strong	sig
x_{10}	Service Trade Area	0.834	0.005	8	Very Strong	sig

Code	Variable	Pearson Correlation	Sig. (2-tailed)	N	Correlation	*p-value*
x_{17}	Number of Government Employee	0.722	0.028	5	Strong	sig
x_{26}	Attraction Area	0.655	0.23	9	Strong	-
x_{14}	School Building Area	0.631	0.068	5	Strong	-
x_{15}	Office Building Area	0.613	0.272	9	Strong	-
x_{11}	Public Service Facility Area	0.595	0.091	5	Strong	-
x_{20}	Number of School	0.559	0.118	9	Strong	-
x_8	Office Area	0.542	0.346	9	Intermediate	-
x_{22}	Number of Student	0.426	0.253	5	Intermediate	-
x_7	Number of Attraction	0.305	0.462	8	Intermediate	-
x_{25}	Attracting Area	0.249	0.687	6	Very Weak	-
x_6	Number of Industry	0.238	0.57	8	Very Weak	-
x_{23}	Number of Industrial Worker	0.199	0.706	9	Very Weak	-
x_1	Number of Mall	0.12	0.821	9	Very Weak	-
x_{18}	Industry Area	0.096	0.878	9	Very Weak	-
x_2	Settlement Area	0.083	0.831	6	Very Weak	-
x_{12}	Industrial Building Area	0.073	0.907	9	Very Weak	-
x_{19}	Housing Area	0.044	0.91	5	Very Weak	-
X_3	Number of Traditional Market	0.266	0.489	5	Very Weak	-

**. Correlation is significant at the 0.01 level (2-tailed).

*. Correlation is significant at the 0.05 level (2-tailed).

Source: Analysis Results, 2019

In other words, if the area of the shop building and the area of trade and services increase, the free will also increase. Then the variable Number of Civil Servants has a strong, significant, and unidirectional correlation with the independent variable. Other variables Office Building Area, Tourism Area, Public Service Facility Area, Office Area, School Building Area, have a strong and unidirectional correlation but not significant with the independent variable. Meanwhile, the variables Number of Students, Number of Traditional Markets, Area of House Building, Number of Malls, Residential Areas, Areas of Industrial Buildings and Industrial Areas have a very weak and insignificant correlation with the independent variables. The following condition is multicollinearities. If there is a correlated variable, the elimination of the variable will be carried out by looking at the correlation number of the variable to the "Free" dependent variable. The variable with a weaker correlation to the dependent variable will be eliminated. The following results of SPSS processing for correlation tests between independent variables can be seen in the table below.

The analysis results conclude a correlation between the independent variables, namely, x_{16} with x_{10}, x_{26}, x_{14}, and x_{11}. Then these variables will be eliminated from the analysis because they have a smaller correlation number with the dependent variable. Then x_{20} is correlated with Public Service Facility Area, Number of Schools, and Number of Students. Then these variables are eliminated from the analysis because the correlation number is smaller than x_{20}. Other variables x_{27} and x_7, are not correlated with other variables. So after the correlation test, the selected variables are "store building area (x_{16}), school building area (x_{20}), population x_{27}, and number of tourist objects x_7.

Table 8. Eliminate Variable

Correlations													
	y	x_{16}	x_{10}	x_{26}	x_{14}	x_{20}	x_{17}	x_{15}	x_8	x_{11}	x_{23}	x_{27}	x_7
y	1	.848**	0.83	0.72	-0.65	0.631	0.6	0.59	0.55	0.54	0.42	0.372	0.305
x_{16}	.848**	1	0.99	0.72	-0.58	0.424	0.84	0.25	0.43	0.81	0.2	0.386	0.329
x_{10}	.834**	.993**	1	0.72	-0.58	0.45	0.8	0.29	0.39	0.79	0.19	0.36	0.24
x_{26}	.722*	.727*	0.72	1	-0.51	0.718	0.89	0.67	0.55	0.72	0.41	0.29	0.44
x_{14}	-0.65	-0.58	-0.5	-0.5	1	-0.68	1	-0.4	0.01	1	-0.2	0.3	-0.12
x_{20}	0.631	0.424	0.45	0.71	-0.68	1	0	0.76	0.58	-0.2	0.7	0.361	-0.15
x_{17}	0.613	0.844	0.82	0.89	1	0.005	1	0.27	0.46	0.8	-0.2	0	0.91
x_{15}	0.595	0.256	0.29	0.67	-0.48	.767*	0.27		0.38	0	0.4	0	0
x_8	0.559	0.438	0.39	0.55	0.01	0.586	0.46	0.38		0.7	0.83	0.78	0.36
x_{11}	0.542	0.812	0.79	0.72	1	-0.28	0.84	0.09	0.79	1	-0.1	0.46	0.88
x_{23}	0.426	0.207	0.19	0.41	-0.27	.701*	-0.2	0.48	0.83	-0.1	1	0.49	0.06
x_{27}	0.372	0.386	0.36	0.29	0.3	0.361	0	0.05	0.78	0.46	0.49	1	0.09
x_7	0.305	0.329	0.24	0.44	-0.12	-0.15	0.91	0	0.36	0.88	0.06	0.09	1

**. Correlation is significant at the 0.01 level (2-tailed).
*. Correlation is significant at the 0.05 level (2-tailed).

Source: Analysis Results, 2019

3.2.3. *Multiple Linear Regression Analysis*

Multiple linear regression is used to model the relationship between the independent variable and the dependent variable [8] with the number of variables more than one. The fixed variable in this study is Total Movement (y) which will be explained by the independent variable, namely "Shop Building Area (x_{16}), School Bang Area (x_{20}), and Total Population (x_{27}), number of tourist objects (x_7). This linear regression analysis uses the OLS (Ordinary Least Squares) method, whose assumptions have been fulfilled by researchers in previous tests.

The results of independent modelling with stepwise analysis model type 1 can be seen in the table above. Based on predetermined criteria, the selected model is the model generated in the 3rd stage. Some of the reasons why the 3rd stage model was chosen are as follows:
a) The corrected Coefficient of Determination (r^2a) has the highest Adjusted R^2 value of 0.732 compared to other stages.
b) The value of the regression constant is the smallest among the other models, which is 1.794. the value of the regression constant (r^2a) is better if it is close to one.
c) The p-value < 0.05, i.e., 0.007 at stage 3 and 0.008 at stage 4, stage 3 was chosen because it has a smaller sig value, so this regression model is feasible to predict movement.
d) The number of variables included in the model is more than in stage 4. Then the sign of the regression coefficient on the variables x_{16} and x_{20} is following the initial hypothesis, which is positive (+).

Therefore, according to the criteria, the multiple linear regression model in the third stage was chosen as the regression model. This section describes the regression equation to determine the constant number and test the significance of the regression coefficient hypothesis:

Table 9. Regression Coefficient

Model		Unstandardized Coefficients		Standardized Coefficients	t	Sig.	Correlations		
		B	Std. Error	Beta			Zero-order	Partial	Part
1	(Constant)	1.794	0.483		3.713	0.01			
	Store Building Area	0.357	0.1	0.707	3.583	0.012	0.848	0.826	0.64
	School Building Area	0.13	0.077	0.331	1.899	0.144	0.631	0.565	0.3

Source: Analysis Results, 2019

Its regression equation:
because the data is transformed into logarithmic form, the equation will be converted back into normal form with the following equation:

$$y = 62{,}23 + 2{,}275\ x_{16} + 1{,}348\ x_{20} \qquad (10)$$

y = Traffic Movement (pcu/hour)
x_{16} = Store Building Area
x_{20} = Education Building Area

4. Conclusion

Based on the results of the study, it can be concluded that it is true that transportation and land use are two related things where transportation plays a role as a medium of community movement in meeting their needs such as work, school, and some other land use plays a role in providing activity space (residential, public infrastructure, industry, trade, and services). Following Khisty's statement, movement is influenced by land-use intensity (size and scale of activity). The result shows that the variables with the criteria for the size of the land use, namely the area of the shop building and the area of the school building, affected the transportation movement.

The results of the analysis show that from 4 variables, namely: store building area, school building area, number of students, and number of tourist attractions, only two variables: Store Building Area and School Building Area which are proven to affect the amount of traffic movement with a regression coefficient of 2.275 for Building Area Shops and 1,348 for School Building Areas. These two variables are included in the regression model with the following regression equation.

This indicates that the development of Trade and Service activities and education increases or decreases. Its development will be directly proportional to the development of transportation movements in the

City of Bandar Lampung, Indonesia. The trade and service building area is defined as the building that functions as a trading activity at the store level to supermarkets and shopping centers. Then the area of the school building is defined as the area of the building to provide primary education to higher education classes.

$$Y = 62{,}23 + 2{,}275\ x_{16} + 1{,}348\ x_{20} \tag{11}$$

y = Traffic Movement (pcu/hour)
x_{16} = Store Building Area
x_{20} = Education Building Area

As one of the important cities in Bandar Lampung, Indonesia already has transportation problems, such as 66% of roads have a low accessibility level. Another problem is that public transportation reliability (BRT and Angkot) cannot accommodate people's mobility. The transportation facilities also insignificantly developed. This condition leads people to use a private car instead of public transport.

So in dealing with transportation problems in Bandar Lampung, Indonesia, the researchers conclude that by using the movement model, which is a representation of real conditions in a simplified form, it can be a reference in calculating the needs of the city community according to the size and activity of land use as well as traffic movement conditions in the coming year. So that the balance and effectiveness between transportation capabilities and land use activities occur and produce an efficient Bandar Lampung City, Indonesia in the function of urban space and the role of clans in serving the people of Bandar Lampung City, Indonesia.

References

[1] L. Liu, H. Chen, and T. Liu, "Study on urban spatial function mixture and individual activity space from the perspectives of resident activity," *IEEE Access*, vol. 8, pp. 184137–184150, 2020, doi: 10.1109/ACCESS.2020.3029177.

[2] G. Le Provost *et al.*, "Contrasting responses of above- and belowground diversity to multiple components of land-use intensity," *Nat. Commun.*, vol. 12, no. 1, 2021, doi: 10.1038/s41467-021-23931-1.

[3] R. Damayanti, D. N. Gandarum, and J. S. Juwana, "Pengaruh Guna Lahan Dan Pola Pergerakan Bandara Soekarno Hatta Land Use and Movement Patterns Influence Against Road Service Level Around Soekarno Hatta Airport," *J. Arsit.*, vol. 15, no. 1, pp. 1–12, 2015.

[4] M. R. E. Manoppo, T. K. Sendow, D. Fakultas, T. Jurusan, S. Universitas, and S. Ratulangi, "Manoppo, Mecky R.E dan Sendow, T.K. 2011. Analisa Bangkitan Pergerakan dan Distribusi Perjalanan," vol. 1, no. 1, pp. 17–23, 2011.

[5] MKJI, "Mkji 1997," *departemen pekerjaan umum, "Manual Kapasitas Jalan Indonesia."* pp. 1–573, 1997.

[6] T. Sobral, T. Galvão, and J. Borges, "Visualization of urban mobility data from intelligent transportation systems," *Sensors (Switzerland)*, vol. 19, no. 2, 2019, doi: 10.3390/s19020332.

[7] B. H. Susilo, *Dasar-dasar rekayasa transportasi*. 2015.

[8] G. K. Uyanık and N. Güler, "A Study on Multiple Linear Regression Analysis," *Procedia - Soc. Behav. Sci.*, vol. 106, pp. 234–240, 2013, doi: 10.1016/j.sbspro.2013.12.027.

IOP Conf. Series: Earth and Environmental Science 1000 (2022) 012007 doi:10.1088/1755-1315/1000/1/012007

Pedestrian Volume Characteristic in The Commercial Area in Yogyakarta

Muchammad Zaenal Muttaqin[12*], Ahmad Munawar[1*], Muhammad Zudhy Irawan[3*]
[1]muchzaenalmuttaqin@eng.uir.ac.id
[2]munawar@ugm.ac.id
[3]zudhyirawan@ugm.ac.id
[1]Civil and Environmental Engineering, Universitas Gadjah Mada, Jl.Grafika no.1, Yogyakarta, Indonesia
[2]Civil Engineering Department, Universitas Islam Riau, Jl Kaharuddin Nasution 113, Pekanbaru, Indonesia

Abstract. Pedestrians are different from vehicles. Pedestrian has its unique characteristic, especially for its flexibility in traffic. Pedestrians play an important role in supporting sustainable roads as the impact from the vehicle such as pollution, even crowded vehicles create more problems than pedestrians. Pedestrians' characteristics can be divided based on their activity, area, and even based on their behaviour when they are walking. All pedestrian management policies must be started from knowing local and then global characteristics. This will serve more details about pedestrian lanes, and can also be used to derive fundamental parameters for pedestrian operations and to create pedestrian models. In traffic research, one of the volume functions related to speed and density was also used to pre-analyze pedestrian behaviour. The purpose of this study was to introduce the local characteristic of pedestrians in Yogyakarta as a basic term for making regulations or policies as well as better planning for pedestrian lanes. The results showed that pedestrian volume had different characteristics between morning flow and afternoon flow. The characteristic volume of the morning flow tended to decrease due to the difference in temperatures which was lower in the morningandhigher temperatures during the day. As for the afternoon flow, pedestrian fluctuations increased duetothe temperatures decreasefromnoonto evening. This was reinforced byan independent T test. Another result showed that pedestrians groupsdominated the shopping area, hospital area, as well as public space. Lastly, the characteristics ofpedestriansin the sidewalk commercial areaalsohad different characteristicsin terms of carrying goods, whereas the shopping areasweremoredominatedbypedestrianscarrying goodsthan others. These basic terms were expected to be the basic foundation for managing and planning pedestrian lanes based on their local characteristics.

1. Introduction

Pedestrians are different from vehicles. Both of them often run into conflicts with each other on the road. Pedestrian has its unique characteristic. In traffic areas, pedestrians play an important role to support sustainable roads as the impact of vehicles such as pollution, even crowded vehicles create more problems than pedestrians (1). Pedestrians' characteristics can be divided on their activity, area, and based on their behaviour when they are walking. All pedestrian management policies must be started from knowing local characteristics. This will serve as the foundation for what is necessary in terms of pedestrian planning, required infrastructure for pedestrian lanes, and can also be used to derive fundamental parameters for pedestrian operations and to create pedestrian models. Pedestrian activity is typically in conflict-free zones or designated lanes. Indonesia, on the other hand, lacks the necessary territory to walk. Pedestrians frequently come into collision with various impediments, such as other vehicles. On the other hand, the highway system's surface area, as a result of vehicle traffic, is constantly expanding. According to the Central Bureau of Statistics, Indonesia's road infrastructure continues to grow year after year. Even now, road infrastructure is being dramatically improved as a result of toll construction. Additionally, pedestrian routes have been steadily constructed throughout Indonesia, including in Yogyakarta. Yogyakarta's rapid development over time has pushed urban conditions closer to urban sprawl (2). Pedestrian characteristics will serve as the foundation for what is necessary in terms of pedestrian planning, the infrastructure required for pedestrian lanes, and can also be used to derive fundamental parameters for pedestrian operations and to create pedestrian models. The volume of pedestrian traffic is one of the features of pedestrian parameters. In traffic research, one of the volume functions is to calculate traffic flow hours in order to estimate the busiest flow for the purpose of designing and evaluating traffic lanes. The purpose of this study was to ascertain the characteristics of pedestrians in the city of Yogyakarta. Additionally, the research examined the area, volume, and sidewalk characteristics in commercial locations. The study was limited to pedestrian profiles solely through group of pedestrian and carrying goods.

2. Theory

Linch (1987) in his research [4] argued that pedestrians are part of public space and an important aspect of urban space. A pedestrian path has a minimum width that serves to provide pedestrian comfort in walking. The effective width of the pedestrian lane seen from the individual needs is 60 cm with additional wiggle room as wide as 15 cm to move without carrying goods. So if it is assumed that one lane is used by two people, either hand in hand or two pedestrians crossing each other without any contact, then the width of the pedestrian path is at least 150 cm [2]. Based on pedestrian regulation in Indonesia, from the Public Works Minister Number 3 of 2014, the dimensions of the pedestrian path should be provided with minimum standards of pedestrian path requirements based on the volume of pedestrians passing through the path as well as the condition of the path area. Therefore, pedestrian lane width (W) can be guided by the following formula [6],

$$W = \frac{P}{F} + n \tag{1}$$

Description: P = Pedestrian volume plan (ped/ meter /minute); W = Width of pedestrian path (meters); F = maximum current plan (ped/meter/min); n = Additional width (meters);

Countries that have placed this formula in the planning of pedestrian paths are Indonesia and Brazil. Indonesia set the F value of 35 ped /meter/minute, while Brazil set b of 25 ped /meter/minute. Additional widths also vary according to assumptions based on applicable references. Indonesia regulation has land use assumptions, including a value of 1.5 for the market areas, a value of 1 for a non-market shopping areas, and a value of 0.5 for other areas. On the other hand, Brazil determines the additional width as a fixed barrier. Each barrier on pedestrians has a discharge width greater than its physical size. In detail, the additional width according to [8] is based on the range of pedestrians with surrounding conditions, such as fences that are 0.45 m, doors, and windows that are 0.25 m apart. In addition to these calculations, there is also a minimum pedestrian path width limit that is determined based on the typical area and pedestrian safety.

3. Research Method

To determine the characteristics of pedestrians, this study used the results of a field survey in the form of video footages that were calculated manually for characteristic of pedestrian located in commercial areas in Yogyakarta. Firstly, this research chose a pedestrian path that had special requirements, for instance having a separate pedestrian lane from vehicle lanes. The research locations were Jalan Sudirman, Jalan Sardjito , Jalan Solo, Jalan Panembahan Senopativ (Taman Pintar), and Jalan Malioboro. Location observations also measured the dimensions of available pedestrian lanes. The main survey was conducted with a video recorder which was used to record the situation at the observation sites. The camera was placed in a location that did not interfere with pedestrians' activities so that the data collected was data from the natural movement of pedestrians. From these data, the number and time of pedestrians in exploring the research site were obtained. The entire locations had sidewalk that were built separately from vehicle lanes and were included in the commercial location in the city of Yogyakarta. The research was conducted for 4 hours at each location where each observation time was assumed to be the busiest time of each observation location.

4. Result and Discussion

This study was located in five sidewalks in the commercial area in Yogyakarta. In detail, the five locations were located on Sudirman Street, Solo Street, MalioboroStreet, Panembahan Senopati Street, and Sardjito Street. All five roads had separate sidewalks form vehicle traffic lanes. The research time was taken four hours which was adjusted to the regulation of the Ministry of Transportation in 1997 which stated that in observing the pedestrian paths, the time for collecting observation data was four hours.

The results showed that the width of the sidewalk at the observation site had met the requirement where the minimum width for pedestrian paths in commercial area was two meters. In addition, the observation time looked different from one side to the other. This was due to the researcher's assumption that visitors to pedestrian attractions in commercial areas in Yogyakarta dominated on weekends compared to a normal day. However, this was a different situation for the pedestrian in the hospital area, where the busy time is at the beginning of the week because of the accumulation of patients who were not served optimally on the weekend. The complete details of the research location are as follows,

Table 1.Table of characteristics of the observation location

No.	Location Name	Location Characteristics	Observation time	Weather	Daily Temperature (^{0}C)
1	Sudirman Street Sidewalk	Office/Public space	Sundays, 7:30 a.m. - 11:30 a.m.	Sunny	22.5 – 30.8
2	Sardjito Street Pavement	Hospital	Mondays, 9:15 a.m. - 1:15 p.m.	Sunny	22.6 – 31.4
3	Solo Street Sidewalk	Shopping	Saturdays, 11:45 a.m. - 3:45 p.m.	Sunny	22.3-31.4
4	Panembahan Senopati Street Sidewalk	Shopping	Sundays, 2:30 p.m. - 6:30 p.m.	Sunny	22.5-30.8
5	Malioboro Street Sidewalk	Shopping	Saturdays, 11:30 a.m. - 3:30 p.m.	Sunny	23-30

The observation times listed are the peak condition of the pedestrian, such as on the Malioboro sidewalk at 11.30-15.30 WIB, where the current is higher in the afternoon because it is approaching the weekend and many people spend time walking and enjoying the location. In general, a total of 2872 pedestrians were recorded in five locations during four hours of observation for each location. This is in accordance with the pedestrian regulation which states that the observation of pedestrian paths can be carried out for a minimum of four hours [14]. Analysis results state that the location with the highest pedestrian volume detected is Jalan Malioboro, with a graph of currents that increase significantly from the first hour to the last hour. One of the high-current pedestrian volumes is above 100 pedestrians per hour [15], so that the sidewalks of Jalan Panembahan Senopati and Jalan Malioboro become high-current pedestrian paths, with a maximum current per hour during observation exceeding 100 ped/hour. In addition, the results from the current data show practically no similar time pattern of the traffic flow event. Traffic growth is generally uneven for each observation location. Pedestrian volume data indicate that fluctuations in pedestrian volume will be based on the function of the reviewed area. Sudirman location, for example, it was detected that during the day the volume was decreases. This was because, in public spaces, the temperature affected pedestrian activity.

As previously explained, there was a link between the increase temperature in the morning to afternoon or evening with fluctuation in pedestrian volume. In the process of proving the comparison, an independent T sample test was used with data on the volume of pedestrian flow conditions in the morning. Paired T-tests has normal distribution requirements required for each data [16]. Therefore, normality tests were conducted against the PHF values of each PHF variety in order to be further processed. Peak Hour Factor value will be statistically analyzed using Kolmogorov Smirnov method at a confidence level of 95% (α=0.05) to test the distribution of data and the results are shown in the table below. The results of the analysis concluded that the distribution of data for all FJS values with the four varieties of PHF was normally distributed so that the T test can be conducted.

Table 2. Normal distribution test

Survey Location	Asymp. Sig. (2-tailed)	Conclusion
Jalan Sudirman	0.17	Normal
Jalan Sardjito	0.2	Normal
Jalan Solo	0.2	Normal
Jalan Panembahan Senopati	0.08	Normal
Jalan Malioboro	0.2	Normal

As previously explained, the observation of Sudirman Street and Sardjito Street was taken in the morning, while for Solo Street, Panembahan Senopati, and Malioboro Street, the volume data was taken during the day. The two data sets were then tested for average differences through independent T-samples to prove the compariso pf the influence of low temperatures in the morning to high temperatures during the day and high temperatures during the day to low temperatures in the evening. Due to the unequal amount of data, which is 32 amount of data for the morning and 48 amount of data in the afternoon, the independent sample test was conducted with the assumption of unequal variance [17]. Table 1 shows the result of the t-test. It can be assumed that the population variances between commuters and older adults in the morning and afternoon flow is significantly different. The two-tail significance of pedestrian volume for unequal variances indicates that there is a significant difference in walking volume between the morning and afternoon flow. This can be seen by the significance value of zero (less than 0.05). This concludes that the difference in pedestrian volume characteristics in commercial areas sidewalk was influenced by the ambient temperature of the pedestrian paths. In addition to statistics, this conclusion is also supported by the statement [18]–[22] which explain that one of the considerations for pedestrians to travel is the weather conditions and temperature when going to walk. Daytime conditions with higher temperatures will affect pedestrians' interest in walking. In contrast, afternoon conditions with lower temperatures than during the day will affect the movement of pedestrians. This is visually proven that in locations observed in the morning, such as observations on Sardjito street and Sudirman street, it tends to decrease compared to other locations observed in the afternoon.

Table 3. T-test Paired Sample Table

Data type	t-test value	Sig. (2-tailed)	Conclusion
Morning flow vs Afternoon flow	-5.481	0	Acceptable

Pedestrian movement activity will depend on the path used, one of which is related to the width of the pedestrian. According to [23], the pedestrian width requirement depends on the existing pedestrians volume. This study uses Indonesian pedestrian regulations No.3 of 2014 related to the width of pedestrian requirement. The pedestrian volume input in this calculation is the maximum volume per hour for the entire observation time. This study concluded that the width of the existing pedestrian lanes is still in accordance with the width of pedestrian needs based on the regulation of the Minister of Public Works No. 03/PRT/M/2014 related to pedestrian planning, especially in the sidewalk areas. Overall, the width of pedestrian needs is between 1.1 to 1.3 meters, while all locations are at a pedestrian width of 2 to 5.5 meters. In addition, the same regulation also mentions that the ideal width of the pedestrian path is at least 2 meters mainly related to pedestrian free spaces located in shopping areas or offices. However, this width still does not meet the need for a sense of security for pedestrians to walk, especially for Sarjito Street and Solo Street. According to another reference, the existing width of 2 meters in shopping areas and crowded areas, i.e. hospitals for the Asian region, is still less than the width of safer pedestrians, which is at least 3 meters (14).

Table 4. Table of pedestrian characteristic

Location name	Max volume per hour (ped/meter)	Width of requirement(PU 2014)	Existing width
Sudirman Street	6,42	1,02	5,30
Sardjito Street	40,00	1,04	2,00
Solo Street	50,50	1,05	2,00
Panembahan Senopati Street	65,63	1,10	3,20
Malioboro Street	107,82	1,28	5,50

Pedestrian profiles are often found in sidewalk commercial areas, which are related to the group of pedestrians. Pedestrians tend to walk in groups rather than individually in commercial areas for pedestrian convenience. The following graph shows the profile of pedestrians at the research site. The results showed that in shopping locations, the movement of pedestrians was dominated by groups rather than individual. In this study, the research site located at Jalan Solo, Panembahan Senopati Street (Taman Pintar) and Jalan Malioboro. These three locations are located in shopping centers in Jogjakarta. The opposite result is seen in commercial areas such as offices, hospitals and other public spaces, pedestrians tend to walk alone rather than in groups. This difference is due to the purpose and comfort of pedestrians walking on the path. This is supported by [25], in shopping locations, pedestrians need more comfort. This is because there are more diverse types of activities in the shopping area, such as shopping activities, entertainment activities, or just walking activities such as lane functions in urban space, but for office areas, the movement is quite high dominated by individuals who do their own activities, such as workers who enter and exit the office, or self-comfort when in urban space or other activities. In addition, pedestrians tend to walk in groups to protect each other when moving or doing activities in the area. Moreover, the shopping is one of the busiest areas where it will be difficult to direct walking. Thus, walking in groups gave rise to a leadership role to guide the movement of pedestrians along with them.

Furthermore, this research identified the profile of Pedestrians who carry goods. There were 3 types that will be discussed, which is Pedestrian not carrying goods, Pedestrian carry goods in arms and Pedestrian bring goods. The difference between bring and carry in arms is that when Pedestrians carry goods, it will be outside of the pedestrian's body such as on top, side, or behind. While Pedestrians bring goods is identified as Pedestrians bring something by protecting the goods close to their body. The results of the study related to the profile of pedestrians carrying goods can be seen in the graph below. Based on the results, among all of the group average, male pedestrian was the highest average group with 1497 pedestrians recorded. In addition, there was an average of 1375 female pedestrians recorded. If the type of pedestrian was interpreted according to carrying bags, the results show that on weekends at Jalan Sudirman, the number of pedestrians who do not carry bags increased. It happened because in urban spaces area during weekend, many people do activities for leisure, like sports, jogging etc. The same profile pattern can be observed at Jalan Panembahan Senopati during the surveys, although the location was sidewalk's shopping area. This location was interconnected with vehicle parking for the tourist destination, thus people would walk from the parking lot to their destination without carrying a bag. In contrast, the result in Jalan Solo shows a different pedestrian pattern where women dominated with no carrying and holding bag. Moreover, Malioboro Street showed that people who holding bags dominated from the time of the survey. It is because the locations are shopping areas that have many stores to create an attraction for pedestrians. People walking in the shopping areas will tend to bring any goods that they purchased and go to their vehicle to end their activity, as stated by [27], (18).

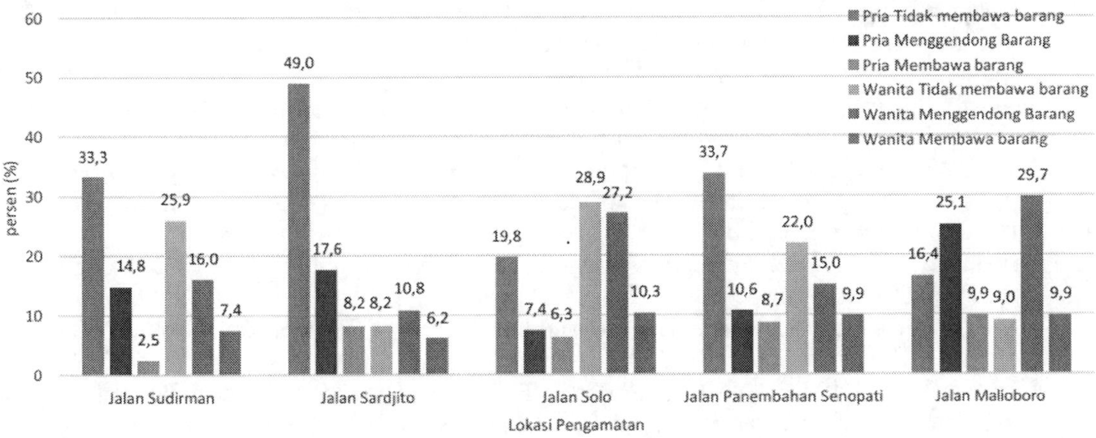

Figure 1. Graphic of percentage for pedestrian profile with carrying bag

5. Conclusion

In this paper, we presented more about pedestrian characteristic volume for commercial areas sidewalk in Yogyakarta. Pedestrian characteristic volume was focused on fluctuation based on the time characteristics and behavior. Pedestrian volume showed different characteristics between morning flow and afternoon flow. The volume of characteristics in morning flow tends to decrease due to the difference in the low temperatures in the morning with the higher temperatures during the day. As for afternoon flow, pedestrian fluctuations will increase due to temperatures decrease from noon to evening. This is reinforced by an independent T test. In addition, the characteristics of the pedestrians' groups dominate the shopping area, the hospital area, as well as the public space. Finally, the characteristics of pedestrians in the commercial area sidewalk also have different characteristics in terms of carrying goods, whereas in the shopping areas it is more dominated by pedestrians carrying goods than others. This research is limited to a different research times for each research site and is limited to only one observation for each location. It is a suggestion for future research to evaluate the volume of pedestrians with more than one observation time in order to see volume fluctuations more accurately and to evaluate the volume of pedestrians with consideration of peak hour volume for the purposes of further investigation in the future.

Reference

1. Timms P, Tight M, Watling D. Imagineering mobility: Constructing utopias for future urban transport. Environ Plan A. 2014;46(1):78–93.
2. Subekti SR. Analisis Perencanaan Fasilitas Pejalan Kaki (Studi Kasus : Jl . Ir . H . Juanda , Jakarta Pusat). In: SImposium FSTPT 19. Yogyakarta: UII; 2016. p. 11–3.
3. Ramadhan MAA, Pratama GNIPNIP, Hidayah R, Universitas DI, Yogyakarta N, Ramadhan MAA, et al. Penataan Sistem Jalur Pejalan Kaki Di Universitas Negeri Yogyakarta. Inersia. 2018;15(1):101–17.
4. Tanan N, Darmoyono L. Achieving walkable city in Indonesia: Policy and responsive design through public participation. AIP Conf Proc. 2017;1903(November).
5. Umum KP. Pedoman perencanaan, Penyediaan dan Pemanfaatan Prasarana dan Sarana Jaringan Pejalan Kaki di Kawasan Perkotaan, Kementrian Pekerjaan Umum, 2014. Indonesia: Kementerian Pekerjaan Umum; 2014 p. 1–65.
6. Paula Manoela dos Santos, Caccia LS, Samios AAB, Ferreira LZ. The 8 Principles. 2015;1–9.

Available from: http://www.rcn.org.uk/development/practice/principles/the_8_principles
7. Galiza RJ, Ferreira L. Converting mixed pedestrian flows into equivalent commuters using standard pedestrian equivalent factors. Transp Plan Technol. 2014;37(3):235–46.
8. Shaaban K, Muley D. Investigation of Weather Impacts on Pedestrian Volumes. Transp Res Procedia [Internet]. 2016;14:115–22. Available from: http://dx.doi.org/10.1016/j.trpro.2016.05.047
9. Jegham I. Pedestrian Detection in Poor Weather Conditions Using Moving Camera Pedestrian detection in poor weather conditions using moving camera. 2017;(October).
10. Miranda-Moreno LF, Lahti AC. Temporal trends and the effect of weather on pedestrian volumes: A case study of Montreal, Canada. Transp Res Part D Transp Environ [Internet]. 2013;22:54–9. Available from: http://dx.doi.org/10.1016/j.trd.2013.02.008
11. Ariffin RNR, Zahari RK. Perceptions of the Urban Walking Environments. Procedia - Soc Behav Sci. 2013;105:589–97.
12. Attaset V, Schneider RJ, Arnold LS, Ragland DR. Effects of Weather Variables on Pedestrian Volumes in Alameda County , California. Transp Res Rec. 2010;(510):1–18.
13. Kementerian PU. PM PU No. 03/Prt/M/2014 Tentang Pedoman Perencanaan, Penyediaan, Dan Pemanfaatan Prasarana Dan Sarana Jaringan Pejalan Kaki Di Kawasan Perkotaan. 03/Prt/M Indonesia: Kementerian Pekerjaan Umum; 2014.
14. UNESCAP. "Development of Technical Standards on Road Infrastructure Safety Facilities and Model Intelligent Transport Systems (ITS) Deployments for the Asian Highway (AH) Network [Internet]. Asian; 2016. Available from: https://www.unescap.org/sites/default/d8files/knowledge-products/Recommednded DESIGN GUIDELINES.pdf
15. Cheng L, Yarlagadda R, Fookes CB, Yarlagadda PK. A review of pedestrian group dynamics and methodologies in modelling pedestrian group behaviours. World J Mech Eng [Internet]. 2014;1(1):2–13. Available from: http://eprints.qut.edu.au/78716/
16. Moussaïd M, Perozo N, Garnier S, Helbing D, Theraulaz G. The walking behaviour of pedestrian social groups and its impact on crowd dynamics. PLoS One. 2010;5(4):1–18.
17. Lai Y, Kontokosta CE. Landscape and Urban Planning Quantifying place : Analyzing the drivers of pedestrian activity in dense urban environments. Landsc Urban Plan [Internet]. 2018;180(September):166–78. Available from: https://doi.org/10.1016/j.landurbplan.2018.08.018
18. Huang S, Wei R, Lo S, Lu S, Li C, An C, et al. Experimental study on one-dimensional movement of luggage-laden pedestrian. Physica A [Internet]. 2018; Available from: https://doi.org/10.1016/j.physa.2018.09.038

IOP Conf. Series: Earth and Environmental Science 1000 (2022) 012008 doi:10.1088/1755-1315/1000/1/012008

Potential tourist destinations for priority transportation infrastructure development in East Kalimantan

Rosa Agustaniah[1,3], **Achmad Wicaksono**[2,3], **Ludfi Djakfar**[2,3]
[1] Doctoral Program of Civil Engineering, Universitas Brawijaya, Veteran Street, Malang City, East Java 65145, Indonesia.
rosaagustaniah@yahoo.com
[2,3] Department of Civil Engineering, Brawijaya University, Veteran Street, Malang City, East Java 65145, Indonesia

Abstract. Transport and tourism infrastructure are interrelated and have the ability to strengthen regional development and have a major impact on the rate of economic growth. East Kalimantan province has many potential mainstay tourism objects that have not been managed and promoted properly. The weakness of tourism in East Kalimantan lies in the transportation infrastructure. Access to several favorite tourist sites related to travel costs is considered relatively high, and the low accessibility of the road network impacts tourist visits to tourist attractions. This research is the basis for determining potential tourist destinations for the priority development of transportation infrastructure in East Kalimantan Province. Determination of tourist destination areas using the location quotient index approach (LQ > 1), namely the business sector that has the largest potential contribution to regional budget revenues in the transportation and tourism sector and reviewing policy directions contained in the regional regulations of East Kalimantan province regarding spatial plans for designated areas tourism is spread over an area of ± 97,442 ha. The areas that have been designated as transportation infrastructure developments are Kutai Kertanegara Regency, Berau Regency, Balikpapan City, Samarinda City, and North Penajam Paser Regency as the state capital.

1. Introduction

Transport and tourism infrastructure are interrelated and have the ability to strengthen regional development, improve people's living standards, and have a significant impact on the rate of economic growth [11]. Increasing tourism growth is the key to enhance income, job creation, business development, and its strategic value is the primary key of national development sectors in the future, so the government pays greater attention to this sector [1] [2] [5] [7].

East Kalimantan Province has many potential tourism objects such as freshwater dolphins, forest tribes, mangrove ecotourism, tropical rain forests, and marine tourism. They have not been managed and promoted properly, so they have not contributed to it the tourism sector. The weakness of tourism in East Kalimantan Province lies in the inadequate transportation infrastructure to support tourist travel activities. It does not yet have good road access to tourist destinations and many isolated tourist areas, still using rough land made by local people. Access to several favorite tourist sites related to travel costs is considered relatively high, and the low accessibility of the road network impacts tourist visits to tourist attractions.

This research is the basis for determining potential tourist destinations in East Kalimantan Province so that tourist destinations can be selected to develop transportation infrastructure. In this study, the determination of tourist destination areas using the location quotient (LQ) approach. This approach uses business sector activities or activities that have the largest potential contribution to regional budget revenue in the transportation and tourism sector and reviews policy directions in the regulations on a regional spatial plan (RTRW) of East Kalimantan Province.

East Kalimantan Province is administratively bordered on the north by North Kalimantan, in the east by a portion (12 Mill) of the Makassar Strait and the Sulawesi Sea, in the south by the Province of South Kalimantan, in the west by the Province of Central Kalimantan and West Kalimantan and The State of Sarawak, East Malaysia and has 10 (ten) districts/cities (Table 1). East Kalimantan has a land area of 127,267.52 km^2 and a marine management area of 25,656 km^2 located between 113° 44′ East Longitude and 119° 00′ East Longitude and between 2° 33′ North Latitude and 2° 25′ South Latitude (Figure 1) [11].

Table 1. Area of regencies/cities in East Kalimantan Province

Regency/City	Capital	Land Area (Ha)	Area of Marine Management (km^2)
Paser Regency	Tanah Grogot	1.119.293	8.200
West Kutai Regency	Sendawar	1.563.060	-
Kutai Kertanegara Regency	Tenggarong	2.634.895	1.891
East Kutai Regency	Sangatta	3.189.649	2.641
Berau Regency	Tanjung Redeb	2.220.033	11.962
North Penajam Paser Regency	Penajam	321.155	400
Balikpapan City	Balikpapan	56.128	287
Samarinda City	Samarinda	71.783	-
Bontang City	Bontang	19.256	275
Mahakam Ulu Regency	Long Bagun	1.531.500	-
East Kalimantan Province		12.726.752	25.656

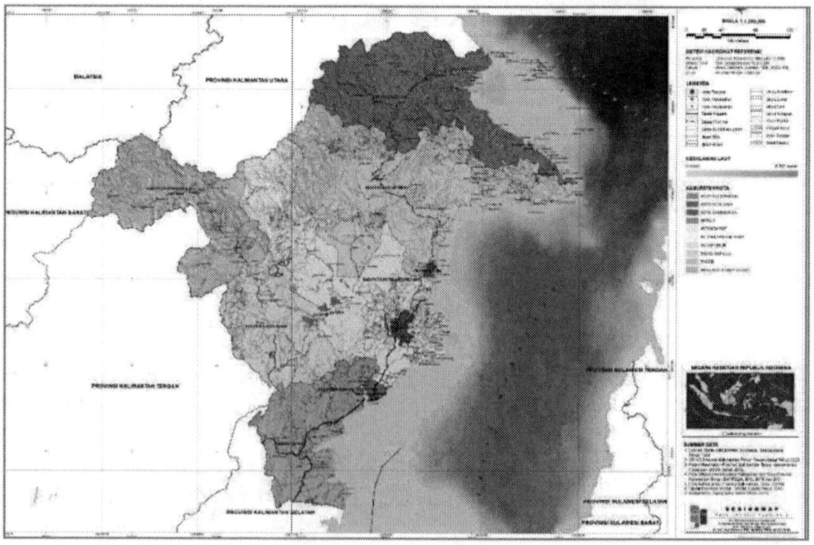

Figure 1. Map of the administrative area of East Kalimantan Province

2. Literature review

According to its definition, tourism is a temporary movement of individuals/groups to a destination outside their normal place of residence; the relaxation activities carried out while they are in the destination area and the facilities provided to meet their needs. The role of transportation is to connect various destinations and transport people, goods, and services. Tourism is all about travel, and the role of transport in tourism operation is very important. If there is the development of transportation, then tourism develops. Advances in aviation have narrowed the world, and motorized vehicles have made travel possible anywhere. These two realities, coupled with changing work patterns and marketing innovations, have driven tourism around the world throughout the year [13].

Some of the potential benefits of the development of the transportation sector are; [9] 1) changes in the relative costs of specific means of transportation to other means of transportation; 2) increasing the income per capita of the community; 3) increasing the availability of transportation facilities; 4) improving the quality of travel (speed, comfort, trust) and infrastructure technology; 5) influence on land use due to inter-regional migration and changes in settlement patterns; 6) increase in economic activity affects the change in the pattern and structure of public consumption; 7) demographic changes (age structure and gender); 8) changes in the operational behavior of the local business world. Ford (2014) [3] states "accessibilities of the tourist destination" is the ability to reach a certain destination, it can be easier or more challenging to get it, and it can be seen how easy it is to get a place from other nearby locations. For tourism to develop, tourist destinations must be accessible, meaning that they must have a high level of accessibility, including road conditions, distance, time, available modes of transportation, and a comparison of the costs of visiting tours [6]. Elements that affect accessibility are road conditions, available transportation facilities, transportation networks, frequency of departure, and distance. Accessibility consists of various infrastructures and transportation facilities, namely parking lots, bus terminals, airports, train stations, ports, docks, tourist buses, taxis, airplanes, trains, private vehicles, ships, highways, toll roads, etc. [9]. The basis for determining potential tourist destinations for the development of transportation infrastructure in East Kalimantan Province using a spatial concentration analysis approach using the location quotient (LQ) method or more commonly referred to as the Hoover-Ballasa coefficient with the LQ formula:

$$LQ = \frac{Si}{Xi} = \frac{vij/vtj}{Vi/Vt} \quad (1)$$

Where: *Si*, the number of users of sub-sector i in a certain area; *Xi*, number of users of subsector *i* in all regions; *vij*, the total number of city/district users; *vtj*, number of users of sector i city/district; *Vi*, the number of users in the sector *i* area; *Vt*, total user area [12]

3. Method of collecting data

This study uses secondary data, empirical data processed by relevant agencies, published by the Central Statistics Agency (BPS), Public Works Agency, Spatial Planning & Public Housing Prov. East Kalimantan, Prov. East Kalimantan, Provincial Tourism Office. East Kalimantan and publication sources from the internet. Furthermore, the data is processed quantitatively so that the results are in accordance with the objectives of the final research results. The data needed in this study are 1) East Kalimantan Gross Regional Domestic Product (GRDP) from 2016 to 2020 [4]; 2) Regional Regulation of East Kalimantan Province Number 1 of 2016 concerning Regional Spatial Planning (RTRW) of East Kalimantan Province 2016 – 2036 [11]; 3) East Kalimantan Province Map

4. Results and discussion

Analysis of the LQ method is used to see sectors in East Kalimantan Province that have a significant regional role and are prospective to be developed. This LQ calculation uses East Kalimantan GRDP data which consists of nine sectors/business fields based on constant prices. GRDP data is one of the regional macroeconomic indicators that can identify the condition and economic development of a region every year. This study uses East Kalimantan Province GRDP data for 5 years from 2016 - 2020 as a time series (data sequence). Based on the price factor for goods and services, there are two models for presenting GRDP data. First, it is based on Current Prices (ADHB), where the price for calculating the added value or value of final goods and services uses the price prevailing price in each year of GRDP calculation. The second is based on Constant Price (ADHK), where the cost to calculate the added value or the final value of goods and services uses a specific year price that is fixed for each year of GRDP calculation. Thus GRDP at Current Prices (PDRB - ADHB) describes the development of the added value of goods and services calculated using prices every year. In contrast, GRDP at Constant Prices (PDRB - ADHK) illustrates the growth in the value-added of goods and services calculated using annual expenses.

Tabel 2. East Kalimantan Province LQ Index

No	Code	Business Field (Based on GRDB data)	Years					*Average LQ Index
			2016	2017	2018	2019	2020	
1	A	Agriculture, forestry and fisheries	0,79	0,84	0,88	0,87	0,80	0,83
2	B	Mining and excavation	1,12	1,03	1,01	1,05	1,14	1,07
3	C	Processing industry	1,04	1,12	1,15	1,12	1,05	1,10
4	D	Electricity and gas supply	1,11	1,11	1,14	1,11	1,06	1,11
5	E	Water supply, waste management, waste and recycling	0,99	1,05	1,06	1,03	0,98	1,02
6	F	Construction	0,81	0,87	0,86	0,82	0,78	0,83
7	G	Wholesale and retail; car and motorcycle repair	0,91	0,98	1,00	0,95	0,89	0,94
8	H	Transportation and warehousing	0,76	0,81	0,83	0,79	0,78	0,79
9	I	Provision of accommodation and food and drink	0,83	0,90	0,91	0,87	0,82	0,87
10	J	Information and communication	1,13	1,24	1,25	1,20	1,15	1,19
11	K	Financial and insurance services	0,87	0,94	0,95	0,91	0,87	0,91
12	L	Real estate	0,93	1,01	1,04	1,00	0,96	0,99
13	M	Company services	0,86	0,92	0,94	0,91	0,86	0,90
14	N	Mandatory government administration, defense and social services	0,77	0,85	0,88	0,85	0,80	0,83
15	O	Education services	0,84	0,91	0,92	0,86	0,79	0,86
16	P	Health services and social activities	0,84	0,93	0,94	0,89	0,83	0,89
17	Q	Other services	0,80	0,85	0,87	0,83	0,78	0,83

* Analysis result

The classification of GRDP according to business sector contains 17 indicators with codes A – Q (Table 1). For research on potential tourist destinations for priority development of transportation infrastructure in East Kalimantan in the formulation of the location quotient (LQ) method, only four indicators are used, namely; (H) transportation and warehousing; (I) provide accommodation and food and drink; (J) information and communication; (Q) other services (Table 2),

IOP Conf. Series: Earth and Environmental Science 1000 (2022) 012008 doi:10.1088/1755-1315/1000/1/012008

Tabel 3. Regencies and cities in East Kalimantan Province LQ Index

Regency/City	Business Field Code (GRDP)	Years					*Average LQ Index
		2016	2017	2018	2019	2020	
Paser Regency	H	0,89	1,00	1,02	0,96	0,88	0,95
	I	0,84	0,95	0,96	0,89	0,82	0,89
	J	1,09	1,23	1,26	1,20	1,11	1,18
	Q	0,78	0,85	0,87	0,82	0,76	0,82
West Kutai Regency	H	0,94	1,02	1,04	0,97	0,91	0,98
	I	0,85	0,92	0,93	0,88	0,84	0,88
	J	1,13	1,23	1,26	1,21	1,16	1,20
	Q	0,84	0,87	0,86	0,78	0,74	0,82
Kutai Kertanegara Regency	H	0,81	0,89	0,92	0,85	0,80	0,86
	I	0,75	0,80	0,79	0,72	0,69	0,75
	J	1,03	1,18	1,20	1,13	1,08	1,12
	Q	0,79	0,84	0,83	0,77	0,74	0,79
East Kutai Regency	H	0,81	0,95	0,97	0,92	0,81	0,89
	I	0,92	1,06	1,09	1,02	0,89	1,00
	J	1,05	2,20	1,25	1,19	1,06	1,35
	Q	0,81	0,93	0,94	0,88	0,76	0,86
Berau Regency	H	0,83	0,89	0,90	0,86	0,81	0,86
	I	0,77	0,84	0,85	0,82	0,77	0,81
	J	1,15	1,25	1,26	1,21	1,13	1,20
	Q	0,92	0,97	0,98	0,92	0,84	0,92
North Penajam Paser Regency	H	1,05	1,08	1,06	1,03	1,01	1,04
	I	0,74	0,77	0,79	0,79	0,80	0,78
	J	1,15	1,20	1,21	1,18	1,22	1,19
	Q	0,86	0,87	0,89	0,88	0,89	0,88
Mahakam Ulu Regency	H	1,06	1,06	1,02	0,99	0,99	1,02
	I	0,98	0,97	0,94	0,90	0,92	0,94
	J	1,33	1,36	1,35	1,37	1,40	1,36
	Q	1,01	0,98	0,93	0,88	0,87	0,93
Balikpapan City	H	0,64	0,63	0,66	0,65	0,68	0,65
	I	0,79	0,80	0,83	0,83	0,80	0,81
	J	1,05	1,07	1,11	1,12	1,10	1,09
	Q	0,82	0,81	0,81	0,79	0,75	0,80
Samarinda City	H	0,93	0,95	0,97	0,96	0,96	0,95
	I	0,95	0,97	0,98	0,98	0,96	0,97
	J	1,23	1,29	1,34	1,35	1,34	1,31
	Q	0,88	0,88	0,89	0,90	0,89	0,89
Bontang City	H	1,08	1,10	1,09	1,08	1,07	1,08
	I	0,90	0,92	0,91	0,90	0,89	0,91
	J	1,25	1,29	1,27	1,25	1,24	1,26
	Q	0,93	0,91	0,91	0,86	0,85	0,89

* Analysis result

Tabel 4. Average LQ index and economic potential of Regencies and cities in East Kalimantan Province

Regency/City	*Average LQ index and economic potential	H Transportation and warehousing	I Provision of accommodation and food and drink	J Information and communication	Q Other services
Paser Regency	Average LQ index	0,79	0,87	1,19	0,89
	economic potential	non-base	non-base	base	non-base
West Kutai Regency	Average LQ index	0,95	0,89	1,18	0,89
	economic potential	non-base	non-base	base	non-base
Kutai Kertanegara Regency	Average LQ index	0,98	0,88	1,20	0,81
	economic potential	non-base	non-base	base	non-base
East Kutai Regency	Average LQ index	0,86	0,75	1,12	0,86
	economic potential	non-base	non-base	base	non-base
Berau Regency	Average LQ index	0,89	1,00	1,35	0,97
	economic potential	non-base	base	base	non-base
North Penajam Paser Regency	Average LQ index	0,86	0,81	1,20	1,03
	economic potential	non-base	non-base	base	basis
Mahakam Ulu Regency	Average LQ index	1,04	0,78	1,19	0,90
	economic potential	base	non-basis	base	non-base
Balikpapan City	Average LQ index	1,02	0,94	1,36	0,93
	economic potential	base	non-base	base	non-base
Samarinda City	Average LQ index	0,65	0,81	1,09	0,79
	economic potential	non-base	non-base	base	non-base
Bontang City	Average LQ index	0,95	0,97	1,31	0,96
	economic potential	non-base	non-base	base	non-base

* Analysis result

The location quotient (LQ) calculation result has a different meaning; 1) LQ > 1, it indicates that a region has high specialization (base); 2) LQ < 1, it indicates that a region has low specialization (non-basis); 3) LQ = 1, it indicates that a region is self-sufficient (same specialization).

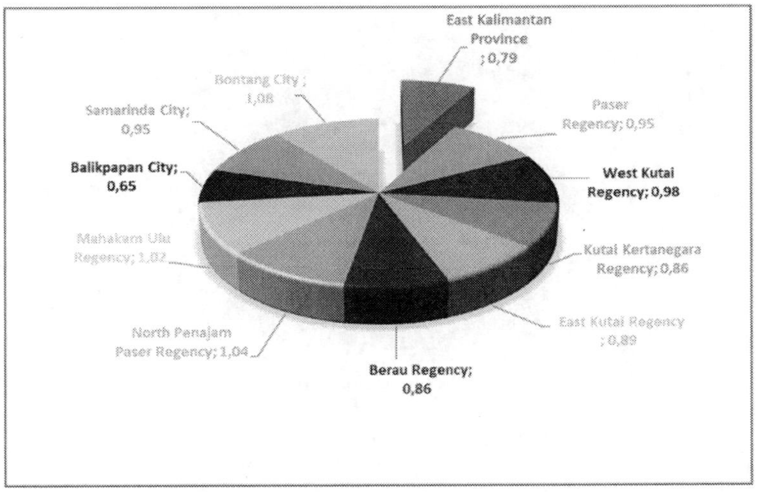

Figure 2. Potential economic chart for Transport and warehousing

The results of the analysis of the LQ > 1 indicate that an area that has a high specialization (base) for transportation and warehousing is in the North Penajam Paser Regency, Mahakam Ulu Regency, and Bontang City. Figure 2 becomes the basis or source of growth and commodities that have a comparative advantage, and the results can be used to meet the region's needs. Still, also it can be exported outside the region.

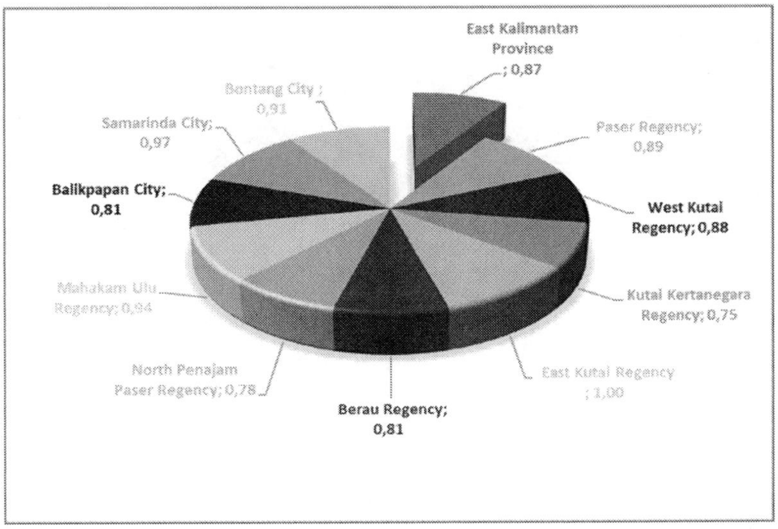

Figure 3. Potential economic chart for the provision of accommodation and food and drink

The results of the LQ = 1 in the East Kutai Regency area indicate that this area is self-sufficient (same specialization) for providing accommodation, food, and beverage. Figure 3 commodity is classified as non-basic, does not have a comparative advantage. Its production is only sufficient to meet the needs of its region and cannot be exported.

IOP Conf. Series: Earth and Environmental Science 1000 (2022) 012008 doi:10.1088/1755-1315/1000/1/012008

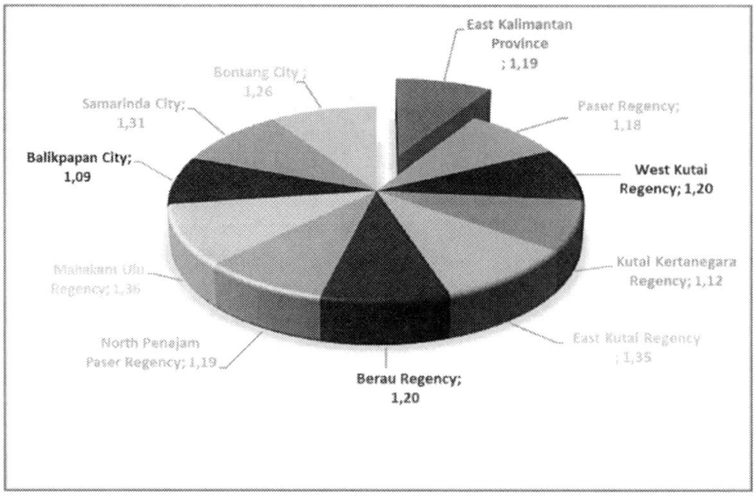

Figure 4. Potential economic charts for information and telecommunications

The results of the analysis of the LQ > 1 indicate that an area has a high specialization (base) for information and telecommunications in all districts and cities in East Kalimantan Province. Figure 4 becomes the basis or source of growth. Commodities have a comparative advantage; the results can not only meet the needs of their region but can also be exported outside the region

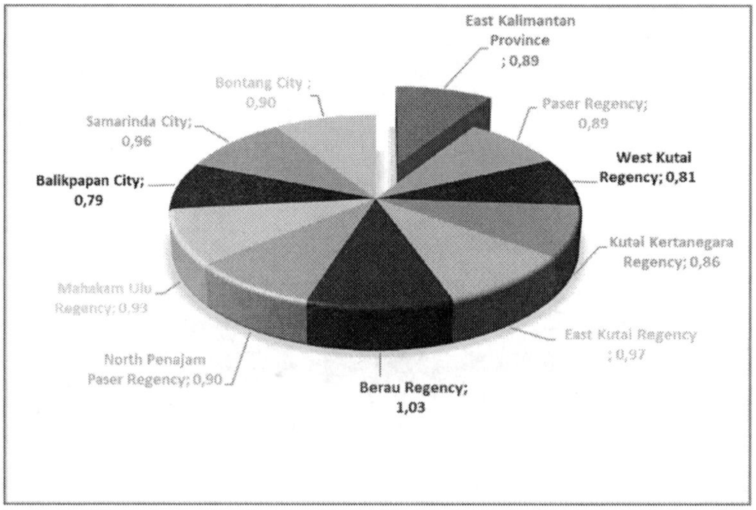

Figure 5. Potential economic charts for health services and social activities

The results of the analysis of the LQ > 1 indicate that an area that has a high specialization (base) for health services and social activities is the Berau Regency area. Figure 5 becomes the basis or source of growth. Commodities have a comparative advantage; the results can meet the region's needs and export outside the region.

The next analysis reviews the policy direction of the regional regulation of the province of East Kalimantan Number 1 of 2016 concerning the Regional Spatial Plan (RTRW), namely the tourism designation area spreads over an area of ± 97,442 Ha (Table 5). So that mapping can be carried out following the right target and according to the direction of regional policies formulated previously, especially in reviewing the suitability of the area between the existing conditions and their designation in the existing RTRW.

Table 5. Details of the development plan for the designated tourism area (per tourist attraction)

No	Regency/City	Type of Tour
1	Kutai Kertanegara (Mahakam River Corridor upstream, Tanjung Isuy and Mancong Village, Kersik Luway)	Habitat for freshwater dolphins and Bekantan
2	Berau (Tanjung Redeb Beach, Derawan Island, Sangalaki Island, Semama Island, Kakaban Island and Maratua Island)	Derawan Islands Cluster
3	Kutai Kartanegara	Kumala Island, Mulawarman Museum, Tenggarong Wood Museum, Bangkirai Hill
4	Samarinda	Pampang Cultural Village, Batik and Botanical Gardens, Citra Niaga Crafts
5	Balikpapan	Karang Joang Tourism Area, Crocodile Breeding, Manggar Beach, Balikpapan Botanical Gardens

The spatial plan in the province of East Kalimantan also provides directions for the components of the spatial system, including those related to spatial structure and spatial use patterns. It is a form of strategy for developing the economic center system of East Kalimantan to develop the function and hierarchy of the settlement zone as an urban system and supporting infrastructure following the RTRW. The hierarchy of the economic center system of Samarinda, Balikpapan, and Bontang is the National Activity Center (PKN). It can be identified that the movement of passengers in the province of East Kalimantan has a radial pattern, where the city of Balikpapan and the city of Samarinda become the central area or center of activity within the province. Almost all main routes form the radius from the center of the central to the sub-urban areas or surrounding districts. The movement of road modes seems to dominate the movement between districts and cities within the province of Kalimantan, followed by the river vessel and flight modes.

5. Conclusions

Many tourism activities depend on road infrastructure, transportation and communication because of the distance and time factors that significantly affect a person's desire to travel. The most critical element in accessibility is transportation, which means the frequency of use, the speed it has can make distances seem to be close. In addition to transportation related to accessibility, infrastructure includes roads, bridges, terminals, stations, and airports. This infrastructure serves to connect one place to another. The existence of transportation infrastructure will affect the growth rate of transport demand itself, and the condition of good infrastructure will make the transport demand's growth rate optimal. Therefore, it is necessary to determine potential tourist destinations and priorities for developing transportation infrastructure to improve transportation infrastructure in East Kalimantan.

Analyzing the location quotient (LQ) method of economic potential shows that the base sector and non-base sector are factors for regional selection for transportation infrastructure development. The base sector is a priority sector or a leading sector that can increase or make a major contribution to growth economy in districts and cities in East Kalimantan. There are 4 (four) indicators for determining the business field in the gross regional domestic product (GRDP), namely; 1) transportation and warehousing; 2) providing accommodation and food and drink; 3) information and communication; 4) other services. Based on the results of the location quotient index formulation (LQ > 1) and the policy directives of the East Kalimantan Provincial Regulation Number 1 of 2016 concerning Regional Spatial Planning (RTRW), there is a potential tourism designation area spread over an area of ± 97,442 Ha. These areas designated as transportation infrastructure development are Kutai Kertanegara Regency, Berau Regency, Balikpapan City, Samarinda City, and North Penajam Paser Regency as the state capital.

References

[1] Ali, L., Jianing, M., Shah, M., Khan, A. and Imran, M. (2017a), Transport culture akin to China Pakistan economic corridor, Journal of Human SystemMangement, Vol. 36 No. 4, pp. 381-396.

[2] Asomani-Boateng, R., Fricano, R.J. and Adarkwa, F. (2015), Assessing the socio-economic impacts of rural road improvements in Ghana: a case study of transport sector program support (Ii), Case Studies on Transport Policy, Vol. 3 No. 4, pp. 355-366.

[3] Ford, A. C., Barr, S. L., Dawson, R. J., & James, P. (2015). Transport accessibility analysis using GIS: Assessing sustainable transport in London. ISPRS International Journal of Geo-Information. https://doi.org/ 10.3390/ijgi4010124

[4] Gross Regional Domestic Product Of Kalimantan Timur Province By Industry 2016-2020, Bps-Statistics Of Kalimantan Timur Province

[5] Ikioda, F. (2016), The impact of road construction on market and street trading in Lagos, Journal of Transport Geography, Vol. 55 (July), pp. 175-181.

[6] Jin, F., Jiao, J., Qi, Y., & Yang, Y. (2017). Evolution and geographic effects of high-speed rail in East Asia: An accessibility approach. Journal of Geographical Sciences. https://doi.org/10.1007/s11442-017-1390-8

[7] Kasraian, D., Maat, K., Stead, D., and Van Wee, B. (2016), "Long-term impacts of transport infrastructure networks on land-use change: an international review of empirical studies," Transport Reviews, Vol. 36 No. 6, pp. 772-792.

[8] Law of the Republic of Indonesia No. 10 of 2009 concerning Tourism

[9] Li, Q., Zhang, T., Wang, H., & Zeng, Z. (2011). Dynamic accessibility mapping using floating car data: A network-constrained density estimation approach. Journal of Transport Geography. https://doi.org/10.1016/ j.jtrangeo.2010.07.003

[10] Njoya, E. T. (2020). An analysis of the tourism and wider economic impacts of price-reducing reforms in air transport services in Egypt. Research in Transportation Economics.

[11] Regional Regulation of East Kalimantan Province Number 1 of 2016 concerning Regional Spatial Planning (RTRW) of East Kalimantan Province 2016 – 2036

[12] Warpani, Suwardjoko. 2001. City and Regional Analysis, ITB Publisher, Bandung

[13] Yoeti Oka A. (2008). Tourism Economics: Introduction, Information, and Implementation. Compass Publisher. Jakarta

Factor Analysis of Commuters' Willingness to Use Public Transport

Nabila Baqarizky[1], R Jachrizal Sumabrata[2]

Departemen Teknik Sipil, Fakultas Teknik, Universitas Indonesia, Kampus Baru UI Depok, 16424, Indonesia

nabila.baqarizky17@gmail.com[1]

Abstract. Jabodetabek is the largest Indonesian metropolitan city with estimated daily trips of 47.5 million. According to Priadmaja, Anisa, Prayogi (2017), only 16.7% of the population uses public transport, contributing to 53% of traffic congestion in Jabodetabek. Furthermore, the continued increase of urban migration in search of employment, education, and other services has heightened the traffic congestion within the city and its surrounding areas. To mitigate this challenge, the Transit-Oriented Development concept was initiated to maximize the use of public transport. However, not many people prefer to travel using public means and therefore, this research sought to analyze the factors that influence the commuters' willingness to use the available modes. Six variables were considered, including security, safety, amenities, affordability, equity, and regularity with limitations to KRL, MRT, and BRT modes. Questionnaires were issued to the respondents who filled the required information and sent them back. The collected data was analyzed with the help of multiple linear regression equations. The results indicated that amenities, regularity, equality, safety, and affordability variables influenced the use of KRL mode. Furthermore, the MRT mode was affected by regularity, affordability, and equality variables while the variables that influenced the use of BRT mode included amenities, safety, orderliness, and equality.

Keywords; Commuters' willingness, public transport, KRL (Kereta Rel Listrik), MRT (Mass Rapid Transport), BRT (Bus Rapid Transport)

1. Introduction

Jabodetabek, is the largest city in Indonesia with a population of at least 27,957,194, according to the 2020 census. The city is the central control place for the national economy and Indonesian capital. This shows why it has attracted many people and, therefore, in need of a streamlined transportation system to ease the daily traffic snarls. Statistics show that about 47.5 million trips are made daily in the Greater Jakarta area (Abiyoga, 2020), with public transportation having a total of 16.7% while cars and motorbikes account for 17.4% and 62.9 %, respectively, and other means taking 3%. According to Sitanggang & Saribanon (2018), the number of motorized vehicles in Jakarta and its surroundings has greatly increased from 5,500 to 6,000 units per day. The increased vehicles have resulted to traffic congestion, which has negatively impacted the quality of life besides affecting Jabodetabek's economy due to increased fuel consumption and loss of time in traffic. Overall, the city loses approximately IDR 8.3 trillion annually due to traffic challenges.

To mitigate the congestion challenge, the concept of Transit Oriented Development (TOD) was adopted by DKI Jakarta Provincial Government (Petra. S.U, 2015). TOD is a spatial arrangement project that is pedestrian-friendly and whose activity centers are located around the transit. One of such establishments includes the Dukuh Atas area, which is equipped with components that support the TOD concept, including pedestrian paths, bicycle lanes, mix-land use, and green open spaces (Sodri et al., 2021). Notably, the development of the TOD concept majorly depends on commuters' willingness, who are the key players. This research aimed to investigate the factors that affect the commuters' willingness to use public transport.

2. Literature Review

2.1 Transit-Oriented Development

Transit-Oriented Development (TOD) is a spatial arrangement project that is pedestrian-friendly and whose activity centers are located around the transit. TOD combines homes, retail places, offices, open spaces, and public centers to a walkable environment in an effort to make it easier for pedestrians to travel by public transport, bicycles, and on foot (Hasoloan, 2018; Priadmaja et al. (2017).

Individual security concerns and the safety of property come first when people want to select the transportation means. Harahap (2018) defined security as a condition experienced with people free from physical harm, threat, or accidents. In this regard, passengers want assurance of their safety when using public transport means. According to Rukfianti, safe riding or driving is an effort to reduce the level of danger exposed to all road users. Ramadhayanti (2018) stated that the safety of users is crucial, and therefore, public transport must provide facilities such as safety equipment for emergencies, first aid kits, and the competence and physical condition of the vehicle crew.

Convenience involves a situation that makes something useful or easy for an individual by reducing the time or effort needed to perform an activity. It is one of the factors that influence the desire of many people to prefer private transportation instead of using public means. Factors that attract its use include comfort, measured from the satisfaction of services provided, including friendly service, protection from hot and rainy weather, availability of seats, and comfortable and attractive interior design (Enrekang, 2017).

In the marketing world, price is one of the variables that play an important role because it affects a consumer's desire to buy or use a product (Augusty, 2010). According to Triyadi (2018), price plays the role of allocation besides providing information regarding quality in the decision-making process.

Equality in public transportation comprises special services such as accessibility, service priorities, and service facilities for people with disabilities, the elderly, children, and pregnant women (Jayati et al., 2019).

Regularity when used in public transport involves items such as the quality of technical services, including operational, load factor, travel speed, headway, travel time, and service time. According to Soeparno (2014), other regularity examples are frequency (how many trips are made each hour or day), the number of vehicles operating, waiting time (timely arrival and departure).

2.2 Hypothesis

- H_1: The security variable influences the willingness to use public transportation
- H_2: The safety variable has a relationship with the willingness to use public transportation
- H_3: The amenities variable influences the willingness to use public transportation
- H_4: The affordability variable influences the willingness to use public transportation
- H_5: The equality variable influences the willingness to use public transportation
- H_6: The regularity variable influences the willingness to use public transportation

3. Methodology

3.1 Methodology and Variables

The research adopted a cross-sectional descriptive design where quantitative data was collected by administering questionnaires to the respondents. A site survey was conducted on Sunday, February 28, at 10 am in the Dukuh Atas area by looking at the surrounding conditions and determining the critical points of the location. Questionnaires were administered directly to users of KRL, MRT, and BRT public transport to determine the factors that influenced the commuters' choice of transport. Additionally, some questionnaires were distributed to the respondents using online google forms. A validity test was conducted to accurately measure the variable under research, while a reliability test was done to ensure the variables yielded the same results. The data was analyzed with the help of descriptive statistical packages, and the variables were analyzed using multiple linear regression in the form of a t-test. The research adopted six variables derived from the literature review and the Regulation of the Minister of Transport of the Republic of Indonesia Number PM 98 of 2013, as illustrated in Table 1.

Table 1. Research Variables and Factors

Variable	Factor
Security	Vehicle Crew Identity, Lighting, Danger Signal Lights
Safety	Vehicle Crew (Competence and Physical Condition), Facilities, Infrastructure
Amenities	Transport Capacity, Room Temperature Control Facilities, Cleaning Facilities
Affordability	Rates/Fees
Equality	Priority Seating, Wheelchair Room
Regularity	Service Information, Stop Time at the Bus Stop, Headway

4. Results and Discussions

4.1. Respondent's Demographics

From a total of 250 respondents, it was established that 46% of the respondents were living in Jakarta, 29% in Bogor, 12% in Tangerang, 9% in Depok, and 4% in Bekasi. Furthermore, 64% of the respondents were female, and 36% male. More than half of the respondents (57%) were known between the age of 20-30 years, 20% between 40-50 years, 11% below 20years, 10% between 50-65 years, and 2% comprised those aged between 30-40 years as shown in Figure 1.

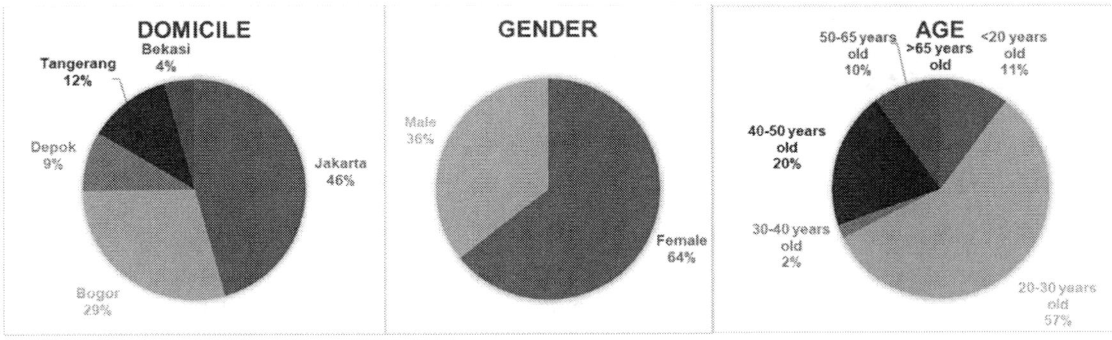

Figure 1. Respondent's Demographics

4.2. Research Variables

The research established various variables that influenced the commuters' willingness to use public transport in a priority manner, as indicated in the results. Amenities (X_3) was in the top priority, with transport capacity, room temperature control facilities, and cleaning facilities being the highest considerations. The second variable was identified as safety (X_2), with the following factors being considered, vehicle crew (competence and physical condition), facilities, and infrastructure. The third variable identified was regularity (X_6) with service information, stop time at the bus stop, and headway being the factors reflected. The fourth variable was security (X_1), with vehicle crew identity, lighting, danger signal lights as the most sought-after factors. The fifth variable was affordability (X_4) which considered, rates/fees, and the sixth variable was equality (X_5) which considered priority seating and wheelchair room. The findings are presented in figure 2.

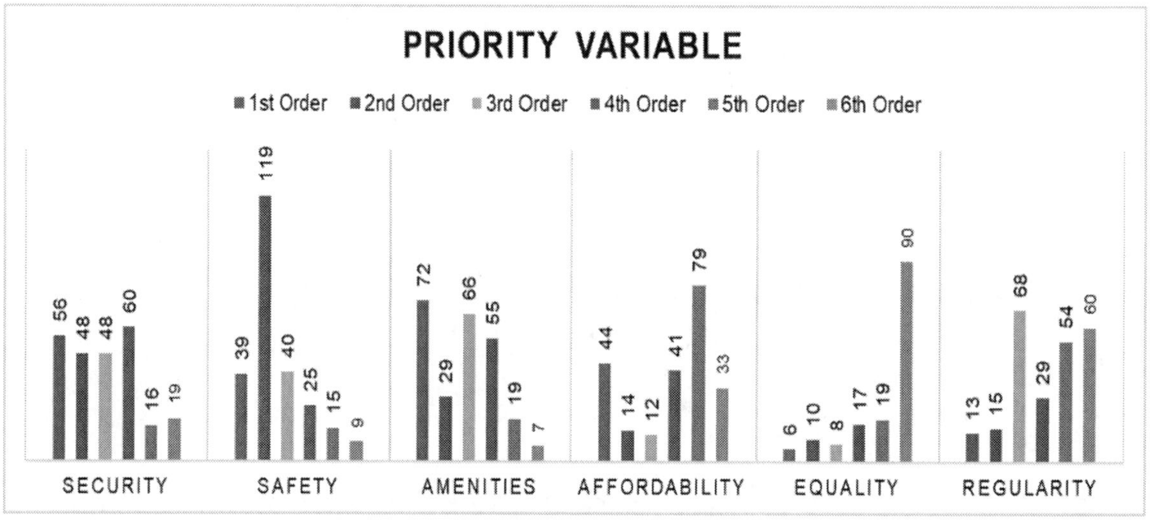

Figure 2. Research variables

4.3 Factors influencing Commuters' Willingness to Use KRL

4.3.1 Coefficient of Determination (R^2) and T-Test

The correlation of influencing variables was determined in relation to the commuters' willingness to use public transport. The tests were then analyzed using SPSS with the (R^2) value of 0.98, where the dependent variable simultaneously affected the dependent variable and the remaining 2% influenced by other variables not studied in the equation. Based on the results of the t-test on SPSS, the t-count values for X_2, X_3, X_4, X_5, X_6 are bigger than the t-table values at a confidence level of 1.96. However, for X_1, the results of the t-count < t-table were obtained. The value of the t-table was obtained from the distribution table using n (number of respondents) and α by 0.05. The research concluded that the X variable under safety (X_2), amenities (X_3), affordability (X_4), equality (X_5), regularity (X_6) positively influenced the commuters' willingness to use public transport. Additionally, the security variable (X_1) had a partial negative influence on the commuters' willingness to use KRL mode. The t-test derived the regression equation for the KRL mode shown below, and the results are displayed in Table 2.

$$Y = 0.093 - 0.024X1 + 0.262X2 + 0.401X3 + 0.237X4 + 0.596X5 + 0.406X6 \quad (1)$$

Table 2. Coefficient of Determination (R^2) and t-Test on KRL

	Variable	B	T-Count	T-Table	Description	R Square
	Constant	0.093	0.876	1.96		
X_1	Security	-0.024	-0.599	1.96	Uninfluential	
X_2	Safety	0.262	3.315	1.96	Influential	
X_3	Amenities	0.401	8.980	1.96	Influential	0.98
X_4	Affordability	0.237	3.745	1.96	Influential	
X_5	Equality	0.596	6.365	1.96	Influential	
X_6	Regularity	0.406	7.623	1.96	Influential	

4.3.2 Hypothesis Testing Results on KRL

The research conducted a hypothesis test on the variables that influenced the commuters' use of the KRL mode of transport. All factors tested positively influenced the mode of public transport chosen by commuters apart from the security, which was uninfluential hence rejected as illustrated in Table 3.

Table 3. Hypothesis Testing Results on KRL

Hypothesis	T - count	T - Table	Conclusion	Decision
1	-0.599	1.96	Uninfluential	Hypothesis H_1 rejected
2	3.315	1.96	Influential	Hypothesis H_2 accepted
3	8.980	1.96	Influential	Hypothesis H_3 accepted
4	3.745	1.96	Influential	Hypothesis H_4 accepted
5	6.365	1.96	Influential	Hypothesis H_5 accepted
6	7.623	1.96	Influential	Hypothesis H_6 accepted

4.3.3 Effective Contribution to KRL

The following results were obtained after calculating the effective contribution of the independent variable on the KRL mode. The security variable (X_1) contributed negatively to commuters' influence using KRL mode at (-1.6%). This implied that the variable caused the independent variable to increase as the dependent variable decreased. The safety variable (X_2) contributed 12.49%, amenities (X_3) contributed 33.66%, affordability (X_4) 11.8%, equality (X_5) 12.97%, and regularity (X_6) 28.7%. In conclusion, the amenities variable had the greatest influence on commuters' willingness to use public transport with a contribution value of 33.66%, as elaborated in Table 4.

Table 4. Effective Contribution on KRL

Variable	b	Cross Product	Regression	Effective Contribution	Total Effective Contribution
X_1	-0.024	7586.43	11141.877	-1.60 %	98%
X_2	0.262	5429.30		12.49 %	

Variable	b	Cross Product	Regression	Effective Contribution	Total Effective Contribution
X_3	0.401	9544.65		33.66 %	
X_4	0.237	5657.06		11.80 %	
X_5	0.596	2476.30		12.97 %	
X_6	0.406	8027.03		28.67	

4.4 Factors Contributing to Commuters' Willingness to Use MRT

4.4.1. Coefficient of Determination (R Square) and T Test

Results of the linear regression test using SPSS, indicated that the R^2 value was 0.979 or equal to 97.9%. The X variable simultaneously (together) affected the Y variable by 97.9%, while 2.1% was influenced by other variables or variables not examined in the equation. A partial test (t-test) was carried out, which indicated that the t-count values for X_3, X_4, X_5, X_6 were bigger than the t table value of 1.96. However, for X_1 and X_2, the results of the t count < t table were obtained. Therefore, based on the t value, the research concluded that the X variable, which consisted of amenities (X_3), affordability (X_4), equality (X_5), regularity (X_6), partially affected the Y variable but security (X_1) and safety (X_2) had no partial influence on the Y variable in the MRT mode. Following the findings, the regression equation for the MRT mode below was obtained, and the illustration is presented in Table 5.

$$Y = 0.153 + 0.004X1 + 0.089X2 + 0.445X3 + 0.487X4 + 0.137X5 + 0.418X6 \quad (2)$$

Table 5. Coefficient of Determination (R^2) and t-Test on MRT

	Variable	B	T-Count	T-Table	Description	R Square
	Constant	0.153	1.324	1.96		
X_1	Security	0.004	0.334	1.96	Uninfluential	
X_2	Safety	0.089	1.041	1.96	Uninfluential	
X_3	Amenities	0.445	6.794	1.96	Influential	0.979
X_4	Affordability	0.487	5.410	1.96	Influential	
X_5	Equality	0.137	1.982	1.96	Influential	
X_6	Regularity	0.418	6.071	1.96	Influential	

4.4.2 Hypothesis Testing Results on MRT

Table 6. Hypothesis Testing Results on MRT

Hypothesis	T - count	T - Table	Conclusion	Decision
1	0.334	1.96	Uninfluential	Hypothesis H_1 rejected
2	1.041	1.96	Uninfluential	Hypothesis H_2 rejected
3	6.794	1.96	Influential	Hypothesis H_3 accepted
4	5.410	1.96	Influential	Hypothesis H_4 accepted
5	1.982	1.96	Influential	Hypothesis H_5 accepted

6	6.071	1.96	Influential	Hypothesis H_6 accepted

4.4.3 Effective Contribution on MRT

The following results were obtained after calculating the effective contribution of the independent variable on the MRT mode. The security variable (X_1) contributed 0.33%, safety (X_2) contributed 4.01%, amenities (X_3) contributed 36.12%, affordability (X_4) contributed 22.94%, equality (X_5) accounted for 5.65%, and regularity (X_6) accounted for 28.85%. In conclusion, the amenities variable had the greatest influence on the commuters' willingness to use public transport with a contribution value of 36%, as demonstrated in Table 7.

Table 7. Effective Contribution on MRT

Variable	b	Cross Product	Regression	Effective Contribution	Total Effective Contribution
X_1	0.004	10572.30		0.33 %	
X_2	0.089	6328.37		4.01 %	
X_3	0.445	11349.66	13679.678	36.12 %	97.9%
X_4	0.487	6587.77		22.94 %	
X_5	0.137	5749.64		5.65 %	
X_6	0.418	9631.82		28.85	

4.5 Factors Contributing to Commuters' Willingness to use BRT

4.5.1 Coefficient of Determination (R Square) and T-Test

The coefficient determination specified that the R^2 value was 0.986 or equal to 98.6%, which indicated that the X variable simultaneously affects the Y variable by 98.6%, while the remaining 1.4% was influenced by other variables or variables not examined in the equation.

A partial test (t-test) was carried out with the following results, the t-count values for X_1, X_3, X_5, X_6 were greater than the t-table value of 1.96. However, for X_2 and X_4, the results of the t-count < t-table. Therefore, the research concluded that the X variable, which consisted of security (X_1), amenities (X_3), equality (X_5), regularity (X_6), partially affected the Y variable. Further, the research indicated that the safety variable (X_2) and affordability (X_4) had no partial effect on the Y variable in BRT mode, hence the regression equation for the BRT mode below. The findings are presented in Table 8.

$$Y = 0.088 + 0.446X_1 + 0.101X_2 + 0.590X_3 + 0.0914X_4 + 0.279X_5 + 0.235X_6 \quad (3)$$

Table 8. Coefficient of Determination (R2) and t Test on BRT

	Variable	B	T-Count	T-Table	Description	R Square
	Constant	0.088	1.334	1.96		
X_1	Security	0.446	4.107	1.96	Influential	
X_2	Safety	0.101	0.765	1.96	Uninfluential	
X_3	Amenities	0.590	7.496	1.96	Influential	0.986
X_4	Affordability	0.091	0.996	1.96	Uninfluential	
X_5	Equality	0.279	3.345	1.96	Influential	
X_6	Regularity	0.235	2.943	1.96	Influential	

4.5.2 Hypothesis Testing Results on BRT

Table 9. Hypothesis Testing Results on BRT

Hypothesis	T - count	T - Table	Conclusion	Decision
1	4.107	1.96	Influential	Hypothesis H_1 accepted
2	0.765	1.96	Uninfluential	Hypothesis H_2 rejected
3	7.496	1.96	Influential	Hypothesis H_3 accepted
4	0.996	1.96	Uninfluential	Hypothesis H_4 rejected
5	3.345	1.96	Influential	Hypothesis H_5 accepted
6	2.943	1.96	Influential	Hypothesis H_6 accepted

4.5.3 Effective Contribution on BRT

The research calculated the effective contribution for the independent variable on the BRT mode, and the following results were obtained. The security variable (X_1) contributed 20.41%, safety (X_2) contributed 4.66%, amenities (X_3) contributed 41.75%, affordability (X_4) contributed 4.07%, equality (X_5) accounted for 11.79%, and regularity (X_6) accounted for 15.96%. The findings showed that the amenities (X_3) variable had the greatest influence on commuters' willingness to use public transport at 41%, as described in Table 10.

Table 10. Effective Contribution on BRT

Variable	b	Cross Product	Regression	Effective Contribution	Total Effective Contribution
X_1	0.446	5947.07	12816.713	20.41%	98.6%
X_2	0.101	5980.88		4.66 %	
X_3	0.590	9192.91		41.75 %	
X_4	0.091	5831.65		4.07 %	
X_5	0.279	5480.02		11.79 %	
X_6	0.235	8818.09		15.96	

5. Conclusions

The research established that safety, comfort, affordability, equality, and regularity influence the commuters' willingness to use public transport using KRL mode. In establishing factors that affected MRT mode, it was found that there was an influence between the variables of convenience, affordability, equality, and regularity on the commuters' willingness to use public transport. Moreover, the results indicated an influence between the variables of safety, comfort, affordability, equality, and regularity in BRT mode on the commuters' willingness to use public transport.

Conclusively, the factors that influenced the commuters' willingness to use the KRL, MRT, and BRT modes included vehicle crew identity, lighting, danger signal lights, transport capacity, temperature control facilities, cleaning facilities, priority seating, wheelchair rooms, service information, stopping times and headway. Furthermore, the variables found to have influenced commuters' use of public transport based on priority included amenities, safety, security, affordability, regularity, and equality. However, there was no significant association between the security and safety variables on the willingness to use public transport in the modes examined.

References

[1] Abiyoga R 2020 *Pengembangan Indikator Kesiapan Kawasan Berorientasi Transit* p 19

[2] Ari widayanti, Soeparno B K 2014 *Permasalahan dan Pengembangan Angkutan Umum di Kota Surabaya* Jurnal Transportasi **14** (1) 53-60

[3] Astuti P 2013 *Pengaruh Event Marketing Terhadap Keputusan Pembelian Produk Rokok Envio Mild*

[4] Augusty F 2010 *Metode Penelitian Manajemen* (Semarang: Badan Penerbit Universitas Diponegoro) p 55-59

[5] Enrekang D 2017 *Analisis Pemilihan Moda Angkutan Umum Dalam* p 23

[6] Harahap A 2018 Kepuasan Pengguna Jasa Transportasi Online Grab *Analisis Dampak Keamanan, Harga, dan Promosi terhadap Kepuasan Pengguna Jasa Transportasi Online Grab* p 14

[7] Hasoloan J T 2018 *Defining Transit Oriented Development (TOD) Potential Along the Commuter Line Stations in Jakarta* Massachusetts Institute of Technologi 1-97 *dspace.mit.edu/handle/1721.1/118253*

[8] Jayati D 2019 *Analisis Kebijakan Peraturan Menteri Perhubungan Nomor Pm 27 Tahun 2015 Tentang Standar Pelayanan Minimal Angkutan Massal Berbasis Jalan (Study Kasus Bus Trans Metro Pekanbaru) Analisis Kebijakan Peraturan Menteri Perhubungan Nomor Pm 27 Tahun 2015 Tent* p 32-33

[9] Peraturan Menteri Perhubungan RI Nomor PM 98 Tahun 2013

[10] Petra S U 2015 *Stasiun Kereta Api Sudirman dan Transit Oriented Development Dukuh Atas*

[11] Priadmaja A, Anisa, Prayogi L 2017 *Penerapan Konsep Transit Oriented Development (TOD) pada Penataan Kawasan di Kota Tangerang* Purwarupa Jurnal Arsitektur **1** (2) 53-60

[12] Raharjo S 2014 *Cara Melakukan Uji-t Parsial Dalam Analisis Regresi dengan SPSS http://spssindonesia.com*

[13] Raharjo S 2017 *Makna Koefisien Determinasi (R Square) dalam Analisis Regresi Linier Berganda. http://spssindonesia.com*

[14] Raharjo S 2018 *Cara Menghitung SE dan SR dalam Analisis Regresi Linier Berganda. http://www.spssindonesia.com*

[15] Ramadhayanti A 2018 *Pengaruh Pengguna Transportasi Berkelanjutan Dan Displin Berlalu Lintas Terhadap Dampak Tingkat Keselamatan Berkendara (Safety Riding) Dalam Studi kasus Penumpang Angkutan Umum M.19 Kranji (Bekasi)-PGC (Cililitan)* Jurnal Kajian Ilmiah **18** (1) p 43-53 *https://doi.org/10.31599/jki.v18i1.192*

[16] Sidjabat S 2015 *Revitalisasi Angkutan Umum Untuk Mengurangi Kemacetan Jakarta* Manajemen Bisnis Transportasi Dan Logistik **1** 309-330

[17] Sitanggang R, Saribanon E 2018 *Faktor-Faktor Penyebab Kemacetan di DKI Jakarta* Jurnal Manajemen Bisnis Transportasi dan Logistik **4** (3) 289-296

[18] Sodri A, Harmain R, Hasibuan H 2020 *Model Spasial Lingkungan Buatan Kawasan Transit-Oriented Development (TOD) DKI Jakarta*. Majalah Ilmiah Globe **22** (1) 41 *https://doi.org/10.24895/mig.2020.22-1.1157*

[19] Triyadi F 2018 *Pengaruh Kualitas Pelayanan, Fasilitas, Dan Tarif Harga Terhadap Kepuasan Konsumen Angkutan Umum Di Terminal Non Bus Lodoyo Kabupaten Blitar (Studi Pada Dinas Perhubungan Kabupaten Blitar)* Universitas Maritim Amni Semarang

[20] Yuliara I 2016 Modul Regresi Linier Berganda *Regresi Linier Berganda* 18

IOP Conf. Series: Earth and Environmental Science 1000 (2022) 012010 doi:10.1088/1755-1315/1000/1/012010

Index of Walkability to and from Public Transport Stops or Terminals in Greater Jakarta to Enhance Walking Environment

L S Putranto[1], **and R B Khuana**[1]

[1] Civil Engineering Department, Tarumanagara University, Jakarta 11440, Indonesia
Corresponding author: leksmonop@ft.untar.ac.id

Abstract. Almost all travel between an origin to a destination requires walking as first-mile and last-mile transport mode. Walking can be conducted either in the sidewalks, zebra-crosses, and pedestrian bridges. This paper adopts the index of walkability developed by D'orso dan Migliore in 2020 to be used for 150 respondents in Greater Jakarta. This index consists of three constructs (factors), i.e., practicability, safety and, pleasantness. A confirmatory factor analysis was used using principal component analysis in SPSS 27 and rotated using varimax with Kaizer Normalization. Instead of three factors in the original index, in this Indonesian adaptation, only two factors were extracted. Based on the discussion on this paper, it was recommended to increase the number of respondents to get a more valid result.

1. Introduction

Walkability can be generally defined as the extent to which the built environment, allows walking [1] and is pedestrian-friendly [2-3]. However, walkable is multi-dimensional [4], with studies stressing different environmental features or means of creating walkable environments, which are traversable, compact, physically attractive, and safe, creating vibrant locations, adding sustainable travel choices, and supporting outdoor physical activities and recreation [5-7].

Index of walkability developed by D'orso & Migliore (2020) [8] consist of three factors, i.e., practicability, safety and, pleasantness. Practicability consists of the condition and cleanliness of the sidewalks, architectural obstacles, and other elements limiting accessibility. Safety defines as protection from various risks during the walking experience such as sidewalk fences, sidewalk lightings and safety, and perception of security against crime. Pleasantness relates to sidewalk attractiveness and the presence of attributes along the sidewalks elevating the degree of walking quality.

According to the Minister of Public Work Regulation No. 03/PRT/M/2014 [9], pedestrian facilities include green belts, lightings, benches, sidewalk fences, trash bins, markings, signs, information boards, bus stops, and public phones. The width of green belts should be at least 150cm and to be planted by shading trees. The lightings should be mounted in 4m height with spacing 10m between each light pole. The dimension of benches is 0,4-0,5m in width dan 1.5m in length with a spacing of 10m between benches. The height of the sidewalk fence should be 90cm. Spacing between trash bins is 20m.

2. Literature Review

According to D'orso & Migliore (2020) [8], the following was the description of each item in the index of walkability:

Practicability:

- Sidewalk slope: manageable (<5%) vs too steep for elderly and/ or wheelchair users (>=5%).
- Pedestrian level of service: high pedestrian flow/ limited sidewalk width/ some obstacles vs low pedestrian flow/ sufficient sidewalk width/ no obstacles.
- Surface degradation: some holes or dips/ degraded sidewalk vs no holes or dips/ adequate sidewalk

Pleasantness:
- Street furniture: no trash bins/ benches/ other street furniture vs some trash bins/ benches/ other street furniture.
- Shelter for rain and sun: not available vs available.
- Green areas: not available vs available.
- Shops: not available vs available.
- Building context/ land use mix/ urban design: degraded urban landscape (damage urban furniture, dirty, some graffiti, some abusive posters, some buildings with degraded facades) vs nice urban landscape (perfect functionality of urban furniture, adequate cleaning, some well-maintained buildings.

Safety:
- Lighting: poor or lack of lighting vs proper and efficient lighting.
- Traffic volume and vehicle speed: high traffic volume/ high speed vs low traffic volume/ low speed.
- Pedestrian protection from vehicles: not available vs were available.
- The traffic control signal at the intersection: not available vs available.
- Driveways: some driveways vs no driveways

According to Lee et al (2020) [10], the audit-based school walkability index can be used as a complementary tool for measuring walkability near low-income elementary schools along with the existing GIS-based school walkability index. The audit-based school walkability index consists of three variables and several items as follows:
- Land use (density of multi-family housing, the density of park, density of vacant land).
- Street characteristics (density of sidewalk, sidewalk completeness rate, flat sidewalk rate, wide sidewalk rate, sidewalk buffer rate, sidewalk connectivity rate, density of uneven surface, density of trashes on the street, density of graffiti, density of drainage deficiencies, streetlight density, density of traffic calming equipment, noise from factories/ pets, and density of zebra cross).
- Neighborhood perception (easiness to observe sidewalk from home, no cracks/ holes/ overgrown grass, cleanliness from trash, pedestrian/ cyclist safety, pedestrian/ cyclist comfort, and scenery surrounding the street).

Christiansen et al (2014) [11], combining school site, perceived environment, and social environment to model active school travel. Perceived environments include perceived safe route, many paths, safe crossing, traffic flow, and traffic speed. Social environments include parents cycle weekly, friends cycle daily, and parents support cycling.

Koohsari et al (2021) [12] conducted data collection between July and December 2013 and April 2014 to February 2015 from a randomly chosen sample of residents in 2 Japanese cities, Koto Ward and Matsuyama City. They found that walkability correlated with population density, access to shops, access to public transport, availability of sidewalks, availability of cycle lanes, access to recreational facilities, aesthetics, traffic safety, and security from crime.

Conderino et al (2021) [13] analysed the 2019 Walk Score across 500 large cities in the U.S. They found that high-income and majority White geographic units had the lowest walkability overall. However, this association was reversed within the majority of Black neighbourhoods, where tracts in lower-income tertiles had the lowest walkability

3. Method

The respondents were 150 pedestrians who use public transport frequently in Greater Jakarta. The general data includes gender, age, residence address (just to indicate the residence location within the Greater Jakarta; full address not required), travel objective, monthly personal expenses, frequency of using public transport, walking distance. The perception data was an adaptation to 13 items of the index of walkability (D'orso & Migliore, 2020) [8] as follow:

Practicability:
- PR1: I prefer to walk on a sidewalk that can be easily accessed by everybody.
- PR2: I prefer to walk on a wide sidewalk.
- PR3: I prefer to walk on a sidewalk without obstacles.
- PR4: I prefer to walk on a well-maintained sidewalk.

Pleasantness:
- PL1: I prefer to walk on a sidewalk equipped with street furniture such as trash bins and benches.
- PL2: I prefer to walk on a sidewalk equipped with shelter for rain and sun.
- PL3: I prefer to walk on a sidewalk equipped with minimarkets.
- PL4: I prefer to walk on a sidewalk surrounded by well-maintained and clean buildings.
- PL5: I prefer to walk on a sidewalk surrounded by greeneries.

Safety:
- S1: I prefer to walk on a sidewalk with proper lighting.
- S2: I prefer to walk on a sidewalk when road traffic is heavy.
- S3: I prefer to walk on a sidewalk equipped with a fence.
- S4: I prefer to walk on a sidewalk with the signalized pedestrian crossing.

Likert scale was used as responses of the perceptional part of the questionnaire, i.e. (1) strongly disagree (2) disagree (3) agree, and (4) strongly agree.

A confirmatory factor analysis (CFA) was conducted using principal component analysis in SPSS 27 and rotated using varimax with Kaizer Normalization. The extraction was based on eigenvalues greater than 1. There were two criteria related to sampling adequacy, i.e., Kaiser-Meyer-Olkin (KMO) Measure of Sampling Adequacy, and Measures of Sampling Adequacy (MSA). KMO should be at least 0.6 and MSA's in the main diagonal of the anti-image correlation matrix should be at least 0.5. The other criterion is Bartlett's test of sphericity tests, i.e., the hypothesis that the correlation matrix is an identity matrix, which would indicate that the variables are unrelated and therefore unsuitable for structure detection. Therefore, the significance of the test should be less than 0.05. A variable's communality ranges from 0 to 1. In general, one way to think of communality is as the proportion of common variance found in a particular variable. A variable that does not have any unique variance at all (i.e., one with an explained variance that is 100% a result of other variables) has a communality of 1. An average value between 0.5 and 0.6 is acceptable for sample sizes between 100 and 200 (Samuel, 2017) [14].

4. Respondent Profiles

Of 150 respondents, most of them (73%) came from the younger-adult age group. The respondent's mean age of 36 years old and a standard deviation of 11 years old. Most of the respondents (61%) lived in Jakarta. Most of the respondents (67%) monthly expenses were less than the minimum regional wage of 4.5 million rupiahs (USD 314) with mean monthly expenses of USD 390 and a standard deviation of monthly expenses of USD 674. Most of the respondents (81%) did not use public transport daily but were frequent enough to be eligible to be the respondent. Most of the respondents (46%) were willing to walk 1000 m or more a day with a mean willingness to walk 2,945m with a standard deviation of 5,073m. Most of the respondents (43%) travel for work

5. Results

To be able to fulfill all the requirements stated in Data Analysis Method, the CFA should be conducted more than once. In the first trial, the KMO Measure of Sampling Adequacy was 0.677 (more than 0.5) and Bartlett's Test of Sphericity <0.001 (far under 0.05) and therefore the requirement was fulfilled. Table 1., shows the MSA in the first trial. MSA for PR4 (0.490), S1 (0.318), and S2 (0.274) were less than 0.5, and therefore the requirement was not fulfilled, and consequently, PR4, S1, and S2 were removed before further trial was conducted. Table 2., shows the communalities in the first trial. Communalities extraction of PL3 (0.280) was less than 0.5 and therefore the requirement was not fulfilled and consequently, PL3 was removed before further trial was conducted.

Table 1. MSA from the first CFA trial

Item	MSA
PR1	0.765
PR2	0.573
PR3	0.792
PR4	0.490
PL1	0.832
PL2	0.814
PL3	0.756
PL4	0.850
PL5	0.790
S1	0.318
S2	0.274
S3	0.591
S4	0.798

Table 2. Communalities from the first CFA trial

Item	Communalities
PR1	0.723
PR2	0.858
PR3	0.762
PR4	0.835
PL1	0.543
PL2	0.770
PL3	0.280
PL4	0.766
PL5	0.802
S1	0.879
S2	0.805
S3	0.842
S4	0.757

In the second trial, the KMO Measure of Sampling Adequacy was 0.794 (>0.6) and the significant level of Bartlett's Test of Sphericity was less than 0.001 (<0.05). Therefore, the requirement was fulfilled. Table 3., shows the MSA in the second trial. All MSA's were more than 0.5 and therefore the requirement was fulfilled. Table 4., shows the communalities in the second trial. All communalities were more than 0.5 and therefore the requirement was fulfilled. Table 5. describes the number of factors that can be formed based on eigenvalue > 1,0 and the total variance explained. Table 6. shows the rotated component matrix consists of 2 components (factors). The original walkability index (D'orso & Migliore, 2020) [8] consists of 3 factors. Therefore, our findings were 2 new combined factors called Pleasantness-Practicability (component 1) and Safety-Practicability (component 2).

6. Conclusion and Recommendation

Our findings were 2 new combined factors in the Indonesian Walkability Index called:

- Pleasantness-Practicability (component 1) consists of PL1 (I prefer to walk on a sidewalk equipped with street furniture such as trash bins and benches), PL2 (I prefer to walk on a sidewalk equipped with shelter for rain and sun), PL4 (I prefer to walk in a sidewalk surrounded by well-maintained and clean buildings), PL5 (I prefer to walk in a sidewalk surrounded by greeneries) and PR1 (I prefer to walk in a sidewalk which can be easily accessed by everybody).
- Safety-Practicability (component 2) consists of S3 (I prefer to walk in a sidewalk equipped with a fence), S4 (I prefer to walk in a sidewalk with signalized pedestrian crossing), PR2 (I prefer to walk in a wide sidewalk), and PR3 (I prefer to walk in a sidewalk without obstacle).

Based on the discussion on this paper, it was recommended to increase the number of respondents to get a more valid result.

Table 3. MSA from the second CFA trial

Item	MSA
PR1	0.794
PR2	0.748
PR3	0.778
PL1	0.877
PL2	0.817
PL4	0.846
PL5	0.792
S3	0.735
S4	0.781

Table 4. Communalities from the second CFA trial

Item	Communalities
PR1	0.721
PR2	0.845
PR3	0.626
PL1	0.877
PL2	0.817
PL4	0.846
PL5	0.792
S3	0.829
S4	0.694

Table 5. Total variance explained

Component	Initial Eigenvalues			Extraction Sums of Squared Loadings			Rotation Sums of Squared Loadings		
	Total	% of Variance	Cumulative %	Total	% of Variance	Cumulative %	Total	% of Variance	Cumulative %
1	3.751	41.678	41.678	3.751	41.678	41.678	3.571	39.682	39.682
2	2.829	31.435	73.113	2.829	31.435	73.113	3.009	33.430	73.113
3	0.639	7.095	80.208						
4	0.561	6.233	86.441						
5	0.382	4.245	90.686						
6	0.291	3.237	93.923						
7	0.223	2.480	96.403						
8	0.167	1.855	98.259						
9	0.157	1.741	100.000						

Table 6. Rotated component matrix

Items	Components	
	1	2
PL1	0.735	
PL2	0.862	
PL4	0.885	
PL5	0.880	
PR1	0.848	
PR2		0.917
PR3		0.787
S3		0.910
S4		0.832

References

[1] Kelley E A Kandula N R Kanaya A M and Yen I H 2016. Neighborhood Walkability and Walking for Transport among South Asians in the MASALA study *J. Phys. Activity and Health* **13 (5)** pp 514–519.

[2] Gebel K Bauman A and Owen N 2009. Correlates of Nonconcordance between Perceived and Objective Measures of Walkability *Ann. Behav. Med.* **37** pp 228–238.

[3] Moura F Cambra P and Gonçalves A B 2017 Measuring Walkability for Distinct Pedestrian Groups with a Participatory Assessment Method: A Case Study in Lisbon *Landscape Urban Plann* **187** pp 282–296.

[4] Forsyth A and Southworth M 2008 Cities Afoot—Pedestrians, Walkability and Urban Design. *J. Urban Des.* **13 (1)** pp 1–3.

[5] Forsyth A 2015 What is a Walkable Place? The Walkability Debate in Urban Design *Urban Des. Int.* **20 (4)**, pp 274–292.

[6] Saelens B E and Handy S L 2008 Built Environment Correlates of Walking: A Review *Med. Sci. Sports Exerc.* **40** pp S550–S566.

[7] Hall C M and Ram Y 2018 Measuring the Relationship between Tourism and Walkability?: Walk Score and English Tourist Attractions. *J. Sust. Tourism* **27 (2)** pp 223-240.

[8] D'Orso G and Migliore M 2020 A GIS-Based Method for Evaluating the Walkability of a Pedestrian Environment and Prioritised Investments *Journal of Transport Geography* **82** pp 1-7.

[9] Minister of Public Work Regulation No. 03/PRT/M/2014.

[10] Lee S Lee C Won J Abbey-lambertz M and Mendoza, J A 2020 School Walkability Index: Application of Environmental Audit Tool and GIS *Journal of Transport & Health* **18** pp 1-11.

[11] Christiansen L B Toftager M Schipperijn J Ersbøll A K Giles-corti B and Troelsen J 2014 School Site Walkability and Active School Transport – Association, Mediation and Moderation *Journal of Transport Geography* **34** pp 7–15.

[12] Koohsari M J Mccormack G R Shibata A and Ishii K 2021 The relationship between walk score® and perceived walkability in ultrahigh density areas *Preventive Medicine Reports* **23** 1-6.

[13] Conderino, S. E., Feldman, J. M., Spoer, B., Gourevitch, M. N., & Thorpe, L. E. 2021 Social and Economic Differences in Neighborhood Walkability Across 500 U.S. Cities *American Journal of Preventive Medicine*, 1–8.

[14] Samuels P 2017 *Advice on Exploratory Factor Analysis (Technical Report)* Available online at https://www.researchgate.net/publication/319165677... [Accessed on 11 June 2021]

Modeling the performance of passenger public transportation service in Salatiga City

M Handajani[1], F Firmawan[1] and Harmini[1]

[1] Faculty of Engineering Semarang University Semarang, Indonesia

E-mail: [1]mudjiastuti@usm.ac.id

Abstract. The Public transportation system is one of the main indicators to show the increase in efficiency and productivity of a city. Meanwhile, the public transportation services in Salatiga City were observed to be averagely good but have some classic obstacles such as the absence of bus stops to pick up passengers and non-determination of the fare to be paid by the passengers per kilometer. This study was, therefore, conducted to model the performance of public transportation in Salatiga City. The results showed that 9 fleets with a route length of 6.2 km which has a load factor of 72% because Tamansari – Blotongan is one of the routes most traveled by the passengers are sufficient for the needs of the passengers. It was also discovered that 70% of the people prefer public transportation due to its cheapness, 55% fastness, and 77.5% because it is safe while 10% were found to be satisfied with the waiting time. Moreover, a real-time passenger information system was observed to have the ability to determine the position of public transport passengers while the Radio Frequency Identification Device (RFID) network was able to estimate the number of passengers currently limited due to the COVID-19 pandemic.The first section in your paper

1. Introduction

Transportation has an important role to encourage increased economic growth. Economic growth is of development for each region so that various efforts are made to make it happen. This subsequently indicates its participation in the creation of economic stability, the continuation of community activities, and the effective functioning of government processes. Public transport was, however, defined as the movement of people and cargo from one place to another in an urban area. Therefore, the development of an public transportation system is an important means to solve urban problems like traffic jam, air poluttion and save fuel consumption and this is part of the Smart Transportation efforts towards realizing an environmentally friendly Smart City for cities in Indonesia, especially Salatiga [1]. Meanwhile, increasing demand for quality of life have led to the need for more appropriate means of mass transportation, affordable fares, and a definite time to reach a destination. This led the Salatiga City Government to plan a transportation system in the form of passenger public transportation which is environmentally sound, reliable, safe, comfortable, cheap, regular, scheduled, and more modern [2]. This means a Real-Time Passenger Information System Modeling is needed for the users of the Salatiga City Public Transportation which provides information on public transportation routes for passengers. Therefore, this study was conducted to determine the length of the route, the number of public transportations on the route, schedule, speed, boarding/alighting stop, and headway which is the distance between two public transport vehicles after which the performance of the public transportation services was modeled.

1.1. Literature review

Academic information was sourced from data obtained from the field and several previous studies in international and national journals which are related to the (a) evaluation of public transportation in Semarang City in terms of technical, economic, and environmental aspects, (b) evaluation of boarding aligning public transportation in Demak City, (c) traffic and road transportation technology, (d) Mangkang Semarang Integrated Terminal Master Plan, (e) monitoring system and installation of Information System in Trans Semarang Bus. Categorized the behavioral characteristics of passenger public transportation on the road into three and these include traveling at a low speed which leads to the reduction of other vehicles' speed, lack of bus stops which makes the cars stop at any place, and violation of traffic laws.[3]

Table 1 shows the criteria for Public Transportation of Passengers measured through Government Regulation no. 10 of 2012 Director General of Land Transportation [4]. This means the services are adjudged to be good as long as they meet the standards set by the government.

Table 1. Public transport performance

Variable	Parameter
Headway	1 – 12 minutes
Waiting Time	
a. Average	a. 5 – 10 minutes
b. Maximum	b. 10 -20 minutes
Load Factor	70 %
Travel Distance	200 km/ vehicle/day
Operating Capacity	80 -90%
Travel time	
a. Average	a. 1 – 1,5 hours
b. Maximum	b. 2 – 3 hours
Travel Speed	
a. Congested Area	a. 30 km/hours
b. Less crowded area	b. 50 km/hours

Source: Government Regulation No. 10 of 2012 Directorate General of Land Transportation

The service quality indicators presented in Table 1 provide the limits on the reliability or precision parameter values required to be met. The condition or classification of the city size is observed to be very important due to the variation of the service to be provided according to the size of the city. The Public Passenger Vehicle in Salatiga City is a vehicle that accommodates 10 passengers. There is, however, no stopping place for public transportation in the city and this means the passengers usually pay according to the fares stated by the driver. Meanwhile, a Mayor's Certificate has been prepared to determine fares on public transportation except for those traveling the whole route who are required to pay according to the specified fare. There is, however, the possibility of implementing a real-time bus monitoring and passenger information system by installing GPS in every city bus to pass information to the central control unit [5]. The system is designed to stand alone and can display the bus location in real-time. It is important to note that a web server is used to monitor its movement while a mobile application is developed for bus users for the same purpose. This is based on the concept of location determination (AVL) with the help of GPS and transmission [6].

2. Methods

The location selected for this study is the Tamansari – Blotongan public transportation route in Salatiga City and the government of the city and the transportation service collaborated to implement the plan on this route. Therefore, this study was conducted using both qualitative and quantitative methods this involved the collection of primary and secondary data through field surveys and review of existing studies. The primary data boarding alighting, headway, number of passengers while secondary data focused on number of vehicles, route,speed and time schedule, existing condition of public transport. This was followed by data analysis and a model of the system's performance. The flow chart of this study is presented in the following Figure 1.

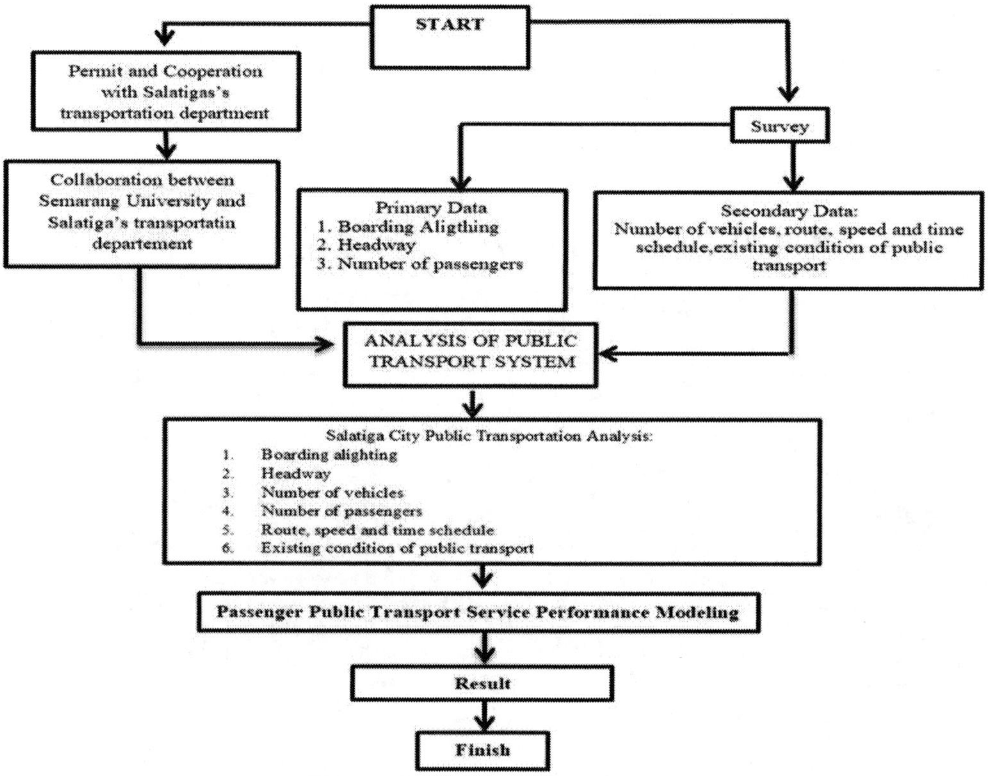

Figure 1. Research Flowchart.

3. Research Results

3.1. Passenger Overview

The data collected from the field was used to compare the filling level with the seating capacity on public transportation modes using a load factor of 72%. It is important to note that 40 respondents that are residents of Salatiga City with different gender and age were used in this study. The objective was to determine their perceptions and also conduct field observations to determine the reason for the use of public transportation, level of satisfaction as well as the level of security and waiting time.

IOP Conf. Series: Earth and Environmental Science 1000 (2022) 012011 doi:10.1088/1755-1315/1000/1/012011

3.1.1. Reasons for using Public Transportation

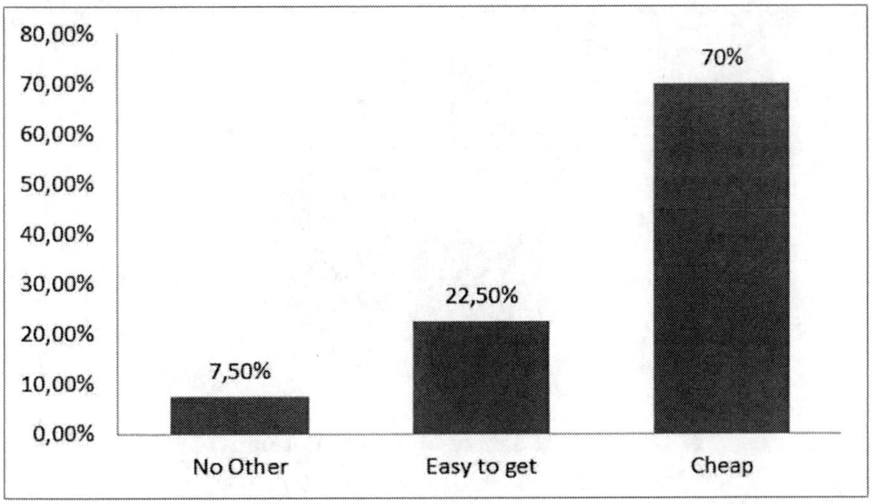

Figure 2. Reasons for Using Public Transportation.

The results showed most of the people use public transportation due to the low cost as indicated by 70%, easy to reach as suggested by 22.5%, and the absence of other modes of transportation as answered by 7.5% as indicated in Figure 2. This means the major reason they use public transportation is cheap Satisfaction with Vehicle Speed.

3.1.2. Satisfaction with Vehicle Speed

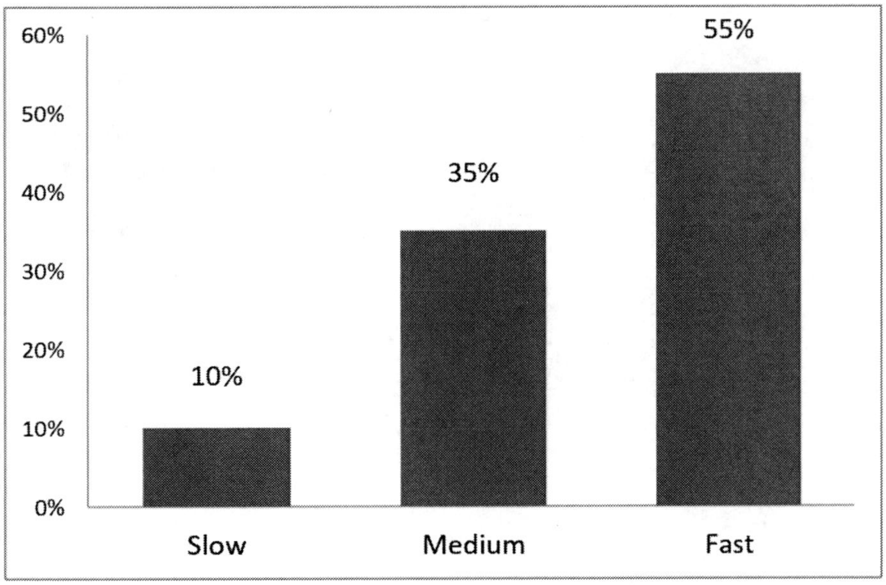

Figure 3. Satisfaction with Transport Speed.

The results showed 10% of the respondents prefer slow speeds, 35% prefer medium speeds while the remaining 55% want the fastest speed as indicated in Figure 3. This means the respondents are more satisfied with the fastest speed of public transportation.

3.1.3. Passenger Satisfaction with Safety

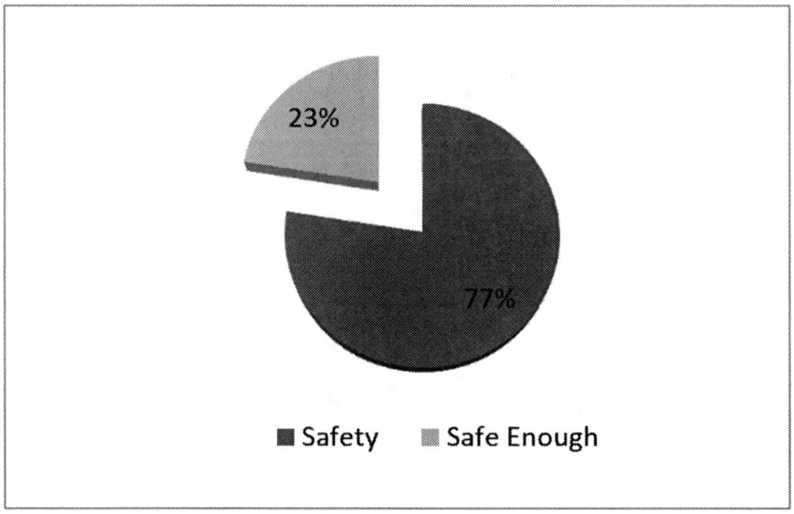

Figure 4. Satisfaction with Transportation Safety.

Figure 4 shows most of the passengers are satisfied with the level of safety in public transportation as indicated by 77% that believe it is quite good while 23% indicate it is quite safe. This means the people use public transportation because they feel it is safe.

3.1.4. Satisfaction with Waiting Time

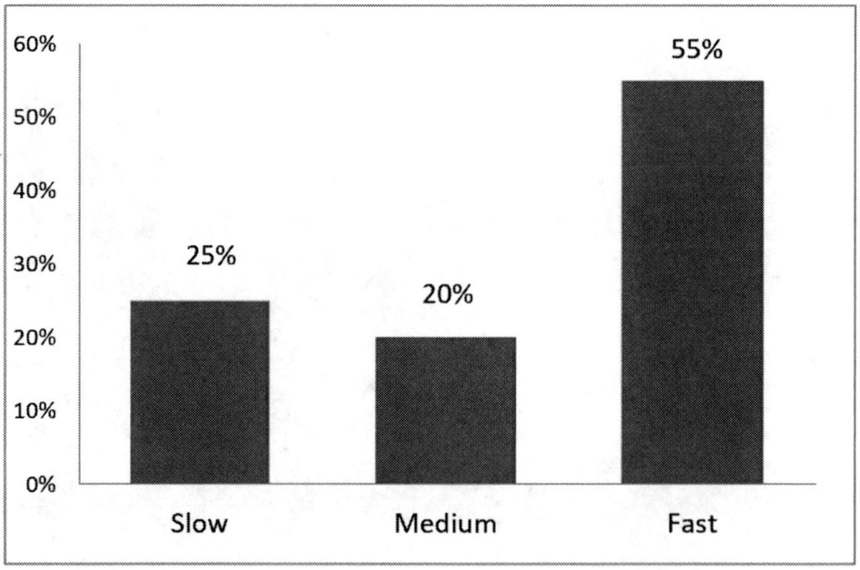

Figure 5. Passenger Satisfaction with Waiting Time.

The people of Salatiga City were discovered to prefer public passenger transportation with a relatively small waiting time as indicated by 55% that chose fast waiting time, 8% for medium waiting times, and 10% for slow waiting time. This means the community is not satisfied with the current waiting time, thereby, leading to the conduct of this study to apply the Real-Time Passenger Information System.

3.2. Economical Overview

The certainty of saving travel time was calculated using the Real-Time Passenger Information System model and the following was observed:

3.2.1. Travel Time

The certainty of travel time for private vehicles using Salatiga City Public Transportation can be obtained through Passenger Information System which provides information on public transportation routes for passengers. Moreover, the distance and travel time at each stop traversed by public transportation is useful information for passengers and this indicates the ability of the travel time certainty to minimize waiting time at each designated stop. This, therefore, helps in the efficient and effective use of time. For example, students do not need to wait for public transportation with longer arrival times to avoid getting late for school.

i. Mode Choice Approach
This method was used to determine the time value to estimate the ratio of selecting a transportation method. Moreover, a choice comparison was assumed in the form of the function of 2 variables which include operational costs and time costs. Therefore, the time value is defined as the ratio of the travel time to the cost factors.

$$\text{Choice ratio (Pi)} = a_0 + a_1 + (C_i - C_j) + a_2(T_i - T_j) \quad (1)$$

Description:
Pi = Choice ratio of first mode
i,j = Alternative mode,
C, T = Cost (C) and Time(T),
a_0, a_1, a_2 = Coefficient.

ii. Income Approach
The time value based on capita income (GRDP) can be formulated as follows:

$$\text{Time Value} = \frac{PBRB/JP}{WKT}\text{ss}$$

Description:
PDRB = Gross Regional Domestic Income (per capita /IDR),
JP = Total population (person),
WKT = Annual Working Time (hours).

3.2.2. Fuel Usage

A real-time passenger information system can reduce waiting time for passengers. Moreover, there is a need to replace private vehicles with Salatiga City public transportation for community trips to 'rest' a significant number of vehicles for a certain period such as Monday to Friday. This means assuming a private car consumes an average of 10 liters of fuel per day, there is a possibility of saving 10,000L/day for 1000 cars.

3.3. Environmental Overview

The transportation sector is very important to the assessment of the efforts towards achieving global competitiveness. Moreover, the ability of national services to compete depends on fast and precise access which is usually measured by connectivity, accessibility, and mobility. It is also important to prioritize the safety and health of transportation and movement in the rescue plan designed for transportation management. Meanwhile, one of the challenges observed is to ensure the current transportation process does not aid the transmission of the Covid-19 virus [7]. Salatiga City has 194,084 inhabitants and this means it requires public transportation for its urban status. The present public transportation in the city usually accommodates 8 passengers but is reduced to 5 due to the emergence of the Covid-19 pandemic. It is important to note that the use of this mode of transportation can save fuel consumption and this is part of the Smart Transportation efforts towards realizing an environmentally friendly Smart City for cities in Indonesia, especially Salatiga.

3.4. Architecture and Modeling of Real-Time Information System for Salatiga City Public Transportation

System design is the post-analysis stage of the system development cycle which is directed towards determining the functional requirements needed to implement a system [8]. The present Covid-19 pandemic, therefore, requires the design of a Passenger Information System to provide information to passengers on the status of certain modern and real-time transportation modes. It is intended to assist passengers in finding information, saving time, and increasing their comfort [9]. The system currently consists an information LED screen to display information on indoor or outdoor applications [10], drivers to monitor and integrate each device as well as a GPS module to determine the actual location of public transport, announce and broadcast different stops, and provide wireless communication with a central network system. Moreover, the main parts of the Salatiga City passenger public transport information system are the simulator applications, public transport simulators, and processing servers. The architecture and modeling of the system are, therefore, presented in Figure 7 and explained in the following subsections.

3.4.1. Simulator app

It is a web and android based system that is used to display at passenger public transport stops, mobile applications, and control room applications. It always requires updating new information on the central server.

3.4.2. Public transportation simulator

Its main function is to download the name or code of public transportation and the coordinates of its stopping points, calculate the distance and direction, and send information to the server using the GPRS network. The information usually sent includes passenger IDs obtained through the Radio Frequency Identification Device (RFID) network which are required to be tapped by every passenger when boarding and alighting. Moreover, the fare is determined based on the ID card. Moreover, the public transport location calculated in real-time by the GPS is stored on a simulator in the vehicle while the longitude and latitude are gradually transferred to the central server using the GPRS network. The units inside the public vehicles are, however, allowed to download the name or code and the coordinates of the public transportation points on the server. It is, however, important to note that the analysis and calculation of the transportation time contains an algorithm to determine the arrival time based on the route traversed.

3.4.3. Processing server

This is located at the center of the information system and its functions include the following:

i. Maintaining a database of all routes, public transport serving all routes, and public transport stops.
ii. Receiving the location and speed of the public transportation unit.
iii. Calculating the estimated arrival time of public transportation with one another according to the place where it stops.
iv. Replying to requests from android users based on queries sent.
v. Hosting an internet web page that allows administrators to track public transport in real-time and to obtain time estimates between public transportation.

The server stores information on public transportation, routes, and stops in the form of database tables to reduce memory requirements, increase access speed, and reduce the number of database queries. Meanwhile, the database table was divided into static and dynamic to increase the query speed. This means the information is deleted after it has been permanently stored on the server. Moreover, the database table containing the position of public transportation stores data statically or temporarily while the data logger of public transport such as code/id, route number, and name stores dynamically. It is also important to note that the updated position is stored in the public transportation position database table and log. Meanwhile, the distance traveled is calculated and compared with the value of the initial position using the appropriate route at a certain time. Furthermore, the status of public transportation changes from active to invalid when the driver gives a signal that there is a damage or signal on the vehicle which is not detected by the server. This, therefore, significantly helps transportation companies in taking appropriate action. It is also important to note that the public transport position log database table automatically saves a copy of the updated position.

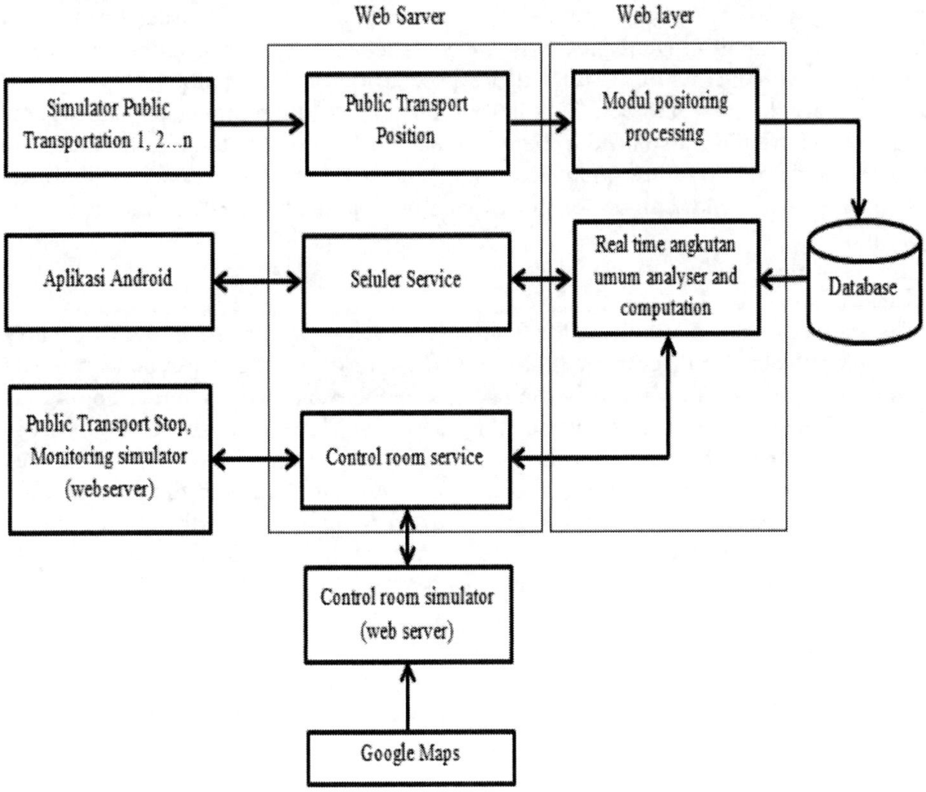

Figure 6. Architecture and model of Real-Time Passenger Information System of Salatiga City Public Transportation.

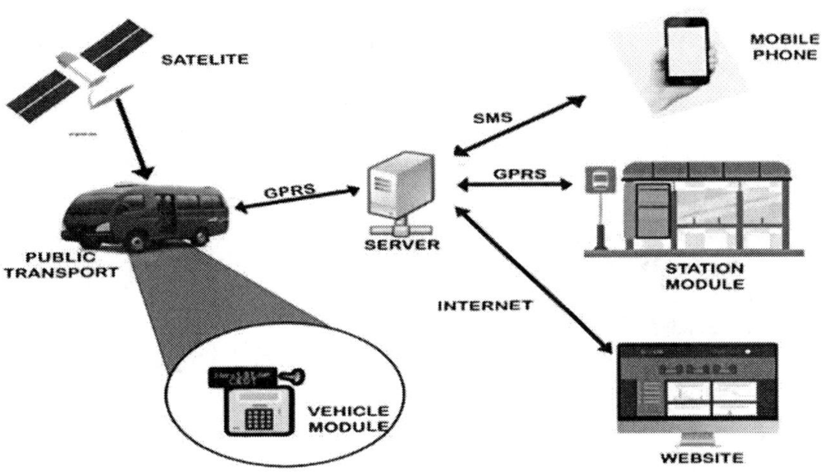

Figure 7. Diagram of Salatiga City's public transportation information system.

Figure 7. describes the application of information systems to public transportation in Salatiga City using satellite communication and GPRS. The satellite communication designed based on Google Maps will be used to detect the location and movement of the public transport vehicles after which the position data is stored on the database server via GPRS communication. Meanwhile, the existing data will be stored in position logging and the public transport will be equipped with a module to receive and send signals to a server called the vehicle module. The data on this server will be processed and displayed on the website via the internet and also made accessible to users through Android OS or SMS. Moreover, a monitoring display will be installed at public transportation stops to show the movement of the vehicles while RFID will be used to detect the identity of every passenger in the vehicle to estimate the total number. This is required to limit the number of passengers boarding one vehicle. Several restrictions also need to be implemented in line with the regulations formulated due to the Covid-19 pandemic and these include limiting the number of passengers in public vehicles. The system will, therefore, send a signal or notification to a passenger to take the next vehicle when the present is full.

4. Conclusion

The results showed that the length of the Tamansari - Blotongan route is 6.2 km with 9 units of the buses available. It was also discovered that the load factor of Salatiga's public transportation was 72% even during the pandemic because it is the route to reach most offices and shopping centers and this means revenue generated remains stable for the operators. Moreover, 70% of the passengers preferred this transportation system because it is cheap, 55% because it is fast, and 77.5% because it is safe. It is also important to note that 10% of the respondents are not satisfied with the present waiting time. The use of a real-time passenger information system was discovered to have the ability to show the number of public transport passengers based on the Radio Frequency Identification Device (RFID) network to estimate the number of those currently disenfranchised due to the Covid-19 pandemic.

5. Acknowledgment

The authors are grateful to the University of Semarang for providing Professorship Grants and support to analyze and model the public transportation service performance of Salatiga city.

6. References

[1] Gao Junpeng, et al 2021 Intelligent public transport cloud platform dispatching operation management system development Jurnal of Physics: Conference Series 1982 (2021)

[2] Handajani Mudjiastuti 2016 Inauguration of Civil Engineering Professors.*Faculty of Engineering, University of Semarang* Fuel Oil (BBM) Efficient Solution towards Sustainable Transportation

[3] Pratomo S A 2015 Study on the Behavioral Characteristics of Public Transport Passengers and Its Influence on Traffic Performance *Scaffolding* Volume 4 No 1

[4] Government Regulation of the Directorate General of Land Transportation No. 10 of 2012

[5] Swati and Chandurkar 2013 Implementation of Real-Time Bus Monitoring and Passenger Information System *International Journal of Scientific and Research Publication* Volume 3, Issue 5, May 2013, ISSN 2250-3153

[6] Handajani Mudjiastuti 2020 Implementation of Passenger Information and Monitoring System in Trans Semarang Bus and Assessment of the Community Perception. *International Journal of Innovative Technology and Exploring Engineering (IJITEE)* Volume 9, Issue 4, February 2020, ISSN 2278-3078

[7] Wismadi Arif, Mulyo Agus Taufik., et al 2020 Strategy for the Recovery of the Logistics Service Industry After the Covid-19 Pandemic Jurnal Transportasi Multimoda Volume 18 (2): 71-82.

[8] Samsir, Sitorus Jimmi Hendrik P. Sitorus 2021 Vehicle Location Monitoring System Design Using U-Blox Gps Based on Android Jurnal Bisantara Informatika (JBI) Volume 5 No 1, Juni 2021, ISSN (online) 2686-5319

[9] Suakanto Sinung, Herry Sitepu, et al 2017 Passenger Information System Design and Implementation *SNFA Proceedings (National Seminar on Physics and Its Application)* E-ISSN: 2548-8325 / P-ISSN 2548-8317

[10] Matsumoto K, Nakada K and Azuma K 2014 Development of On-board Passenger Information Display *Hitachi* Volume 63 No 10

IOP Conf. Series: Earth and Environmental Science 1000 (2022) 012012 doi:10.1088/1755-1315/1000/1/012012

Factors Affecting the Interest of Urban Public Transport Users in Jember

Willy Kriswardhana[1], Nunung Nuring Hayati[2], Achmad Reza Kusdiyanto[1]

[1]Department of Civil Engineering, Universitas Jember, Jember, Indonesia
[2]Urban and Regional Planning Study Program, Universitas Jember, Jember, Indonesia

Email: willy.teknik@unej.ac.id

Abstract. In this current condition, people's interest in using public transportation in Jember decreasing with a low load factor value below 50%. It is caused by several factors such as service coverage, lyn information, safety, fare, urban planning, and the quality of services provided by service providers to the satisfaction of public transport users. The Analytical Hierarchy Process (AHP) method is used to determine the weight of the factors that influence the interest of public transport users in Jember. The effort to be made is to formulate a policy strategy to support people who originally use private transportation switching to public transportation. The results showed that there were 5 selected factors: service coverage, lyn information, safety, fare, and urban planning. The weights of the factors that influence the interest of public transport users in Jember are 40% of the safety factor, 17% of the service coverage factor, 16% of the urban planning factor, 14% of the lyn information factor, and 13% the fare factor. Directions for future studies are presented.

1. Introduction

Public transportation is one of the modes of urban transportation that's needed for the implementation of economic activities and urban development. Apart from being a means of supporting the allocation of goods and services, public transportation is also used for social purposes such as work, school, shopping and others. Urban transportation services must be implemented efficiently and effectively. Criteria such as fast, safe, more space capacity, comfortable and affordable transportation fares are some of the goals to achieve good service. Public Transportation services such as stops for boarding and dropping passengers who can be at any place and the existence of routes make this an advantage and one of the attractions for service users. However, bus often has a different system which provides a particular stop for passenger [1].

There are several main problems of urban public transportation in Indonesia, such as lack of driver discipline and low vehicle breeding funds. Urban public transportation in Indonesia is considered to have a relatively low level of quality. This problem is the cause of the decline in the quality of urban public transportation service [2]. Consequently, private motorised vehicles are really popular in Indonesia. Two-wheeled scooter and private car are inundating the road. Traffic jam and pollution problem are not only found in the metropolitan area. Medium cities in Indonesia are now suffering from many transportation problems. One of the cities are Jember.

Urban public transportation in Jember is a means of mobility for some people to meet the needs of daily life. The main type of public transportation that serves transportation within the city is "lyn". Public transportation in Jember serves 17 transportation routes and 16 routes that seve several terminals such as the Tawang Alun, Arjasa, Ambulu, and Pakusari [3]. According to [4], stated that public transportation in Jember has a low load factor, which is below 50%. This value is still below the criteria based on SK 678/AJ.206/DRJD/2002 concerning Technical Guidelines for The Implementation of Public Transportation in Urban Areas of Fixed and Regular Routes. Based on data from the Department Transportation Jember, it was recorded that 80% of 298 urban transportation needed repairs because the age of the vehicle was approximately 20 years. Users are of course increasingly disinterested in the condition of the vehicle which is no longer feasible to operate. The large investment cost for fleet renewal, while the potential demand is still low, makes many fleets in bad condition [5]. A study conducting a factor analysis of increasing interest in public transportation users in Palangka Raya City found that 8 factors were selected based on the ranking of the respondents that's safety, urban planning, service coverage, subsidies, vehicle information, income, fare, and vehicle ownership. Safety in driving using public transportation is the most influential factor in user interest [6].

Moreover, the condition is exacerbated by the nowadays' popular online transportation. The popularity of online transportation leads people to become reluctant to ride public transportation. Therefore, a study of exploring factors affecting public interest to public transportation is needed. This study will provide some beneficials insight for local government to promote and increase the service quality of public transportation that meets the needs of people. To date, there is no study exploring this issue in Jember.

2. Literature Review

2.1. Factors affecting public transport use

Studies exploring factors affecting the use of public transport have been well published previously. A study in Makassar was performing Analytical Hierarchy Process (AHP) method to understand the causes of the decline of interest in microbus. The dominant factor that affects the decrease in the interest of microbus public transport users in Makassar City is the tangible factor, where cleanliness, comfort and comfortable public transport facilities during the trip are still considered by the public to use public transportation [1].

In Kupang, a study showed that many people switched to using private transportation modes due to the influence of public transportation performance factors, comfort, distance, time, and other factors. It is known that several dominant factors that cause people to change modes are the lack of public transportation, time factors such as lack of service time and long waiting times for transportation, service routes such as limited public transportation routes and public transportation not serving their destination, distance factors such as distance walking distance to a place to wait for public transportation which is far away and passenger comfort factors such as less friendly drivers and conductors and the temperature in public transportation is not good [7].

Based on [8] research, the root of transportation problems in Medan City where the existing condition of public transportation in Medan City is still inadequate in terms of quality and quantity so that public transportation is starting to be abandoned by the community and switch to private vehicles which use a lot of road space.

2.2. Analytical Heirarchy Process (AHP)

Multi-Criteria Decision Making (MCDM) has been generally used to deal with selection issues. The Analytical Hierarchy Process (AHP) is one of the MCDM methods that is widely used in solving complex decision making [9]. However, the AHP method is generally applied, where high accuracy is not needed [10]. Some researches were performing AHP to deal with the ranking and weighting the aspects of urban mobility and transportation problems. A study used AHP to solve group decision-making support problem of emergency alternatives in Unattended Train Operation metro system of China [11]. Meanwhile, another study applied the AHP method to assess the level of customer satisfaction for the rail transit lines of Istanbul [12].

3. Method

3.1. Case Study

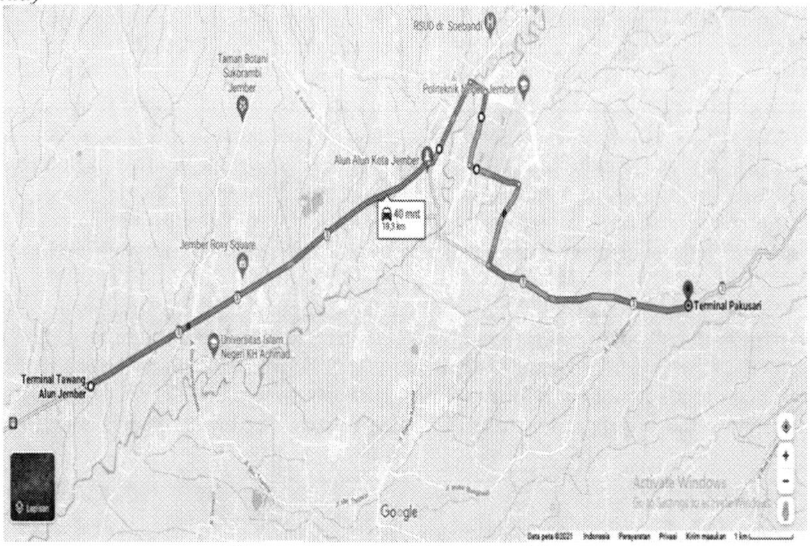

Figure 1. Research Location Map

Jember Regency is part of the East Java Province which borders Bondowoso, Lumajang and Probolinggo Regencies. This research was conducted at the location of the stop on the route lyn Tawang Alun – Campus, namely in the area around the city centre. Urban public transportation is transportation that serves passenger transportation in urban areas. The available urban public transportation in Jember Regency is in the form of a lyn with several route routes. Urban public transport routes usually connect between terminals by passing through parts of the city where it is deemed necessary to have urban public transport services. One of the urban public transportation routes with many passengers serves the route from Tawang Alun Terminal to Pakusari Terminal with the code lyn D. Lyn with code D crosses the school area and the Universitas Jember campus. The route traversed plays an essential role in the operating income of urban public transport. With the current pandemic conditions, the reduced number of transport passengers has made some urban public transport fleets no longer operate as they should. The absence of face-to-face schooling has resulted in urban public transportation, with the code lyn D impacting operating fleets and the decreasing transportation income. According to data from the Jember Regency Transportation Service, in 2020, there were around 250 urban public transport fleets operating before the pandemic. The current condition is in stark contrast to the fleet that operates only about 50 vehicles.

3.2. Data Collection and Analysis

The data needed in this study are primary data and secondary data. Primary data were obtained directly from the field by distributing questionnaires to service users. While secondary data was obtained from the relevant agencies, namely the Department of Transportation Jember, in the form of data on the number of fleets operating based on routes and vehicle codes.

In this study, primary data were obtained directly from the field by distributing questionnaires to respondents using public transportation lyn with the route from the Tawang Alun-Kampus Terminal. The questions contained in the questionnaire are respondent's name, gender, age, last education, occupation, monthly income, the purpose and purpose of the respondent's trip, the quality of public transportation services in Jember Regency, and factors influencing the selection of criteria for public transportation services in Jember Regency.

Explore the questionnaire.

The research method used is the Analytical Hierarchy Process (AHP) aims to determine the weight of the public transport users in Jember. According to [13] the Analytical Hierarchy Process (AHP) is a decision support model that is describing multi-factor problems or complex criteria into a unified hierarchy. The hierarchy consists of the first level, namely the goal, and the level of factors, criteria, sub-criteria and alternatives. This method is used for problem-solving with the consequences of selecting criteria and sub-criteria also having a tolerance limit for inconsistency as a calculation of the validity of the criteria and alternatives chosen by the decision-maker.
The steps that need to be taken in using the analytical hierarchy process method are defining the problem and determining the solution to be achieved. After that, make a structure with the first level, namely the research goal. The next step is to create a pairwise comparison matrix that describes the relative contribution. It defines the comparison so that n x [(n-1)/2] appraisers are obtained with the value of n being the number of elements being compared. It is calculating the eigenvalues and eigenvectors from each pairwise comparison matrix which is the weight of each element for determining the priority of elements at the lowest hierarchical level to achieve the research goal.

Table 1. Pairwise Comparison Assessment Scale

The intensity of interest	Description
1	Both elements are very important
3	Elements that one a little more important than other elements
5	Elements which one is more important than other elements
7	One element is very important from the other elements
9	One element is absolutely very important from the other elements
2,4,6,8	The value between two adjacent considerations

4. Results and Discussion

4.1. Result Analysis of Factors Affecting the Interests of Public Transport Users

Based on the results of the questionnaire data, further analysis was carried out using the Analytical Hierarchy Process (AHP) method. The purpose of this analysis is to determine weighting factors that affect the interests of transport users in that will be used to search the priority recommendations for improvement of public transport services in Jember. Criteria Factors used in this analysis are Service Coverage Factors, Lyn Information, Security, Tariffs, and Urban Planning. The following is an overview of the overall hierarchy of priorities in Fig. 1.

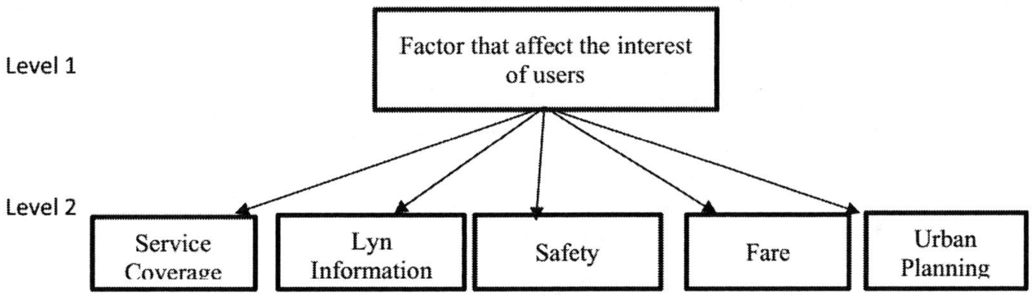

Figure 2. Research Hierarchical Structure

A pairwise comparison matrix grading scale results are obtained from the end of the questionnaire in the form of the numbers 1 through 9 with the subjective assessment of respondents. The next stage is to evaluate the comparison between one criterion and another. The purpose of this pairwise comparison matrix is to define the significance of the assessment results using the Saaty scale. The final results of questionnaires with respondents numbered 400 carried the accumulated data using software expert choice.

Table 2. Pairwise Comparison Matrix Values Between Criteria

Criteria	Service Coverage	Lyn Information	Safety	Fare	Urban Planning
Service Coverage	1	1.4702	0.4162	1.4144	0.8728
Lyn Information	0.68012	1	0.4226	0.9750	0.8777
Safety	2.4029	2.3665	1	3.3598	2.7267
Fare	0.7070	1.0257	0.2976	1	0.9964
Urban Planning	1.1457	1.1393	0.3667	1.0036	1
Total	5.9358	7.0017	2.5031	7.7527	6.4736

Based on the previous process's pairwise matrix results from the accumulation of all the data obtained from the expert choice. The next step is the eigenvector by calculating the number of matrices in each row and then normalising. After normalisation is done, the results are obtained from the eigenvector - an average of all elements.

Table 3. Normalization and Eigen Vector Matrix Pairwise Comparison Between Criteria

Criteria	Service Coverage	Lyn Information	Safety	Fare	Urban Planning	Criteria	Average
Service Coverage	0.1685	0.2100	0.1663	0.1824	0.1348	0.8620	0.1724
Lyn Information	0.1146	0.1428	0.1688	0.1258	0.1356	0.6876	0.1375
Safety	0.4048	0.3380	0.3995	0.4337	0.4212	1.9969	0.3994
Fare	0.1191	0.1465	0.1189	0.1290	0.1539	0.6674	0.1335
Urban Planning	0.1930	0.1627	0.1465	0.1295	0.1545	0.7862	0.1572
Total	1	1	1	1	1	5	1

After knowing the eigen values of each criterion, the next step is to calculate the level of consistency of the results obtained. The consistency test aims to determine whether the calculation results are consistent. The terms of the consistency test are if the value of CR <0.1, this data can be used, but if CR> 0.1, the results of the pairwise comparison matrix are necessary for the review. The first step that needs to be done in conducting a consistency test is to find the maximum eigenvector value (λ max). After getting the eigenvector values, it is continued by looking for the Consistency Index (CI) value. The calculation of the Consistency Index (CI) value is carried out in all matrices.

Table 4. Consistency Indeks Values (CI)

Matrix	Consistency Indeks
Criteria	0.0096

Furthermore, calculations are carried out to get the Consistency Ratio (CR) value where the RI value is obtained from table 4. With the matrix size used, n = 5.

Table 5. Consistency Rasio Values (CR)

Matrix	Consistency Rasio
Criteria	0.0086

Determination of weight factors affecting the interests of public transport users in the District Jember is to determine the priority recommendations for improvement of public transport services.

Table 6. Results Weight Rating Factors Influencing Public Transport User Interest

Criteria	Weight
Service Coverage	17%
Lyn Information	14%
Safety	40%
Fare	13%
Urban Planning	16%

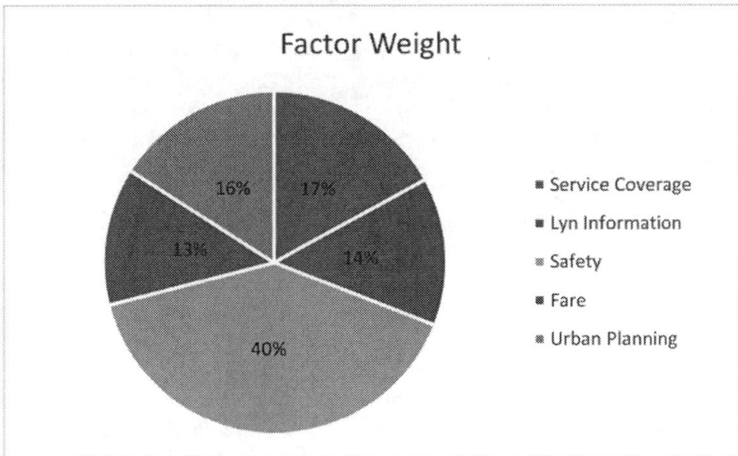

Figure 3. Factor Weight

It can be seen from the table that the respondents' assessment of the factors that influence the interest of public transport users is the safety factor with a factor weight of 40%. Then followed the coverage of services with a weight factor of 17%, with the Urban Planning Factors weight 16%, Lyn Information with weighting factor of 14%, with a weighting factor Fare of 13%.

The most dominant factor influencing public transport users' interest in Jember is the safety factor, accounting for 40%. It is followed by factors of service coverage, city planning, lyn information, and transportation fares. The safety factor is considered very important according to public transport users. The current level of safety in the operation of urban public transportation in Jember Regency is still lacking. There needs to be awareness from the transport owner or service provider in order to increase the safety factor so that people switch to using public transport. User safety becomes a value for comfort and security factors that are desired for their existence in good service.

A study by [6] howed that the factor of increasing interest in public transport service users in Palangka Raya City was sorted by the highest priority level to the lowest factor, namely safety 33%, urban planning 30%, service coverage 11%, subsidies 6%, bus information 5% , 5% income, 5% tariff, 4% vehicle ownership. The study's finding is aligned with our study, which finds that the safety factor is the leading factor affecting people's interest in riding public transportation.

5. Conclusion

For more than a decade, in Jember, the interest of people to ride public transportation has seen a massive decline. The essential factor that needs to be improved is the safety factor. Furthermore, there is a need to broaden the coverage area of public transportation. In order to support the public's need for transportation and to maintain the stability of public transportation in Jember Regency, it is hoped that there will be an update of the existing system and the improvement of services required to increase the interest of public transport users. Future studies can explore the demand for public transport in Jember by performing the stated preference method. Furthermore, exploring the factors related to the demand for public transport in the pandemic condition could be an excellent idea.

References

[1] M. H and L. B. Said, "Analisis Penyebab Penurunan Minat Pengguna Angkutan Umum Mikrolet Di Kota Makassar," vol. 3, no. 2, pp. 94–101, 2020.
[2] A. Munawar, "Perencanaan Angkutan Umum Perkotaan Berkelanjutan," *Unisia*, vol. 29, no. 59, pp. 53–59, 2006.
[3] S. Sulistyono, J. W. Soetjipto, and W. Hariadi, "Analisis Tarif Angkutan Umum Kota Jember Berdasarkan Biaya Biaya Operasi Kendaraan (Bok) Dan Pendapatan," *Simp. XI FSTPT, Univ. Diponegoro*, no. October, pp. 1–11, 2008.
[4] N. N. Hayati, S. Sulistyono, and W. Sabiq, "Strategi Peningkatan Kinerja Trayek Utama Angkutan Umum Perkotaan Jember," *18th FSTPT Int. Symp. Unila, Bandar Lampung, August 28th, 2015*, 2015.
[5] S. Sulistyono *et al.*, "Kebijakan penataan jaringan trayek angkutan umum perkotaan jember," vol. 17, no. 2, pp. 99–110, 2017.
[6] Arif Sulistyo Aji Wibowo, "Analisis Faktor Peningkatan Minat Pengguna Angkutan Umum Di Kota Palangka Raya Menggunakan Metode Analytic Network Process (ANP)," 2020.
[7] J. H. Frans, J. J. S. Pah, and M. G. A. Ikun, "Perpindahan Moda Angkutan Umum Ke Angkutan Pribadi Di Kota Kupang," *J. Tek. Sipil*, vol. 6, no. 2, pp. 151–164, 2017.
[8] S. Sihite and M. Sejahtera Surbakti, "Kajian Pemilihan Moda Transportasi Antara Angkutan Kota Dengan Monorel Menggunakan Metode Stated Preference (STUDI KASUS : RENCANA PEMBANGUNAN MONOREL KOTA MEDAN)," *18th FSTPT Int. Symp. Unila, Bandar Lampung, August 28th, 2015*, no. September, pp. 335–344, 2015.
[9] A. Khaira and R. K. Dwivedi, "A State of the Art Review of Analytical Hierarchy Process," in *Materials Today: Proceedings*, 2018.
[10] E. Eshtehardian, P. Ghodousi, and A. Bejanpour, "Using ANP and AHP for the supplier selection in the construction and civil engineering companies; Case study of Iranian company," *KSCE J. Civ. Eng.*, 2013.
[11] B. Zhao, T. Tang, and B. Ning, "Applying hybrid decision-making method based on fuzzy AHP-WOWA operator for emergency alternative evaluation of unattended train operation metro system," *Math. Probl. Eng.*, 2016.
[12] N. Aydin, E. Celik, and A. T. Gumus, "A hierarchical customer satisfaction framework for evaluating rail transit systems of Istanbul," *Transp. Res. Part A Policy Pract.*, 2015.
[13] T. L. Saaty, "Decision making with the Analytic Hierarchy Process," *Sci. Iran.*, vol. 9, no. 3, pp. 215–229, 1993.

Study Of Health Aspects On Facilities And Infrastructure in Corridor 1 Bus Rapid Transit (BRT) Trans Semarang

Okto Risdianto Manullang, Ragil Haryanto, Danny Rizky Ramadhan*
Urban dan Regional Planning Department, Faculty of Engineering, Diponegoro University, Prof. Soedharto Street, Tembalang, Semarang, Indonesia

Corresponding author's email address: oktomanullang@lecturer.undip.ac.id

Abstract. This study aimed to determine the facilities and infrastructures health aspects of the Corridor I Trans Semarang at Mangkang Terminal-Penggaron Terminal, also to determine the expectations of Corridor 1 Trans Semarang users on the health aspects of future infrastructure. This research method uses customer satisfaction index and importance-performance analysis. The results of the study indicate a percentage level of 50% for facilities and 39% for infrastructure users who feel "less satisfied" with the health aspect of the Corridor 1 Trans Semarang infrastructure facilities that have been provided. Users' expectations in the future are to limit and maintain capacity at the Corridor 1 Trans Semarang bus and shelters, which is a top priority. This was followed by the provision of hand sanitizers, the reduction of seats and handgrip, as well as the use of masks on the Corridor I Trans Semarang bus which became the second priority. Meanwhile, the main priority expectations from users for health infrastructure in addition to limiting and maintaining capacity are the provision of a standing sticker for the seat barrier and an appeal for the application of health protocols/PHBS/cough etiquette at the Trans Semarang shelters. Furthermore, the provision of hand sanitizers, the implementation of non-cash payments, and controlling the use of masks are the second priority expectations of Trans Semarang users.
Keywords. Trans Semarang, Health Aspects, Trans Semarang Service

1. Introduction

Public transportation is a vehicle to carry people and goods that are charged and carried out in large quantities to get to the desired place [12]. The industrial area in Semarang is one of the livelihood centers for the surrounding community.Trans Semarang is the public transportation option for Semarang citizens. This corresponds to the data from the Semarang City Transportation Service 2019 which shows that there is 33,000 users/day taken from a total of 6 Trans Semarang corridors. However, Trans Semarang had to make adjustments after March 2020, due to the cases of the Covid-19 virus in Indonesia.

The spread of this virus can occur between humans [3]. Therefore, the government announced a policy to limit social interaction and movement in the community. Public transportation is part of the impact of this condition, so it needs to be given more attention. Transportation facilities that are used in general can be a source of spread if it does not look at the route, travel characteristics, and exposure time [5]. Surat Edaran Menteri Kesehatan Republik Indonesia Nomor HK.02.01/Menkes/335/2020 tentang Sektor Jasa dan Perdagangan (Area Public) dalam Mendukung Keberlangsungan Usaha [6], which regulates the implementation of health protocols as a new lifestyle during the Covid-19 pandemic for the implementation of the New Normal in the middle of society. This condition affects the Trans Semarang service as public transportation in Semarang. This increasing number of cases needs to be balanced with the provision of healthy public transportation and can reduce the transmission and spread of the virus Covid-19 Semarang provides services that prioritize health aspects for its users. This was previously not included in the Technical Guidelines for the Provision of Public Transportation Facilities. This health aspect needs to be accommodated in Trans Semarang infrastructure services to minimize the transmission of Covid-19.

Corridor I Trans Semarang is the focus of this research because it serves a 40 Km route (roundtrip) using a large capacity bus mode, therefore this corridor can carry a large number of users at one time with a longer trip. This can cause the spread of the virus between fellow users more easily when compared to other Trans Semarang corridors. The previous research conducted by Kusumawardani, et al (2020) [1] showed that there was a relationship between health, time, convenience, and information services in Corridor I Transjakarta services during the pandemic. However, it is not known how the characteristics of each user, so that this study relates the characteristics of users of Corridor I Trans Semarang during the pandemic with the health aspect of the Corridor I Trans Semarang infrastructure that is expected by users in the future. Furthermore, to find out the infrastructure's health aspects of the Corridor I Trans Semarang, it is important to analyze the health aspects of the Corridor I Trans Semarang facilities (buses) and infrastructure (stops) and the expectations desired by users in the future using user preferences.

The characteristics of the Covid-19 spread can last up to 3 hours in the air, 4 hours on copper surfaces, and 24 hours on cardboard, and 2-3 days on plastic or stainless steel surfaces [11]. This is expected to have something to do with user characteristics seen by gender, type of work, and travel patterns. Gender is a biological concept of the difference between men and women, while according to Sadono Sukirno, the type of work is a differentiator of income for certain occupational groups [4. Gender and occupation can be used to determine the infrastructure facilities health aspects of Corridor I Trans Semarang that are suitable for both men and women also to determine the location of providing and improving infrastructure facilities health services in Corridor I Trans Semarang, according to the needs of future users. The observed travel patterns are reviewed based on the frequency of use, distance, travel time, and travel costs for Corridor I Trans Semarang users. Based on data from the Trans Semarang BLUD in 2020, it shows a significant decrease in Trans Semarang users during the pandemic over more than 17,000 passengers from March 2020 to April-May. Furthermore, the travel distance becomes one of the determining factors in the choice of mode, where the closer the distance traveled, the user will choose an easy, safe, and comfortable mode (Overgaard, 1966) [12]. Travel time is the time used to travel a certain distance [2]. Meanwhile, travel costs are the rates paid when using public transportation under the applicable routes and conditions. These three things can influence the choice of transportation mode, ease of access, and the impact of crowds caused during the pandemic.

The health aspect as seen in the Corridor I Trans Semarang infrastructure is determined based on the Peraturan Menteri Perhubungan No.PM 18 Tahun 2020 Tentang Pengendalian Transportasi dalam Rangka Pencegahan Penyebaran Corona Virus Disease (Covid-19) [7], which contains health aspects in the group of facilities and infrastructure which must be available on public transport services. The health aspect group in facilities consists of implementing online or non-cash ticket purchases, periodic spraying of disinfectants, providing hand sanitizers, preparing and controlling the use of masks, giving physical distancing signs, up to 50% capacity limitation in each Trans Semarang bus mode. On the other hand, for the health aspect group, the infrastructure available at the stop mode, there must be a hand sanitizer, a place to wash hands with soap, provide and control the use of masks, take body temperature measurements, provide physical distancing markers, up to a limit of 50% of the total capacity of each mode stop. This research is quantitative by using customer satisfaction index and importance-performance analysis as analytical methods to know the health aspects and sub-aspects of the currently available infrastructure at Corridor I Trans Semarang and user expectations in the future.

2. Methods

This research method contains objects relating to the operational definition and data collection methods used in the study.

2.1. Observation Variables

This study uses several variables that are used to determine the health aspects of Corridor I Trans Semarang. The variables used consist of general services such as travel routes, operating hours, number of modes. Furthermore, user characteristics such as gender, type of work, income, start and end of the trip, needs, frequency of use, distance, travel time, and travel costs. Infrastructure's health aspects variables which will be used in this study are:

Table 1 Variables of Health Aspects Facilities in Corridor I Trans Semarang

Variable Code	Variable
B1	Provision of Hand Sanitizer
B2	Reduction of Seat and Handrails (Handgrip)
B3	Standing Marker Sticker
B4	Appeal for Health Protocols/PHBS/ Cough Ethics
B5	Provision of Non-Cash Payments
B6	Controlling the Use of Masks
B7	Capacity Limitation and Maintenance
B8	Periodic Spraying of Disinfectant

Table 2 Variables of Health Aspects Infrastructures in Corridor I Trans Semarang

Variable Code	Variable
BA1	Provision of Hand Sanitizer
BA2	Provision of Handwashing Places with Soap
BA3	Provision of Body Temperature Measuring Equipment
BA4	Sit and Keep Your Distance Marking Sticker
BA5	Appeal for Health Protocols/PHBS/ Cough Ethics
BA6	Provision of Non-Cash Payment Instruments
BA7	Controlling the Use of Masks
BA8	Capacity Limitation and Maintenance

*PHBS: Clean and Healthy Lifestyle

2.2. Data Collection Technique

This study uses primary and secondary data. Primary data was obtained by distributing questionnaires to Corridor I Trans Semarang users during the pandemic, interviews with the general staff of the Trans Semarang BLUD, as well as observations of all shelters and 20 Corridor I Trans Semarang buses. Primary data collection was carried out at both shelters and at random for 14 days on weekdays and holidays. Questionnaires are distributed using brochures or leaflets containing the QR Code questionnaire using Google Form. The data obtained from primary data collection contains user characteristics, travel patterns, user satisfaction, and expectations of health aspects of the Corridor I Trans Semarang infrastructure, the number of bus fleets, and activities periodic annihilation.

Secondary data is achieved by reviewing documents. Publication review associated with the condition of Corridor I Trans Semarang, operating hours, travel routes, and other related studies.

2.3. *Data Processing Techniques*

Data processing techniques in this study uses sampling techniques and analysis techniques. The sampling technique was used to obtain the number of samples in this study using probability sampling. Because the number of Trans Semarang users fluctuates, the number of samples is taken using the Lemeshow (1997) formula [8]

$$n = \frac{z1 -_{a/P(1-P)}}{d^2}$$

Information:
n: Minimum number of samples required;
z: z score at 95% confidence = 1.96;
p: Proportion of Trans Semarang users served, maximum = 0.5;
d: Limit of error or absolute precision.

From the results of calculations using the formula above, the number of respondents obtained 100 people as a sample at least in this study. Furthermore, this study uses the analysis technique of Customer Satisfaction Index (CSI) and Importance Performance Analysis (IPA). Customer Satisfaction Index (CSI) is a method to determine the level of user satisfaction with the approach of the importance of each variable [9]. This analysis uses the percentage value of the Weight Score (WS) in the maximum value of the weighting used. This process can be done by knowing the value of Mean Importance Score (MIS), Mean Satisfaction Score (MSS), and Wight Factor (WF) so that the percentage value of Customer Satisfaction Index (CSI) is obtained with the description of the CSI value as follows:

Table 3. Description of CSI Value

No	CSI Value (%)	CSI Description
1	0% - 34.99%	Not satisfied
2	35% - 50.99%	Less satisfied
3	51% - 65.99%	Quite satisfied
4	66% - 80.99%	Satisfied
5	81% - 100%	Very satisfied

After analyzing the Customer Satisfaction Index (CSI), then the analysis is carried out using Importance Performance Analysis (IPA). Importance Performance Analysis (IPA) is an analysis used to determine the relationship between consumer perceptions and priorities for improving the quality of goods and services known in the Importance Performance Analysis (IPA) quadrant using a Likert, X-axis represents the level of quality, and Y-axis as the level of satisfaction is used as a tool to determine user expectations for the provision of health aspects on infrastructure in Corridor I Trans Semarang. Furthermore, the X and Y axis values which are averaged are included in the Cartesian diagram. This can be seen in Figure 1.

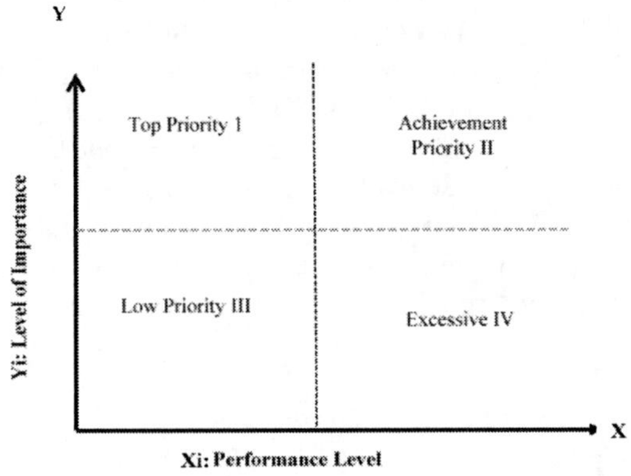

Figure 1. IPA Cartesian Diagram

Information:
Priority I is the attribute with the highest level of importance, but the lowest level of performance
Priority II is an attribute of service quality with a high level of importance and performance
Priority III is an attribute with a low level of importance and performance
Priority IV is a service quality attribute with a low level of importance, but high implementation

3. Results

The characteristics of Corridor I Trans Semarang users consist of gender, type of work, income, and the needs for using Trans Semarang Corridor I and their travel patterns during the Covid-19 pandemic.

3.1. Gender

Survey evidence shows that as many as 54% of users are female and 46% of users are male. This is due to the separation of special seats on the Corridor I Trans Semarang bus mode for women, thus providing comfort for female passengers. In addition, the trend of existing data shows the level of work participation for women is increasing.

3.2. Type of Work

Users of Corridor I Trans Semarang are dominated by private employees by 41%, 36% for students, the rest are entrepreneurs/traders and housewives. This finding is supported by the fact that the Corridor I Trans Semarang crosses several industrial activities.

3.3. Income

User characteristics based on income found that 38% of users have income between Rp1,500,000,000.00 - Rp3,000,000.00; 29% of the income ranged from Rp500,000.00 - Rp1,500,000.00 per month. This income suits the UMR of Semarang in 2020, which is Rp2,810,025 contained in UU Nomor 11/2020 Tentang Cipta Kerja [10].

3.4. User Requirements

Corridor I Trans Semarang users reached 52% for work purposes, 40% for shopping and other social activities, and 8% for educational purposes. This shows that during the Covid-19 pandemic, there are still many movements by Semarang citizens which are carried out using Corridor I Trans Semarang.

3.5. *Travel Pattern*

The travel pattern of Corridor I Trans Semarang users formed during the Covid-19 pandemic is 36% using 4-6 times a week, and 33% using it every day for movement. From the frequency of use, 42% of users can reach the nearest Corridor I Trans Semarang shelters with a distance of 3-5 km from the origin of the movement, 33% within 5-7 km, and only 20% can reach the nearest shelter with a distance of 0- 3 km. Based on the results of the study, public transportation and online motorcycle taxis are the options of many users to reach Corridor I Trans Semarang services. 18% of passengers use city transportation to reach shelters with a distance of 3-5 km, and 17% use online motorcycle taxis for longer distances, which is 5-7 km. The travel time obtained from the research results to reach the nearest shelters is 48%of 1-15 minutes. This is in line with the level of user satisfaction with access from Corridor I Trans Semarang shelters

3.6. *Health Aspects of Facilities at Corridor I Trans Semarang Facilities*

The health aspect of the available facilities at Corridor I Trans Semarang is given to prevent the transmission of the Covid-19 virus from users and officers. The following are health aspects of facilities at Corridor I Trans Semarang provided by the Corridor I Trans Semarang bus manager:

Table 4. Health Aspects of Facilities at Corridor I Trans Semarang

No	Health Aspects in Facilities	Condition of Health Aspects in Facilities	Information
1	Provision of Hand Sanitizer in Corridor I Trans Semarang Bus		Available in all Corridor I Trans Semarang Bus
2	Reduction of Seat and Handgrip		Available throughout Corridor I Trans Semarang Bus
3	Provision of Standing Marker Stickers		Available throughout Corridor I Trans Semarang Bus
4	Provision of Appeals for the Implementation of Health Protocols/PHBS/Cough Ethics		There is an appeal for the application of health protocols in all Corridor I Trans Semarang Bus
5	Provision of Non-Cash Payments		Non-cash payment instruments are available which are managed by all Corridor I Trans Semarang Bus officers
6	Use of Masks by Officers and Users of Corridor I Trans Semarang		Enforcement of the obligation to wear masks for officers and users throughout Corridor I Trans Semarang

3.7. Health Aspects of Infrastructure at Corridor I Trans Semarang

Health aspects of infrastructure at Corridor I Trans Semarang available at the Corridor I Trans Semarang shelters are given to prevent the transmission of the Covid-19 virus at Trans Semarang shelters from users and officers. The following are health aspects of infrastructure at Corridor I Trans Semarang, provided by the manager at Corridor I Trans Semarang shelters:

IOP Conf. Series: Earth and Environmental Science 1000 (2022) 012013 doi:10.1088/1755-1315/1000/1/012013

Table 5. Health Aspects of Infrastructure at Corridor I Trans Semarang

No	Health Aspects in Infrastructure	Condition of Health Aspects in Infrastructure	Information
1	Provision of Hand Sanitizer		Available at Corridor I Trans Semarang Shelters
2	Provision of Four Hand Wash with Soap		Available at 3 Corridor I Trans Semarang Transit Stops
3	Provision of Body Temperature Checking		Available at Simpang Lima Transit Stop
4	Provision of Spacing Seating Marker Stickers		Available at all Corridor I Trans Semarang Transit Stops
5	Provision of Appeals for the Implementation of Health Protocols/PHBS/Cough Ethics		Available at 3 Corridor I Trans Semarang Transit Stops
6	Provision of Non-Cash Payments		Available at all Corridor I Trans Semarang Transit Stops
7	Use of Masks for Trans Semarang Officers and Users		Obligation to Use Masks at All Corridor I Trans Semarang Shelters

3.8. Analysis of Customer Satisfaction Index (CSI) Health Aspects of Facilities at Corridor I Trans Semarang

Based on the results of calculations it was found that Corridor I Trans Semarang users were "Unsatisfied" with the health aspect of the facilities provided by the Corridor I Trans Semarang manager. This can be seen in Table 6 which shows the CSI results are in the 50% percentage category.

Table 6. CSI Health Aspects of Facilities at Corridor I Trans Semarang

NO.	ATTRIBUTE	MIS	MSS	WF	WS	CSI
1	B1	4.37	2.73	14.95	0.41	41%
2	B2	4.31	2.85	14.74	0.42	42%
3	B3	2.88	2.40	9.85	0.24	24%
4	B4	2.34	1.95	8.00	0.16	16%
5	B5	3.90	2.20	13.34	0.29	29%
6	B6	4.16	3.16	14.23	0.45	45%
7	B7	3.90	2.68	13.34	0.36	36%
8	B8	3.38	1.83	11.56	0.21	21%
	TOTAL	29.24	19.80	100	2.53	50%

Information:
MIS : Mean Importance Score
MSS : Mean Satisfaction Score
WF : Weight Factor
WS : Weight Score
CSI : Customer Satisfaction Index

3.9. Importance Performance Analysis Health Aspects of Facilities at Corridor I Trans Semarang

Based on the Importance Performance Analysis (IPA), it can be seen that the expectations given by the users are assessed using a Likert Scale in the form of an assessment of 1-5. The next stage is mapping in a Cartesian diagram which can be seen in Figure 3.

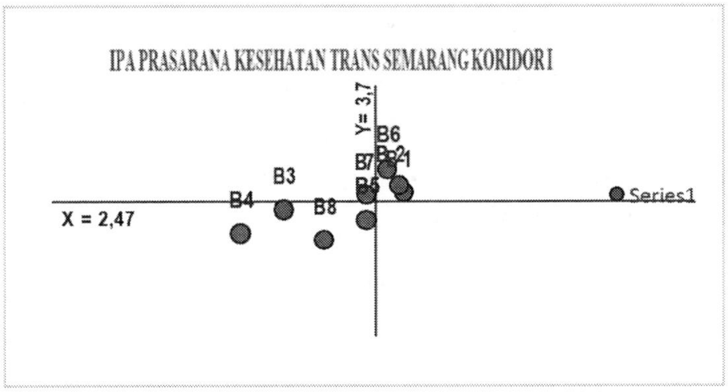

Figure 2. IPA Cartesian Diagram for Health Aspects of Facilities at Corridor I Trans Semarang

Figure 3 shows that the Cartesian diagram of the Health Aspects of Facilities at Corridor I Trans Semarang is filled in quadrants I-III, each of which can be explained as follows:

1. Quadrant I :
   B7 : limiting and maintaining bus capacity
2. Quadrant II :
   B1 : Provision of Hand Sanitizer in Trans Semarang Bus Corridor I
   B2 : Reduction of Seat and Handgrip
   B6 : Controlling the Use of Masks

3. Quadrant III :
   B3 : Standing Marker Sticker
   B4 : Appeal for Application of Health Protocols/PHBS/ Cough Ethics
   B5 : Non-Cash Enforcement
   B8 : Sanitation Activities or Periodic Disinfectant Spraying.

3.10. Customer Satisfaction Index (CSI) Health Aspects of Infrastructure at Corridor I Trans Semarang

Based on the results of calculations it was found that the users of Corridor I Trans Semarang were "Unsatisfied" with the health aspects of infrastructure at Corridor I Trans Semarang provided by the Trans Semarang manager. This can be seen in Table 7 which shows the CSI results in the 39% percentage category.

Table 7. CSI Health Aspects of Infrastructure at Corridor I Trans Semarang

NO.	ATTRIBUTE	MIS	MSS	WF	WS	CSI
1	BA1	4.28	1.7	14.39	0.24	24%
2	BA2	3.03	1.3	10.18	0.13	13%
3	BA3	3.41	1.5	11.45	0.17	17%
4	BA4	3.83	2.5	12.86	0.32	32%
5	BA5	3.27	1.8	10.98	0.20	20%
6	BA6	4.52	2.3	15.18	0.35	35%
7	BA7	4.09	2.4	13.74	0.33	33%
8	BA8	3.34	1.9	11.22	0.21	21%
	TOTAL	29.77	15.31	100	1.95	39.0%

Information:
MIS : Mean Importance Score
MSS : Mean Satisfaction Score
WF : Weight Factor
WS : Weight Score
CSI : Customer Satisfaction Index

3.11. Importance Performance Analysis (IPA) Health Aspects of Infrastructue at Corridor I Trans Semarang

Based on the Importance Performance Analysis (IPA), it can be seen that the expectations given by the users are assessed using a Likert Scale in the form of an assessment of 1-5. The next stage is mapping in a cartesian diagram which can be seen in Figure 4.

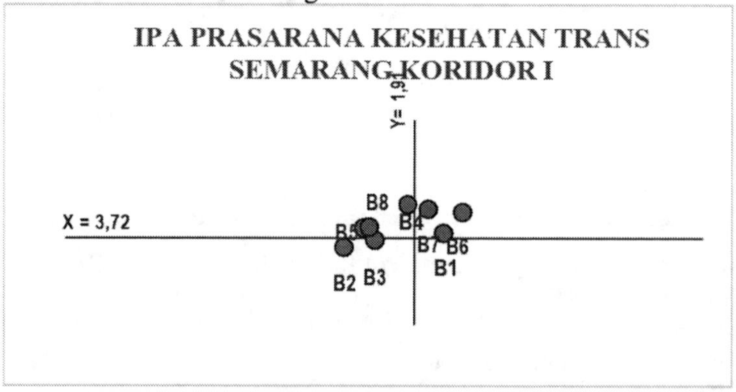

Figure 3. IPA Cartesian Diagram for Health Aspects of Infrastructure at Corridor I Trans Semarang

Figure 4 shows that the cartesian diagram of Health Aspects of Infrastructue at Corridor I Trans Semarang is filled in in quadrants I-III, where each can be explained as follows:

1. Quadrant I :
   BA4 : Stand marker/barrier sticker
   BA5 : Appeal for the application of health protocols/PHBS/cough etiquette
   BA8 : Limitation and maintenance of capacity
2. Quadrant II :
   BA1 : Provision of Hand Sanitizer
   BA6 : Enforcement of Non-Cash Payments
   BA7 : Controlling the Use of Masks
3. Quadrant III :
   BA2 : Provision of a Place for Washing Hands with Soap
   BA3 : Provision of Body Temperature Measuring Equipment.

4. Conclusion

The study of facilities and infrastructure health aspects of Corridor I Trans Semarang resulted in a level of satisfaction in the "Unsatisfied" category. This is indicated by the value of the satisfaction level of 50% for the health aspect of facilities, and 39% for the health aspect of available infrastructure during the Covid-19 pandemic. The provision and improvement of health aspect services at facilities is carried out through reducing chairs and hand grips while improving health aspect services in infrastructure is carried out through the provision of standing/sitting marker stickers, appeals for health protocols/PHBS/cough etiquette, and non-cash payments at Corridor I Trans Semarang shelters.

5. Bibliography

[1] Amanda Dian W.K, dkk 2020 *Identifikasi Kualitas Pelayanan Transjakarta Pada Masa "New Normal" Pandemi Covid-19 (Studi Kasus: Koridor I Blok M-Kota)*. Perencanaan Wilayah Dan Kota 1 SAPPK, 1, 1–10.
[2] Andriansyah 2015 *Manajemen Transportasi dalam Kajian dan Teori*. Jakarta. Manajemen Transportasi Dalam Kajian Dan Teori.
[3] E.Relman 2020 *Deadly China Wuhan Virus Spreading Human To Human Officially Confirmed*. businessinsider.sg.
[4] Hanif, N.,Arshed, N 2016 *International Journal of Economics and Financial Issues Relationship between School Education and Economic Growth: SAARC Countries*. International Journal of Economics and Financial Issues, 6(1), 294–300.
[5] Jin Shen, D 2020 *Prevention and Control of COVID-19 in Public Transportation: Experience from China. Prevention and Control of COVID-19 in Public Transportation: Experience from China*. trid.trb.org
[6] [Kemenkes RI] Kementerian Kesehatan Republik Indonesia 2020 *Surat Edaran Menteri Kesehatan Republik Indonesia Nomor HK.02.01/Menkes/335/20202020 Tentang Sektor Jasa dan Perdagangan (Area Public) dalam Mendukung Keberlangsungan Usaha*. Jakarta. Kemeskes RI
[7] [Kemenhub RI] Kementerian Perhubungan Republik Indonesia 2020 *Peraturan Menteri Perhubungan Nomor PM 10 Tahun 2020 Tentang Pengendalian Transportasi dalam Rangka Pencegahan Penyebaran Corona Virus Disense (Covid-19)*. Jakarta. Kemenhub RI
[8] Lemeshow.S 1997 *Sampling of Populations: Methods and Applications. In Sampling of Populations: Methods and Applications (Vol. 3)*. Wiley-Interscience.
[9] Syukri.S.H 2014 *Penerapan Customer Satisfaction Index (CSI) dan Analisis GAP pada Kualitas Pelayanan Trans Jogja*. Jurnal Ilmiah Teknik Industri, 13(2), 103–111.
[10] Undang-Undang Republik Indonesia, *Cipta Kerja. No. 11,Tahun 2020.*
[11] Van Doremalen. dkk. 2020 *Aerosol and Surface Stability of HCoV-19 (SARS-CoV-2) Compared to SARS-CoV-1.*
[12] Warpani P, S. 2002 *Pengelolaan Lalu Lintas dan Angkutan Jalan*. ITB.

Analysis of The Effects of Development of The Transit Area on Pedestrians at Poris Plawad

Gari Mauramdha[1], R Jachrizal Sumabrata[1]

[1] Civil and Environmental Engineering Department, Faculty of Engineering, Universitas Indonesia, Depok, Indonesia

gari.mauramdha01@ui.ac.id

Abstract. The development of the transit area in Poris Plawad is one of the government's attempts in solving this issue. This implementation consists of construction plans that aim to increase the population of the area. This research aims to analyze the movement of pedestrians to and from the station and provide a recommendation of possible improvement in several aspects of the area's services. In this research, the pedestrian facilities' level of service (LOS) will be the standard reference to define how appropriate the facilities are. The Poris Plawad pedestrian area is categorized as LOS E and LOS F, thus needing improvements. The safety and serviceability of the pedestrian area also need to be evaluated as there are no sidewalks to be found. This research uses Vissim 11 as the leading software for the modelling of the system. The modelling made in this software will be used to compare actual field conditions with the behaviour of the model. The RSME value of the model is below 10%, which means that the model correctly represents its actual conditions. The author then implements several solutions to the existing condition and future conditions of the development area. The solutions for the existing conditions are building sidewalks and pelican crossings for the main road to decrease safety hazards. This increases the safety factors of the existing condition. The future condition will have an increased amount of pedestrians and a modified TOD layout plan. The solution for this is to make a design solely for pedestrians with full attention to their safety and comfort.

1. Introduction

TOD City regional service scale. Transit-Oriented Development is one of several urban development approaches that adopt mixed spatial planning and maximize mass transportation use such as Busway/BRT, City Railway (MRT), Railway Network (LRT) and is equipped with a pedestrian/bicycle network. An inclusive TOD is necessary for long-term sustainability, equity, shared prosperity, and civil peace in cities. In the Jabodetabek area, there are 47 potential TOD areas (22 TOD cities and 25 TOD sub-cities and environments). One of the 47 that is planned to be conducted is the Poris Plawad area. Poris Plawad was chosen because of its strategic location, connecting different modes of transportation. The TOD area will be built near the Poris Plawad Terminal. The Poris Plawad Terminal is a Type-A terminal in Tangerang that houses Angkot, Intercity Buses, Interprovincial Buses, TransJakarta Buses, and TransTangerang Buses. The Poris Plawad terminal is planned to be integrated with the Batu Ceper train station. With the many service facilities that will be built, it is feared that the number of users will increase beyond the capacity of the Transportation Service, thus causing the development of the transit area to be not optimal. Based on this, the purpose of this study is to analyze the service level of the current pedestrian area in Poris Plawad with models validated to actual conditions and model the pedestrian facility development plan along with the construction of the transit area in Poris Plawad.

2. Research Methodology

This research aims to analyze the construction model of the transit area in the Poris Plawad terminal, which is integrated with the Batu Ceper station. The flow of this research consists of several stages. In the preparatory stage, the problems are identified by searching for, in several newspapers, issues regarding the current transit-oriented system development. Afterwards, a search for journals and sources that can provide deeper information regarding the issues raised is conducted. This is continued with making a methodology for the research so that the stages carried out can run optimally. The next stage is data collection, consisting of the collection of primary and secondary data. Primary data is collected from indirect observations of the level of service in the Poris Plawad area. By counting the number of pedestrians passing every 15-minute interval and directly measuring the size of the site, the pedestrian flow can be calculated. The secondary data used for this research is the Poris Plawad TOD Area Layout, which is obtained directly from BPTJ. This layout is used for making the numerical model using Vissim 11. The areas of study limited for this research are the Poris Plawad terminal area, which is integrated with Batu Ceper station, and Jl. Benteng Betawi, which connects the station to the terminal. The time of study limited for this research is weekdays during peak hours, representing the most significant volume of pedestrians during a day. After the model is created, a validation test is carried out with free-flow conditions to determine the model's validity. If the model is valid, it is tested using existing conditions to be compared with the primary data. The primary data used for this comparison is the pedestrian service level in each designated area. The model is analyzed and compared with the primary data so that it corresponds with field conditions. The modelling procedure is carried out by the guidelines from the Vissim 11 user manual. The results from this analysis determine whether the proposed scenario can be carried out. If the analysis is not successful, then a reparation for the model with existing conditions is conducted. The proposed scenario is carried out to create a system that is appropriate for the increased movement that occurs due to the development of the Poris Plawad area. It can be concluded that a good scenario is for each road segment to be made to suit the construction of the transit area in Poris Plawad.

3. Result

3.1. Field Conditions

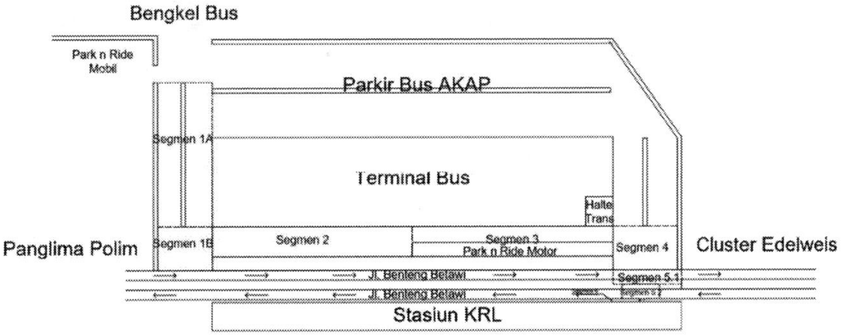

Figure 1. Observed Road Segment.

From field observations, data for a pedestrian's travel time from the segment's entry to the observed segment's exit is obtained. In addition, each type of pedestrian, both individually and in groups, is recorded to determine the volume of pedestrians passing in the area. The data from these results can be processed to obtain the speed of pedestrians and the average number of each type of pedestrian.

Furthermore, all data are combined with the results of layout measurements to be processed according to a data processing to produce the final value of the service level for each road segment. Then, the observation area was measured using a tape meter to validate it with the layout obtained from the terminal manager. Next, the data obtained is organized to be processed to produce quantitative and qualitative assessments. The data is divided based on the observation segments, the direction of travel, and the type of pedestrian. From the data that has been obtained and organized in excel containing observations for each segment every 15 minutes and the differentiated directions, calculations are carried out to obtain the average travel time for each type of pedestrian and the total in one segment. This value is obtained by using the average function used in Excel, and different values are generated. After obtaining the average time, data was collected for each segment's average time and volume. The data generated are based on a duration of 15 minutes with different segments to determine the time of observation that produces the most significant volume at each segment. The observations found that the most significant volume is produced at the 15-30 minute duration of observation in the majority of the observed segments. This becomes a reference to be compared with the current service level in the model. Afterwards, a calculation is conducted to obtain the level of service in terms of quantity and quality.

3.2. Existing Conditions

The modelling in Vissim 11 is done by referring to the acquired layout and the dimensions and measurements obtained at the field.

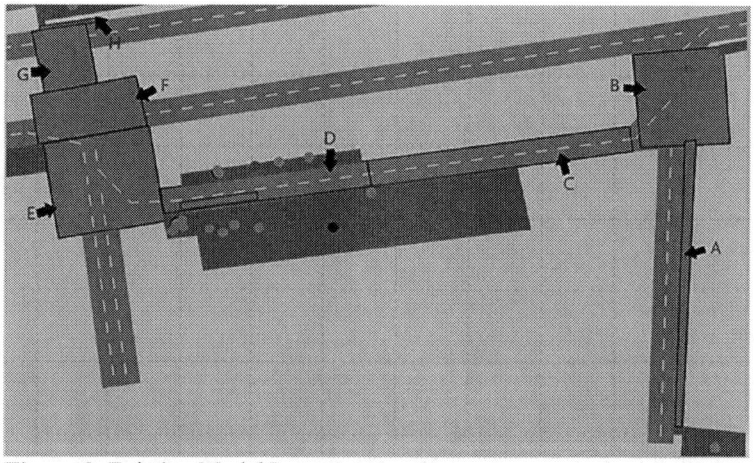

Figure 2. Existing Model Layout

Afterwards, to describe this area as a transit point between modes of transportation, the places of origin and destinations that generate pedestrian trips are assumed. According to the observations, seven places cause pedestrians to generate from pick-up and drop-off points, namely Car Park & Ride, Jl. Panglima Polim, the Terminal, Motorcycle Park & Ride, Bus Stop, Edelweiss Cluster, Roadside, and the Station. From these points of generation, a network of sidewalks can be created by identifying possible pedestrian directions. Moreover, when simulating free-flow conditions, a minimum volume of 10 pedestrians is used for each point of the generation to avoid problems in terms of service levels. Other parameters used are still in the default condition in the program so that the accuracy of designing pedestrian areas can be analyzed. The results show that the condition of each road segment produces LOS A, which means it is by the conditions of free-flow speed.

Table 1. Level of Service for Free-flow Condition.

	Interval Duration (T)	Pedestrian Volume (n)	Pedestrian Density (D=Q/Vs)	Pedestrian Speed (V=L/t)	Pedestrian Flow Rate (Q=D*V)	Pedestrian Space (S=1/D)	Level of Service
Segment 6	0-10	2	0,060	5,028	0,302	16,595	LOS A
Segment 5.2		2	0,003	5,030	0,019	256,607	LOS A
Segment 5.1		4	0,002	5,030	0,011	420,521	LOS A
Segment 4		3	0,002	5,737	0,014	402,738	LOS A
Segment 3		4	0,002	5,735	0,014	409,668	LOS A
Segment 2		2	0,001	5,385	0,010	507,356	LOS A
Segment 1B		11	0,003	5,046	0,015	330,687	LOS A
Segment 1A		2	0,004	5,034	0,024	204,457	LOS A

The free-flow speed obtained from the model simulation can then be compared with the theory, which acts as the input data for pedestrian speed.

Table 2. Validation of Model with Free-flow Condition.

	Speed		Difference	Validation	Notes
	Input	Output			
Segment 6	5,25	5,028	0,221	4,224	Accepted Model
Segment 5.2	5,25	5,030	0,219	4,190	Accepted Model
Segment 5.1	5,25	5,030	0,219	4,189	Accepted Model
Segment 4	5,25	5,737	0,487	9,294	Accepted Model
Segment 3	5,25	5,735	0,485	9,246	Accepted Model
Segment 2	5,25	5,385	0,135	2,586	Accepted Model
Segment 1B	5,25	5,046	0,203	3,879	Accepted Model
Segment 1A	5,25	5,034	0,215	4,095	Accepted Model

The next stage is the analysis of the model, which is validated with field conditions. The analysis uses the service level value as the dependent variable while the independent variable is used in walking behaviour. The walking behaviour is carried out in the analysis by trial and error until it is by the field condition.

In the first iteration, the default parameter from the application is used to see how it fits in the model. Then, the pedestrian volume input is entered with the results from the observations in the field. The field observation results are interpreted into pedestrian volume based on their route. The level of service produced is as follows.

Table 3. Level of Service for the 1st iteration at 0-15 Minute Intervals.

	Interval Duration (T)	Pedestrian Volume (n)	Pedestrian Density (D=Q/Vs)	Pedestrian Speed (V=L/t)	Pedestrian Flow Rate (Q=D*V)	Pedestrian Space (S=1/D)	Level of Service
Segment 1A	0-15	8	0,039	3,895	0,152	25,555	LOS A
Segment 1B		6	0,012	4,168	0,051	80,912	LOS A
Segment 2		12	0,023	4,147	0,098	42,277	LOS A
Segment 3		14	0,034	3,818	0,130	29,262	LOS A
Segment 4.1		55	0,117	1,527	0,179	8,498	LOS A
Segment 4.2		51	0,461	0,587	0,271	2,166	LOS D

Segment 4.3		7	0,026	3,200	0,085	37,432	LOS A
Segment 5.1		60	0,183	2,255	0,414	5,446	LOS B
Segment 5.2		43	0,236	1,892	0,448	4,220	LOS B
Segment 6		10	0,602	2,043	1,231	1,659	LOS D

In the second iteration, changes are made to the walking behaviour parameters. The parameters used will be from the meta-analysis results in previous studies to prove the suitability of the conditions of the people in the Poris Plawad area. The resulting service levels are as follows.

Table 4. Level of Service for the 2nd iteration at 0-15 Minute Intervals.

	Interval Duration (T)	Pedestrian Volume (n)	Pedestrian Density (D=Q/Vs)	Pedestrian Speed (V=L/t)	Pedestrian Flow Rate (Q=D*V)	Pedestrian Space (S=1/D)	Level of Service
Segment 1A	0-15	8	0,039	3,924	0,153	25,555	LOS A
Segment 1B		6	0,012	4,164	0,051	80,912	LOS A
Segment 2		13	0,025	4,118	0,105	39,024	LOS A
Segment 3		12	0,029	3,832	0,112	34,139	LOS A
Segment 4.1		34	0,072	1,814	0,132	13,747	LOS A
Segment 4.2		32	0,289	0,707	0,204	3,453	LOS C
Segment 4.3		6	0,022	3,518	0,080	43,670	LOS A
Segment 5.1		43	0,131	2,769	0,364	7,599	LOS A
Segment 5.2		35	0,192	2,106	0,406	5,184	LOS B
Segment 6		13	0,783	2,036	1,594	1,276	LOS E

At the end of the iteration, adjustments are made to the pedestrian volume and walking behaviour parameters. These parameters are the ones that succeed in achieving error suitability for all segments. The walking behaviour adjustments obtained are as follows.

Table 5. Adjustments for the Walking Behaviour Parameter.

Parameter	Default	Cibubur	Poris
Tau	0,4	0,4	0,4
React To N	8	7	8
A Soclso	2,72	1,5	2,72
Bsoclso	0,2	0,2	0,2
Lambda	0,176	0,1	0,176
A Soc Mean	0,4	0,5	0,6
B Soc Mean	2,8	1,5	1,6
VD	3	3	3
Noise	1,2	0,8	1,2
Side Preference	None	Left	None

Thus, the produced levels of service are as follows.

Table 6. Level of Service for the nth iteration at 0-15 Minute Intervals.

	Interval Duration (T)	Pedestrian Volume (n)	Pedestrian Density (D=Q/Vs)	Pedestrian Speed (V=L/t)	Pedestrian Flow Rate (Q=D*V)	Pedestrian Space (S=1/D)	Level of Service
Segment 1A	0-15	1	0,004	4,844	0,023	204,457	LOS A
Segment 1B		8	0,016	3,927	0,064	60,686	LOS A

Segment 2	14	0,027	3,985	0,109	36,237	LOS A
Segment 3	14	0,034	3,806	0,130	29,262	LOS A
Segment 4.1	25	0,053	2,770	0,148	18,696	LOS A
Segment 4.2	20	0,180	1,222	0,221	5,525	LOS B
Segment 4.3	10	0,038	3,724	0,142	26,202	LOS A
Segment 5.1	37	0,113	2,920	0,330	8,831	LOS A
Segment 5.2	34	0,187	1,902	0,356	5,337	LOS B
Segment 6	9	0,542	3,090	1,675	1,843	LOS D

3.3. Solution Model

In the proposed, existing model, the existing conditions are altered using a new layout to ensure that the pedestrians of the Poris Plawad area feel more comfortable and safer without having to worry about intersecting their paths with passing vehicles.

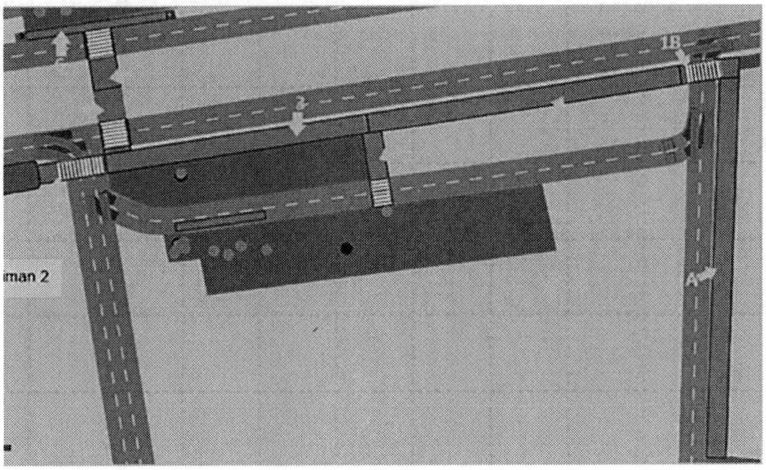

Figure 3. Conditions Existing Solution Layout

Furthermore, for the walking behaviour, pedestrian volume, point of awakening, and other parameters, the existing conditions derived from the results of modelling validation analysis with existing conditions are used. Additionally, in the layout that has been made, additional service facilities are made in the form of a zebra cross & pelican crossing to reduce the waiting time for pedestrians to cross, thus reducing the amount of buildup and providing security. This will ensure that pedestrians feel safe and comfortable when travelling.

Table 7. Level of Service for the Existing Solution.

	Interval Duration (T)	Pedestrian Volume (n)	Pedestrian Density (D=Q/Vs)	Pedestrian Speed (V=L/t)	Pedestrian Flow Rate (Q=D*V)	Pedestrian Space (S=1/D)	Level of Service
Segment 1A	0-15	3	0,006	4,462	0,027	165,865	LOS A
	15-30	3	0,006	4,642	0,028	165,865	LOS A
	30-45	4	0,008	4,126	0,033	124,409	LOS A
	45-60	5	0,010	4,189	0,042	99,522	LOS A
Segment 1B	0-15	7	0,089	3,972	0,353	11,260	LOS A
	15-30	7	0,089	3,944	0,350	11,260	LOS A
	30-45	7	0,089	3,837	0,341	11,260	LOS A
	45-60	6	0,076	3,914	0,298	13,137	LOS A

IOP Conf. Series: Earth and Environmental Science 1000 (2022) 012014 doi:10.1088/1755-1315/1000/1/012014

Segment 2	0-15	14	0,034	4,002	0,136	29,441	LOS A
	15-30	17	0,041	3,967	0,164	24,246	LOS A
	30-45	17	0,041	3,864	0,159	24,246	LOS A
	45-60	14	0,034	3,962	0,135	29,441	LOS A
Segment 2.5	0-15	9	0,092	3,758	0,346	10,871	LOS A
	15-30	8	0,082	3,867	0,316	12,230	LOS A
	30-45	9	0,092	3,740	0,344	10,871	LOS A
	45-60	10	0,102	3,610	0,369	9,784	LOS A
Segment 3	0-15	26	0,075	3,438	0,259	13,253	LOS A
	15-30	29	0,084	3,431	0,289	11,882	LOS A
	30-45	25	0,073	3,402	0,247	13,783	LOS A
	45-60	26	0,075	3,366	0,254	13,253	LOS A
Segment 4	0-15	9	0,102	3,923	0,402	9,766	LOS A
	15-30	9	0,102	3,714	0,380	9,766	LOS A
	30-45	8	0,091	3,753	0,342	10,987	LOS A
	45-60	7	0,080	3,636	0,290	12,556	LOS A
Segment 5.1	0-15	24	0,202	2,360	0,477	4,950	LOS B
	15-30	26	0,219	2,268	0,496	4,570	LOS B
	30-45	31	0,261	2,182	0,569	3,833	LOS B
	45-60	27	0,227	2,223	0,505	4,400	LOS B
Segment 5.2	0-15	24	0,220	1,577	0,346	4,555	LOS B
	15-30	32	0,293	1,523	0,446	3,416	LOS C
	30-45	23	0,210	1,588	0,334	4,753	LOS B
	45-60	31	0,284	1,499	0,425	3,527	LOS C
Segment 6	0-15	13	0,162	3,186	0,515	6,191	LOS A
	15-30	12	0,149	3,211	0,479	6,707	LOS A
	30-45	10	0,124	2,792	0,347	8,048	LOS A
	45-60	9	0,112	3,086	0,345	8,942	LOS A

4. Discussion

4.1. Existing Conditions

From the observations of the existing conditions in the field, there are different results for each segment. The data used for analysis for each segment are the data with the worst service level conditions. Segment 1A has a LOS A category with a value of 13,19 as the worst quality at 15-30 minutes of observation. This location does not have a dedicated crossing area (zebra cross), making it quite dangerous for pedestrians, especially when passing vehicles. Segment 1B has a LOS A category with a value of 32,14 as the worst quality at 30-45 minutes of observation. This location does not have a dedicated crossing area (zebra cross) either, thus also making it quite dangerous for pedestrians, especially when there are passing vehicles. Segment 2 has a LOS A category with a value of 14,08 as the worst quality at 45-60 minutes of observation. This location does not have a dedicated area for pedestrians, which forces pedestrians to take up a portion of the road, thus creating hazards. Segment 3 has a LOS A category with a value of 11,32 as the worst quality at 30-45 minutes of observation. This location also does not have a dedicated area for pedestrians, which forces pedestrians to take up a portion of the road, thus creating hazards. Segment 4, divided into three directions, has the same quality in segments 4.1 and 4.2, namely LOS A, but with different values, namely 9,23 (minutes 45-60) and 25,61 (minutes 0-15) in the worst conditions. Meanwhile, segment 4.3 has LOS C with a value of 3,19 (minutes 45-60) in the worst condition. There is no dedicated crossing area for pedestrians in the field, which makes it unsafe for pedestrians when there are passing vehicles. Segment 5.1 has a LOS B category with a value of 5,50 as the worst quality at 45-60 minutes of observation. This segment is observed to be a place that pedestrians use to cross from the main road where vehicles pass, so it is hazardous when the crossing area is observed not to have traffic signs for pedestrians. Segment 5.2 has a LOS D category with a value of 2,18 as the worst quality at 45-60 minutes of observation. This segment is also observed to be a place that pedestrians use to cross from the main road where vehicles pass, so it is hazardous when the crossing area is observed not to have traffic signs for pedestrians. Segment 6 has a LOS F category with a value of 0,45 as the worst quality at 45-60 minutes of observation. This area is observed to be a place for passengers to enter and exit transportation modes.

4.2. Free-flow Conditions

From the analysis results with free-flow conditions, it can be seen that the condition of each road segment produces LOS A. This means that the analysis is by the theory. This is also shown by the dark blue grid cell area in the simulation layout. From the speed results obtained when running the model, the data can be compared with the theory, which is the data input from pedestrian speed. The simulation results show that all measurement areas have an error value of <10%, which means that the model created is acceptable.
Results from the 1st iteration can be compared with the conditions in the field. Comparisons are made in order to see the suitability of the existing conditions in each road segment. It is found that 3 out of 10 road segments have an acceptable density error, meaning that further changes are needed to change other parameters.

Table 8. Analysis on the Validation of the 1st Iteration Model.

	Field		Model		Difference	Validation	Notes
	LOS	Density	LOS	Density			
Segment 1A	LOS A	0,019	LOS A	0,029	0,010	35,638	Rejected Model
Segment 1B	LOS A	0,020	LOS A	0,014	0,006	40,817	Rejected Model
Segment 2	LOS A	0,048	LOS A	0,041	0,006	15,609	Rejected Model
Segment 3	LOS A	0,048	LOS A	0,041	0,006	15,609	Rejected Model
Segment 4.1	LOS A	0,075	LOS A	0,077	0,002	2,739	Accepted Model
Segment 4.2	LOS C	0,313	LOS C	0,299	0,015	4,865	Accepted Model
Segment 4.3	LOS A	0,039	LOS A	0,027	0,012	46,164	Rejected Model
Segment 5.1	LOS A	0,156	LOS A	0,144	0,012	8,155	Accepted Model
Segment 5.2	LOS C	0,284	LOS B	0,253	0,031	12,215	Rejected Model
Segment 6	LOS F	1,392	LOS E	1,024	0,367	35,853	Rejected Model

The 2nd Iteration results increase to 4 out of 10 segments whose density error value can be tolerated. More iterations still need to be done by changing the parameters that can be adjusted to the conditions in the field.

Table 9. Analysis on the Validation of the 2nd Iteration Model

	Field		Model		Difference	Validation	Notes
	LOS	Density	LOS	Density			
Segment 1A	LOS A	0,019	LOS A	0,029	0,010	35,638	Rejected Model
Segment 1B	LOS A	0,020	LOS A	0,014	0,006	40,817	Rejected Model
Segment 2	LOS A	0,048	LOS A	0,041	0,006	15,609	Rejected Model
Segment 3	LOS A	0,048	LOS A	0,041	0,006	15,609	Rejected Model

Segment 4.1	LOS A	0,075	LOS A	0,073	0,002	2,982	Accepted Model
Segment 4.2	LOS C	0,313	LOS C	0,299	0,015	4,865	Accepted Model
Segment 4.3	LOS A	0,039	LOS A	0,027	0,012	46,164	Rejected Model
Segment 5.1	LOS A	0,156	LOS A	0,159	0,004	2,245	Accepted Model
Segment 5.2	LOS C	0,284	LOS C	0,276	0,009	3,238	Accepted Model
Segment 6	LOS F	1,392	LOS E	1,205	0,187	15,475	Rejected Model

At the nth iteration, a tolerable error value for all road segments is obtained. This shows the suitability of the existing model with the results of observations that have been made using predetermined parameters.

Table 10. Analysis on the Validation of the nth Iteration Model

	Field		Model		Difference	Validation	Notes
	LOS	Density	LOS	Density			
Segment 1A	LOS A	0,019	LOS A	0,020	0,001	3,461	Accepted Model
Segment 1B	LOS A	0,020	LOS A	0,019	0,002	9,521	Accepted Model
Segment 2	LOS A	0,048	LOS A	0,046	0,002	3,440	Accepted Model
Segment 3	LOS A	0,048	LOS A	0,046	0,002	3,440	Accepted Model
Segment 4.1	LOS A	0,075	LOS A	0,079	0,004	5,369	Accepted Model
Segment 4.2	LOS C	0,313	LOS C	0,308	0,005	1,780	Accepted Model
Segment 4.3	LOS A	0,039	LOS A	0,038	0,001	2,315	Accepted Model
Segment 5.1	LOS A	0,156	LOS A	0,147	0,009	5,899	Accepted Model
Segment 5.2	LOS C	0,284	LOS B	0,281	0,003	1,210	Accepted Model
Segment 6	LOS F	1,392	LOS F	1,506	0,115	7,620	Accepted Model

4.3. Solution Model

The existing solution model that is implemented shows the ability to produce LOS A in almost all measurement areas and LOS B/LOS C on two road segments. In segment 5.1, the model produces a good service level with a modulus of space of 3,72-5,57 m2/p. As for segment 5.2, the model produces a pretty good service level with a modulus of space 2,23-3,72 m2/p. The resulting service level is perfect for other segments with a modulus of space of over 5,57 m2/p. It can be ascertained that the layout used is a solution for the services that can be implemented for the problems that occur in the area where the TOD will be built.

5. Conclusion

The service level of pedestrian facilities in the Poris Plawad area, which has LOS E and LOS F, and safety and comfort issues due to the absence of pedestrian facilities, needs to be evaluated. A validated model based on observations with an RSME value below 10%, based on a comparison of actual conditions in the field with the model, has been made. In the existing scenario, a solution is found in making a dedicated crossing area with a pelican crossing system in areas that pass through the main road to produce an increase in the safety factor and the level of service.

6. Recommendations

Stakeholders (BPTJ) responsible for the Poris Plawad area should pay attention to the current lack of pedestrian facilities. The government should pay attention to the principles of TOD regarding pedestrian facilities that allow transportation users to choose to walk to their destination because they feel safe and comfortable. In the "n"th iteration that was successfully validated, walking behaviour parameters were obtained, which could be used as a reference in evaluating and solving the community model in the Poris Plawad area.

References

Artawan, A., Wedagama, D., & Mataram, K. (2013). *ANALISIS KARAKTERISTIK PEJALAN KAKI DAN TINGKAT PELAYANAN FASILITAS PEJALAN KAKI.*

BPTJ. (2019). *TOD Poris Plawad.* Diambil kembali dari Badan Pengelola Transportasi JABODETABEK: http://bptj.dephub.go.id/tod-poris-plawad

Danbury Branch Improvement Program. (2010). *Transit-Oriented Development.* URS Corporation AES.

DCP, N. (2006). *Pedestrian Level of Service Study.* New York City: Transportation Division.

Direktorat Jendral Perhubungan Darat. (1997). *KEPUTUSAN DIREKTUR JENDERAL PERHUBUNGAN DARAT NOMOR: SK.116/AJ.404/DRJD/97 Tentang Petunjuk Teknis Penyelenggaraan Perlengkapan Jalan DIrektur Jenderal Perhubungan Darat.* DKI Jakarta, Indonesia.

Iswanto, D. (2006). *Mengkaji Fungsi Keamanan dan Kenyamanan Bagi Pejalan Kaki di Jalur Pedestrian (Trotoar).* Semarang: Tesis Program Pascasarjana Universitas Diponegoro Semarang Program Studi Magister Teknik Arsitektur.

Kumparan. (2018, March 23). *Kawasan TOD Poris Plawad Rp 1,7 T Mulai Dibangun April 2018.* Diambil kembali dari Kumparan: https://kumparan.com/@kumparanbisnis/kawasan-tod-poris-plawad-rp-1-7-t-mulai-dibangun-april-2018

Kurugod, T. P., Kadam, R. L., & vinayaka, B. (2017). International Research Journal of Engineering and Technology. *STUDY OF PEDESTRIAN LEVEL OF SERVICE BY MICRO-SIMULATION USING VISSIM,* 1-13.

Millonig, A., Brandle, N., Ray, M., Bauer, D., & Van Der Spek, S. (2009). *Pedestrian Behaviour Monitoring: Methods and Experiences.* 32.

Pemerintah Republik Indonesia. (1993). *PERATURAN PEMERINTAH REPUBLIK INDONESIA NOMOR 43 TAHUN 1993 Tentang Prasarana dan Lalu Lintas Jalan Presiden Republik Indonesia.* Indonesia.

Prayoga, W. A. (2019). *Analisis Pergerakan Pejalan Kaki Akibat Pengoperasian Stasiun LRT Cibubur.*

Presiden Republik Indonesia. (2018). *PERATURAN PRESIDEN REPUBLIK INDONESIA NOMOR 55 TAHUN 2018 Tentang Rencana Induk Transportasi Jakarta, Bogor, Depok, Tanggerang, dan Bekasi Tahun 2018-2029.* Indonesia.

Situmorang, L. (2019). *Analisis Skenario Pejalan Kaki Pada Ruang Publik (Studi Kasus: Stasiun LRT Harjamukti, Cibubur) .*

Soerjo, T. A. (2018, March 23). *BPTJ Targetkan Groundbreaking Proyek TOD Poris Plawad pada April.* Diambil kembali dari tirto.id: https://tirto.id/bptj-targetkan-groundbreaking-proyek-tod-poris-plawad-pada-april-cGDg

Vision, P. (2011). *VISSIM 5.30-05 User Manual. Karlsruhe : Planung Transport Verkehr AG .*

Evaluation of the Green Transportation Concept in the Sultan Ageng Tirtayasa University Campus

Rindu Twidi Bethary[1], Arief Budiman[1], Dwi Esti Intari[1], Dandy Ramdhan[1]

[1] Department of Civil Engineering, Sultan Ageng Tirtayasa University, Cilegon, Banten, Indonesia

rindubethary@untirta.ac.id, ariefbudiman@untirta.ac.id

Abstract. A green campus is an environmentally friendly concept that promotes the creation and the use of transportation means with minimal effects on people and the environment. Notably, the green campus program is adapted to create awareness in the campus community to make the environment habitable. This research used UI GreenMetric World University Rankings with 8 green transportation criteria to conduct the assessment. Based on the observation and analysis, a total of 1475 from a maximum value of 1800 was obtained. This was 81.9%, which means that green transportation at Sultan Ageng Tirtayasa University is progressing. However, several improvements need to be made, including special policies to restrict vehicles from entering the campus, developing emission-free transportation, and making an integrated parking building.

1. Introduction

The academic community has the mandate to keep the campus environment free from greenhouse gas (GHG) emissions in an effort to use the resources and technology effectively (1). Applying a green campus can create a healthy environment and build awareness, especially regarding the importance of the environment, which decreases operational costs [2, 3]. The Indonesian government strives to reduce the impact of global warming using various organizations, including the academic community [4]. In 2013, five pilot campuses were set for the green campus program to reduce global warming [5]. The campuses were tasked to play an active role in addressing sustainability issues in energy management and human data sources in their functions, including teaching, research, partnerships, and services such as helping communities to live sustainably [6].

Increased greenhouse gas emissions (GHG) do not only concern Indonesia but the world at large. The research conducted by the environment ministry indicated that one of the sources of GHG emissions is from the transportation sector. Therefore, strategies are in place to minimize GHG in the transportation sector to 26% - 41% [7]. To achieve the set target, the IPB campus developed the concept of green transportation to encourage people to use environmentally friendly public transport [8]. The key idea in this concept was to minimize the use of motorized vehicles by providing public transportation facilities with low emission levels besides promoting a walking culture [9].

Several methods can be used to evaluate green campus indicators, including UNEP (United Nation Environmental Program), Ministry of Environment and Forestry (Green Public Facilities), Green Building Council, and UI GreenMetric. Both international and domestic, Campuses use the UI GreenMetric standard rating system to assess environmental management [10, 11]. The research conducted at the Semarang State University regarding the development of green transportation found that the available infrastructure was not optimal. Consequently, the high pollution within the campus affected the comfort of the academic community [12].

Sultan Ageng Tirtayasa University (UNTIRTA) is also among the campuses implementing a green campus program with a UI GreenMetric. In 2020, the university was ranked 30th at the national level with regard to the implementation of the green campus program. It is hoped that the program will minimize the current environmental problems. Therefore, this research aimed to evaluate the green transportation system at the UNTIRTA campus to increase the UI GreenMetric ranking in the coming years.

2. Methodology

In this research, a qualitative approach was used through direct observations of the criteria for green transportation at UNTIRTA. Also, quantitative approach to make comparisons by assessing the green campus using the UI Green Metric World University Ranking [13]. In 2019, at least 780 universities from 85 countries across the globe participated in the UI GreenMetric assessment with a focus on sustainable green campuses [14].

There are six Green transportation assessment categories and indicators for UI GreenMetric, including the ratio of the vehicles divided by the total population in the campus, shuttle services within the campus, policies regarding emission-free vehicles on campus, the ratio of the number of emission-free vehicles divided by the total population in the campus, the ratio of the parking area to the total area, campus transportation programs designed to limit or reduce parking areas on campus over the past 3 years, and the number of transportation initiatives to reduce private vehicles on campus. Each indicator is presented in the percentage form and divided into 5 levels ranging from the lowest to the highest. Each criterion was categorized as general until the results were processed, and the gross value multiplied by the score's weight to obtain the final figure [13].

3. Analysis and Discussion

Vehicle pollution at the UNTIRTA campus has risen to worrying levels necessitating the implementation of a green campus. The analysis of the assessment on each indicator is as follows:

3.1. The ratio of the number of vehicles divided by the total campus population

This indicator reviewed the ratio of vehicles, both cars and motorcycles, divided by the campus population. The data required for this indicator includes the volume of vehicles with a total of 4905 vehicles. The total population at the UNTIRTA campus is 17664, and the vehicle ratio is 0.51 with a maximum value of 200, thus the score is being (0.5 x 200 = 100).

3.2. Campus Shuttle Service

The shuttle services are used to ease the transportation of passengers from one point to another within the campus. Additionally, specific shuttles ferry the members of staff within the campus while others take the staff to and from Serang, Cilegon, and UNTIRTA's Sindangsari campus, as shown in Figure 3. The assessment criteria looked at the availability of shuttle services provided by the campus with a specified schedule. Notably, the university contributed part of the financing to provide a maximum score of 300, therefore, the score: 0.75 x 300 = 225.

The UNTIRTA campus provides free bus services to support the academic community in accessing various destinations. The bus service operation schedule, divided into B.01 and B.02, runs from Monday to Friday, with Sindangsari being the central bus stop. Route B.01 goes through the New UNTIRTA Sindangsari Campus – Campus D Nursing - Campus B, and Faculty of Engineering Cilegon. Route B.02 serves the New UNTIRTA Sindangsari Campus - Campus C FKIP Ciwaru – Campus A UNTIRTA in Pakupatan. In a bid to reduce the use of private cars with the main campus in Sindangsari, there are plans to have buses operating within to serve the entire academic community.

IOP Conf. Series: Earth and Environmental Science 1000 (2022) 012015 doi:10.1088/1755-1315/1000/1/012015

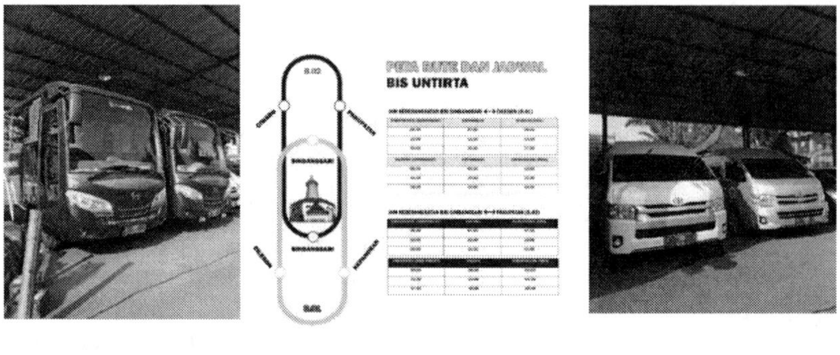

Figure 1. Shuttle Bus and Elf Sultan Ageng Tirtayasa University

3.3. Policy regarding emission-free vehicles on campus

The UNTIRTA has provided free bicycle services to create a pollution-free environment within the campus. The university should continually support this initiative by providing the required infrastructure to encourage the daily use of bicycles as a means of transportation. This will increase the safety of all road users besides helping to reduce the use of vehicles, which are the major pollutants. Figure 2 below presents bicycle users within the campus.

Figure 2. Emission Free Vehicles Sultan Ageng Tirtayasa University

Therefore, bicycle service as an alternative in facilitating the movement of the UNTIRTA academic community to move from one building to another one to avoid vehicle emissions on campus. Also, the availability of campus bicycle services can improve the quality of the environment and the safety of road users on the UNTIRTA campus by starting to reduce the use of motorized vehicles in the campus environment.

3.4. The ratio of Total Parking Area to Total Campus Area

The parking area ratio is calculated by dividing the total campus area covered by the parking space. This calculation is required to determine the percentage of the total parking area on campus as presented in Table 1, which shows a total campus area of 356193 m^2 compared to the parking space of 5127.83 m^2. The percentage of the parking area to the total campus area is 1.44% and belongs to the category < 4 – 1%.

IOP Conf. Series: Earth and Environmental Science 1000 (2022) 012015 doi:10.1088/1755-1315/1000/1/012015

Table 1. Total area and parking area of UNTIRTA Campus

No	Campus	Area (m^2)	Parking Area (m^2)
1	Pakupatan Campus	28.384, 0	3.015, 8
2	Sindangsari Integrated Campus	230.975, 0	3.226,23
3	Cilegon Campus / Faculty of Engineering	61.685, 0	1.546, 85
4	Ciwaru Campus	29.216, 0	574,6
5	Kepandean Campus	5.050,550	1327, 0
	Total Area	356.193, 0	5127,83

3.5. A transportation program designed to limit or reduce the parking area on campus over the past three years (from 2016 to 2018)

Enacting policies regarding entrance and parking within campus premises will help to preserve the environment. Also, some campuses have limited space for parking, in particular, A Pakupatan UNTIRTA. As a result, policies were put in place to ensure only vehicles with stickers park within the campus. Consequently, only vehicles belonging to the University (Dinas), Senior Lecturers (Sepuh), Education Personnel have access to the parking lots within the campus. Additionally, third parties to provide alternative parking areas to the motorists who miss parking within the campus. Furthermore, the University has drafted several additional policies to limit the number of vehicles parking within the campus, especially at the New Sindangsari. The drafting of the new regulations was based on the Rector's Decree No. 637 / UN43 / KPT.PR.00.00 / 2020. The new policies include:

- The application of vehicle parking fees in the UNTIRTA campus
- Enforcement of vehicle plate odd-even system for all vehicles entering the campus, except for official vehicles
- Enactment of the operation of buses serving inter-campus routes that operate from 0700 - 1800 Hrs
- Enforcement of Car Free Day (CFD) at the UNTIRTA, where no car is allowed at least once a week
- Prohibition in bringing vehicles into the campus for one year for the first-semester students

3.6. Sultan Ageng Tirtayasa University's policy is to limit or reduce the number of private vehicles on campus

The Car Free Day is a routine plan by UNTIRTA to support and care for the environment as stipulated in Rector's Decrees and Rector's Letters. By implementing the CFD activity, the campus is protected from vehicle emissions that pose a danger to people and the environment. The policy of the CFD program can create a new culture in transportation, using public transportation, cycling, and walking, which can be seen in Figure 3.

Figure 3. Conditions of Car Free Day Implementation at UNTIRTA

As UNTIRTA's main commitment to realize a green campus, plans are underway to build an integrated public transport service system. A ticketing system with low rates is set to be put in place and provided at no cost in some situations. To support this service, UNTIRTA will implement restrictions on the SRP (Parking Space Unit) as an effort to force motorized users to switch to public transportation. Also, UNTIRTA has provided free campus bus services to each UNTIRTA campus from Monday to Friday.

3.7. Pedestrian Paths

Sidewalks in the UNTIRTA campus are intended to make it easier for pedestrians to comfortably and safely reach their destinations. In this regard, the pathways have shelters to protect pedestrians from heat and rain besides being constructed from the main roads to ensure pedestrian safety. Additionally, there are guide blocks for pedestrians with physical disabilities, as seen in Figure 4.

Figure 4. Pedestrian Paths Implementation at UNTIRTA

3.8. Total of UNTIRTA Green Campus Assessment

The green campus assessment for UNTIRTA is shown in Table 2. Based on the results, UNTIRTA's assessment of UI Greenmetric found that TR1 is weakest due to the absence of vehicle restrictions entering the campus. Furthermore, long-term campus policies should be put in place.

Table 2. Transportations Category and Indicator

No	Category and Indicator	Maximum	Assessment
TR 1	The ratio of the number of vehicles divided by the total population	200	100
TR 2	Campus shuttle service	300	225
TR 3	Policies regarding emission-free vehicles on campus	200	200
TR 4	The ratio of the number of emission-free vehicles divided by the total campus population	200	150
TR 5	The ratio of the parking area to the total campus area	200	150
TR 6	Transportation program designed to limit reducing parking areas on campus over the past 3 years (from 2016 to 2018)	200	150
TR 7	Number of transportation initiatives to reduce private vehicles on campus	200	200
TR 8	Pedestrian policy on campus	300	300
TOTAL		1800	1475

While the total value of green transportation is 81.9% out of the UI GreenMetric maximum value, it is necessary to implement alternative strategies to maintain green transportation. The alternative strategies include drafting policies to encourage green transportation themed activities, such as using emission-free vehicles provided by the campus, coming up with specific plans, monitoring, reporting, evaluating, and creating a special team to ensure sustainability in the green campus program.

4. Conclusion

The green transportation analysis at Sultan Ageng Tirtayasa University based on UI GreenMetric scored 81.9% of the maximum value, which indicates great efforts to keep the environment free from pollutants. However, it is necessary to improve each criterion by checking the ratio of vehicles to the total population and using emission-free vehicles. Furthermore, there is a need for special policy planning to improve the criteria for Green Campus by UI GreenMetric. This will be achieved by restricting the number of vehicles entering the campus, developing emission-free transportation, and making integrated parking buildings. All these require the support and cooperation from all stakeholders to participate in the green transportation program actively.

5. References

[1] Aion, N., Helmandollar, L., Wang, M., & Ng, J.W. (2012). Intelligent Campus (iCampus) Impact Study. 2012 IEEE/WIC/ACM International Conferences on Web Intelligence and Intelligent Agent Technology, 3, 291-295.

[2] Tan, Hongwei & Chen, Shuqin & Shi, Qian & Wang, Lingling. (2014). Development of green campus in China. Journal of Cleaner Production. 64. 646-653. 10.1016/j.jclepro.2013.10.019.

[3] Sahoo, Manoj & Mishra, Sunil. (2013). Green Campus a Competitive Advantage snd Sustainability for Management Institutions. 1. 74-80.

[4] Kementrian Lingkungan Hidup dan Kehutanan (2017). Menlhk. Tersedia di http://ppid.menlhk.go.id/siaran_pers/browse/512

[5] Buana, R. P., Mia, W., & Rindu, E. (2018). Pengembangan Indikator Peran serta Pihak Manajemen Perguruan Tinggi Dalam Penerapan Konsep Green Campus." RekaRacana: Jurnal Teknil Sipil, Volume 4, No 4, 2018, 82-93.

[6] Zainordin, Nadzirah & Judyar, Zamzrina. (2017). Towards Sustainable Campus - a Study on Physical Development Planning aCross Four Different Institutions.

[7] Kementrian Perencanaan Pembangunan Nasional (2013). Kajian pembangunan Transportasi dan Perubahan Iklim Dalam Mendukung Konektivitas dan Pembangunan Berkelanjutan.

[8] Andriani, Dian & Yuliastuti, Nany. (2013). Penilaian Sistem Transportasi yang Mengarah Pada Green Transportasi di Kota Surakarta. Jurnal Pembangunan Wilayah dan Kota.

[9] Naskah akademik dan perencanaan green kampus IPB 2019-2023.

[10] Santoso, N.D., Akmalah, E., & Irawati, I. (2017). Implementasi Konsep Green Campus di Kampus Itenas Bandung Berdasarkan Kategori Tata Letak dan Infrastruktur (Hal. 139-150).

[11] Falakh, F. (2020). Evaluasi Penerapan Green Campus pada Pemeringkatan UI GreenMetric World University Rangkings di Universitas Islam Negeri Walisongo Semarang. Jounal Of Enviromental Science Sustainable, 1(2), 30 - 35.

[12] Prihanto, Teguh. (2017). Strategi dan Program Pengembangan Konservasi di Kampus Hijau Universitas Negeri Semarang (UNNES).

[13] Binta, I., & Maulana, D. (2021). Evaluasi Penataan dan Infrastruktur Kampus Hijau pada Politeknik Negeri Pontianak Berdasarkan UI GreenMetric. GEWANG: Gerbang Wacana dan Rancang Arsitektur, 3(1), 25-30.

[14] UI GreenMetric World University Rankings Guideline 2020.

The Relationship Between Socio-Demographic Environment and Trip Preferences Towards Relaxation Facilities in Urban Area (Case Study: Modern Café in Makassar)

H Yatmar, M I Ramli, M Pasra, and M Ikbal

Civil Engineering, Faculty of Engineering Universitas Hasanuddin

hajriyantiyatmar@unhas.ac.id

Abstract. This study aimed to investigate the trip preferences on relaxation facilities specific to café in Makassar city. For this purpose, 1,184 visitors are the respondents who have visited modern café in Makassar: Anomali, Grid and Pool, Numerica, Fireflies, and Black Canyon Coffee. A descriptive analysis was conducted to evaluate the trip preference due to socio-demography background. The finding shows that the trip purpose preferences among the socio-demography characteristics were similar. The dominant trip purposes sequentially are "hangout and refreshing", "eating and drink", and "study". The significance of this study is to provide a travel demand preference according to the socio-demography background related to trip purpose in the café as one of the relaxation facilities that affect the trip attraction in the urban area.

1. Introduction

Nowadays, people engage in a variety of activities, including studying, working, and socializing. In the modern era, the coffee-drinking lifestyle began to evolve and spread throughout the community, particularly in urban areas. The rapid expansion of coffee shops in Indonesia is also evident in Makassar, a metropolitan city. Today, coffee shops, also known as cafés, serve more than just coffee; they also serve other beverages and a full menu [1]. Their menu may include desserts, regional specialties, and other sweet treats. Additionally, they will provide complimentary internet access and set meals to attract additional customers as gathering spots for family and friends. Social activities increase people's mobility, which may have an effect on time travel and communication across larger geographical areas, thereby altering society's overall geographical structure, as well as the patterns of everyday activities and spaces in various cultures and lifestyles [2].

People are generally expected to be able to be 'present' almost anywhere, to engage in almost anything, and to communicate with virtually anyone via their constant online presence. They can travel quickly to distant activities and use information and communication technologies in their homes to learn about those activities and locations. They engage in social interaction regardless of their geographical location [3]. The trip's requirement to conduct numerous activities concurrently necessitates time and space. Nowadays, the majority of teenagers prefer to work, discuss, study, eat and drink, hang out, and even take a refreshing break in a café [4].

Trip preference information contributes to travel demand information, which in turn influences the trip and attraction based on social demography. The significance of trip intentions can be appreciated and investigated by delving into social demography, such as people's consumption and revealed activities in a particular time and space [5]. The trip to the café has various purposes and the characteristics of visitors based on their socio-demography conditions are interesting to explore. The brief understanding of visitors' characteristics and the purpose of the café may also imply that people are allocating more time for trips and travel thus staying away from home for longer periods.

2. Theoretical Background

Almost everyone travels to take advantage of socioeconomic opportunities such as recreation, education, shopping, and employment, all of which require the support of transportation services. Every human being has a concept for daily trips; this concept is determined by the economic level and the choices made by each individual in compiling daily activities [6,7].

In navigating the current socioeconomic landscape, humans are increasingly confronted with the concept of a lifestyle as a means of relieving fatigue and boredom at home. It is now recognized that, in addition to malls and other family recreation areas, there are more modern establishments that are attracting human interest, namely cafes [8]. Nowadays, the culture of hanging out or simply relaxing in cafes has become ingrained in the Indonesian people. It is no longer just about drinking or eating; cafes have become integral to the goals of individuals or society as a whole as a place to conduct specific activities or as a meeting place. and other items that smell like a group of people but cannot be distinguished from individual items [9], the shift in the function of a cafe and restaurant will result in the emergence of new social and cultural phenomena in society as a result of these behavioral changes.

2.1. Affecting Factor of Trip to Cafe

Travel behavior that includes visits to cafes has become ingrained in society as a whole. According to urbanites, sitting in a cafe and conversing with friends is an integral part of a modern lifestyle, and anyone who does not understand what a cafe is will be considered a member of an outmoded society. Lifestyle as a distinct social group emerges as a result of social stratification. Each group within a particular social structure will have its distinct way of life. One could argue that this way of life is a symbol of social prestige [10].

While some research defines lifestyle as a consumption pattern that reflects an individual's choices regarding how they spend their money and time, other research defines it as a way of life that is defined by how an individual spends their time (activities), what they value in their environment (interests), and how they view themselves and the world around them (opinions) [11].

According to the study, consumption in the modern era is an era in which people purchase goods not for their utility but for their image, which is directed and shaped by advertisements and fashion via television, information time shows, celebrity lifestyles, and so on, which advertisements offer. It is not the utility of an item, but rather its image and style in the eyes of its followers. The attractiveness of a modern cafe, with its design and characteristics, increases the frequency of visits. Numerous factors influence a person's travel behavior, including time, space, social, and economic considerations [12].

The four factors are considered with high impact to influence the behavior of travelers (travel behavior) [13]. These factors are further divided into several variables that can be identified. These variables were assessed quantitatively and qualitatively. These factors or variables are:

1. The purpose of the trip (trip purpose) such as work, school, social, and others.
2. Time of trip (time of trip made) such as morning, noon, midnight, holidays, and so on.
3. Trip length, is the physical distance between origin and destination, including the length of the route/segment, the comparison time if using other modes, here applies that the farther the trip, the more people tend to choose public transportation, and the closer the trip.

2.2. Socio demography characteristics

In this group of factors, all variables relate to individual travelers [14]. These variables contribute to influencing the travel behavior of these variables, including:

1. Income, in the form of purchasing power of the traveler to finance his trip, either by private car or public transportation.
2. Car ownership, in the form of the availability of private vehicles as a means of traveling.
3. Condition of a private vehicle.
4. The population of residential development.

IOP Conf. Series: Earth and Environmental Science 1000 (2022) 012016 doi:10.1088/1755-1315/1000/1/012016

5. Other socio-economic conditions, such as family structure and size (young couple, have children, pension or bachelor, etc.), age, gender, type of work, location of work, have a driving license, and all the variables that affect the choice of mode.

3. Method

The study method is using descriptive analysis of basic features from interviewing surveys due to the trip preference especially trip purpose associated with socio-demography. The responses of respondents to trip purpose and socio-demography are quartiles in crosstabulation to obtain the specific characteristics of customers of cafés. The result is then calculated and quartile into different clusters that according to trip purpose and socio-demography. Then, the result is presented in the quartile chart.

3.1. Descriptive Analysis

Quantitative descriptive analysis is a statistic used to analyze data by describing or describing the data that has been collected [15]. This analytical technique is commonly used for exploratory research. This type of research usually only tries to reveal and describe the results of the research.
Descriptive statistical analysis techniques that can be used include:

1. Presentation of data in the form of tables or frequency distribution and cross-tabulation (crosstabulation). With this analysis, the trend of research findings will be known and categorized into low, medium, or high.
2. Presentation of data in a visual form such as histograms, polygons, ogives, bar charts, pie charts, parallel diagrams, and symbol diagrams.

3.2. Crosstabulation

Crosstab analysis is a basic analysis of the relationship between categorical variables (nominal or ordinal). The Crosstab submenu is used to present data in tabular form, which includes rows and columns. Thus, the characteristic of cross-tabulation is the existence of two or more variables that have a relationship, and generally in the form of qualitative data. Another definition explains that crosstab table analysis is a correlational analysis that is used to see the relationship between variables (at least 2 variables) in nominal or ordinal categories. It is also possible to add control variables [16].

4. Data Collection

This study conducted the interview of visitors in the café as the primary data. The total sampling of respondents according to the visitors' survey during peak hours in workday and weekday. The total sampling from five cafes is 1,184 respondents that were selected randomly from each cafe.

Figure 1. Location of Cafes (Source: Google Earth)

4.1. Study Area

In this study, the location chosen is a modern cafe which is very popular with visitors. In this study, 5 (five) modern cafes were selected. They are Anomali (A), Grid and Pool (GNP), Fireflies (F), Numerica (N), and Black Canyon Coffee (BCC). The location of cafes is shown in the following Figure 1.

4.2. Socio-Demography Characteristics

The categories of socio-demography preferences are shows the distribution of respondent's respond to preference. Each category indicates the marginal percentage for each variable category that is shown in the following Table 1.

Table 1. Socio-Demography Characteristics

Variables		CAFÉ's Respondents (N= 1184), %				
		Anomali (A)	Grid and Pool (GNP)	Numerica (N)	Fireflies (F)	Black Canyon Coffee (BCC)
Age (years old/yo)	Under 20 years old/yo	2,45	2,36	1,01	0,42	3,04
	Between 20 and 25 yo	7,77	6,00	10,73	1,86	8,28
	Between 26 and 30 yo	5,49	4,65	4,73	10,05	4,73
	Above30	5,24	6,76	4,90	6,25	3,29
Gender	Men	14,44	9,63	10,73	10,64	11,06
	Women	6,50	10,14	10,6	7,94	8,28
Occupation	Students	7,18	7,09	7,43	1,10	6,76
	Civil Servant	1,60	3,46	2,45	1,94	2,45
	Private Employee	7,85	7,09	6,08	7,60	6,25
	Entrepreneur	3,55	1,27	2,87	7,09	2,53
	Others	0,76	0,84	2,53	0,84	1,35
Education	Primary School	0,00	0,68	0,00	0,00	0,08
	Junior High School	0,51	0,76	0,08	0,00	0,34
	Senior High School	7,35	7,09	7,18	1,18	7,60
	Diploma (D3)	0,25	1,69	1,01	1,18	1,44
	Bachelor Degree/ D4	12,08	9,46	11,66	15,29	9,38
	Magister and Doctoral	0,76	0,08	1,44	0,93	0,51
Income (IDR)	Under 2 million	7,77	8,11	9,12	1,69	7,77
	Between 2 - 3 million	1,69	1,35	2,87	1,60	2,53
	Between 3 - 5 million	3,72	5,74	4,98	4,39	5,07
	Between 5 - 7.5 million	3,38	3,89	2,87	4,98	2,11
	Between 7.5 - 10 million	2,96	0,59	0,93	3,89	1,44
	Between 10 - 20 million	1,44	0,08	0,59	2,03	0,42

4.3. Trip Preference

The trip preference of respondents indicates the total variables group categories from the respondents' responses that are shown in Table 2. The study is focused on the trip preference that is related to purpose. Most of the trip preference especially for the origin of respondents is from home to café.

Table 2. Trip Preferences of Cafes Respondents

Variables		CAFÉ's Respondents (N= 1184), %				
		Anomali (A)	Grid and Pool (GNP)	Numerica (N)	Fireflies (F)	Black Canyon Coffee (BCC)
Origin	Home	14,36	5,24	13,51	10,98	13,01
	Office	4,56	5,41	4,65	4,81	3,97
	School	0,00	0,42	0,34	0,17	0,17
	Campus	0,51	3,04	1,27	0,42	1,18

IOP Conf. Series: Earth and Environmental Science 1000 (2022) 012016 doi:10.1088/1755-1315/1000/1/012016

Table 2. Trip Preferences of Cafes Respondents (Continued)

Variables		CAFÉ's Respondents (N= 1184), %				
		Anomali (A)	Grid and Pool (GNP)	Numerica (N)	Fireflies (F)	Black Canyon Coffee (BCC)
Origin	Mall	0,68	0,76	0,59	1,35	0,51
	Relations home	0,68	3,21	0,59	0,68	0,25
	Others	0,17	1,69	0,42	0,17	0,25
Transport mode to Café	Motorcycle	9,12	5,49	10,56	4,05	12,50
	Car	9,71	13,51	8,19	10,30	5,66
	Online Taxi (Motorcycle)	0,59	0,00	0,25	0,00	0,59
	Online Taxi (car)	1,52	0,76	2,36	4,22	0,59
Purpose	Food and Drink	1,60	2,36	3,80	1,18	3,04
	Hangout	10,47	10,05	11,32	9,63	10,30
	Study	0,93	0,17	0,76	0,76	1,94
	Refreshing	7,94	7,18	5,49	7,01	4,05
Partner	Friend	10,47	11,32	14,53	8,11	14,53
	Family	0,51	5,15	3,13	4,31	1,94
	Sibling	0,34	0,34	0,51	0,68	0,76
	Relation	0,76	0,00	0,17	0,08	0,00
	Others	8,87	2,96	3,04	5,41	2,11
Destination after	Home	16,72	11,49	18,83	12,25	16,47
	Office	1,44	2,03	1,01	1,44	0,42
	School	0,00	0,08	0,00	0,00	0,00
	Campus	0,00	0,93	0,08	0,00	0,08
	Mall	1,01	1,35	0,17	0,84	0,84
	Relations home	1,10	3,63	0,93	2,87	1,27
	Others	0,68	0,25	0,34	1,18	0,25
Transport mode from Café	Motorcycle	9,12	5,49	10,56	4,05	12,42
	Car	9,71	13,51	8,19	10,30	5,66
	Online Taxi (Motorcycle)	0,59	0,00	0,34	0,00	0,68
	Online Taxi (car)	1,52	0,76	2,28	4,22	0,59
Frequence	Once a week	4,39	11,82	6,17	5,15	5,74
	Twice a week	8,95	1,10	4,22	6,00	4,48
	Three times a week	3,55	0,59	0,76	1,10	2,36
	More than three times a week	2,53	0,00	0,34	2,20	0,59
	Once a month	0,76	5,49	6,84	3,13	3,55
	Twice a month	0,76	0,76	2,79	1,01	2,62
	Others	0,00	0,00	0,25	0,00	0,00
Travel Distance from Origin to Cafe	< 1 km	3,97	4,39	0,84	1,01	0,34
	1 – 2 km	1,86	4,05	3,80	1,60	0,93
	2 – 3 km	0,84	3,80	2,45	2,70	2,20
	3 – 4 km	1,52	1,01	2,45	2,62	2,20
	4 – 5 km	2,87	1,86	1,60	1,44	3,72
	> 5 km	9,88	4,65	10,22	9,29	9,97

The trip preference of respondents while using transport mode "car" is dominated than others mode. The purpose of café of the majority of respondents' choices is to hangout and with friends. The majority of destination and transport mode of respondents from café goes home using the car. The majority of the respondent has to go to café at least once time a week and tend to café which is far away from origin place more than 5 km.

5. Results and Discussion

This session illustrates the trip preference of purpose considering the socio-demography of respondents. It shows the trend of trip preference characteristics of customers in every café.

5.1. Descriptive Result of Trip Preference with Socio-Demography

The distribution characteristics of the respondent are investigated before plotting into quartile mode especially for socio-demographic that investigated this study; age, gender, occupation, education, income, and ownerships as the independent variables while trip purpose is the dependent variable.

5.2. The Trip Purpose Preference with Socio-Demography

The trip preference that is specific to the purpose associated with the socio-demography is shown in the characteristics responses of respondents in every café shown from Figure 2 to Figure 7. The trend of the responses was similar. The response shows the trip purpose of respondents dominated for "Hangout" and "Refreshing", then followed by "Eat and Drink", and the last one is "Study". This is quite interesting and pretends that people come to Cafes for "Relaxation" such as Refreshing and Hangout.

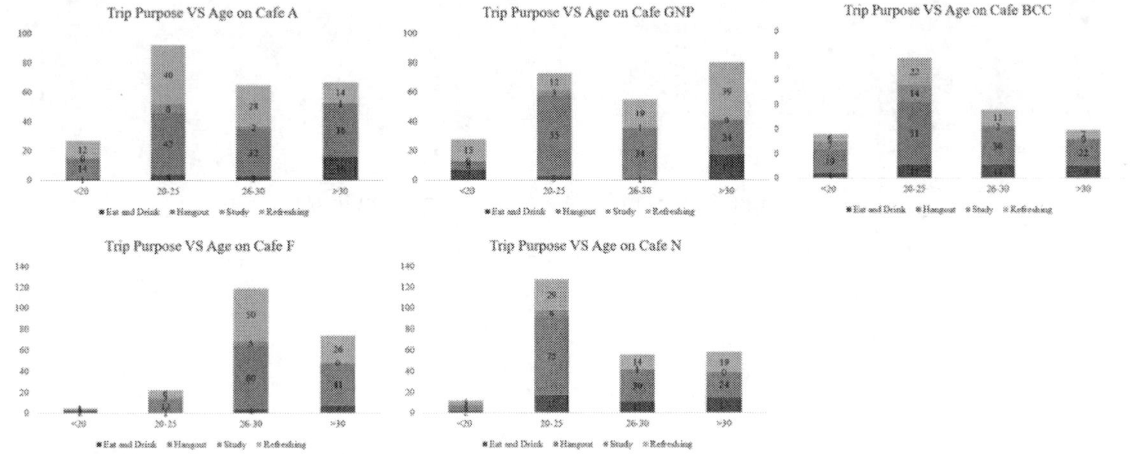

Figure 2. Trip Purpose vs Age

Figure 2 shows the majority of trip purposes in every category of age are similar for all cafes. Figure 3 is shown the trip purpose due to gender. It has shown that the majority of visitors to cafes were Men for Hangout and Refreshing. Figure 4 shows the one who has majority occupation that visits café to Hangout and Refreshing comes from students and private employee.

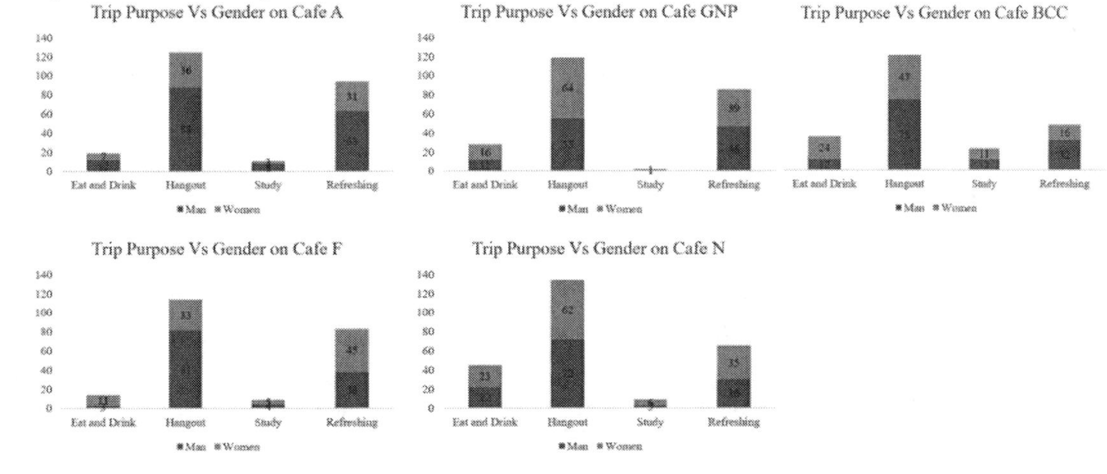

Figure 3. Trip Purpose vs Gender

IOP Conf. Series: Earth and Environmental Science 1000 (2022) 012016 doi:10.1088/1755-1315/1000/1/012016

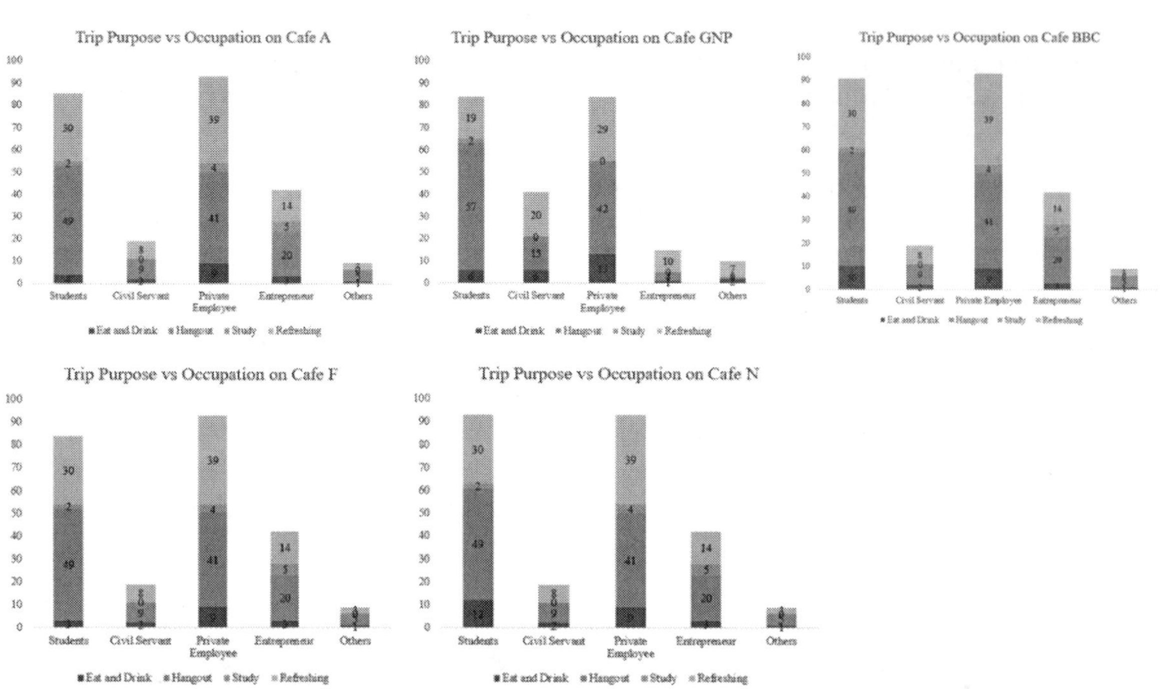

Figure 4. Trip Purpose vs Occupation

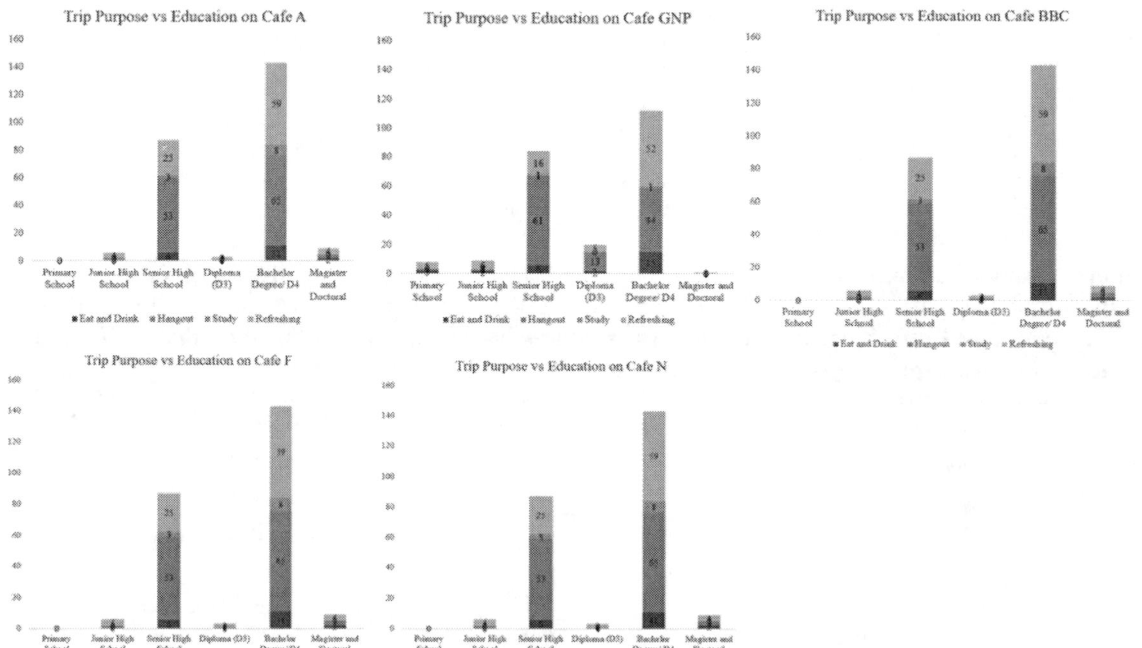

Figure 5. Trip Purpose vs Education

Figure 5 shows the trend of the background education that majority hang out and refreshing in cafes are from Senior Highs School and Bachelor Degree. Figure 6 shows the majority of respondents who have hang out and refreshed are the people who have income categories under two million. Figure 7 shows the response that the majority hang out and refreshed in the café were the ones who have ownership of cars and motorcycles.

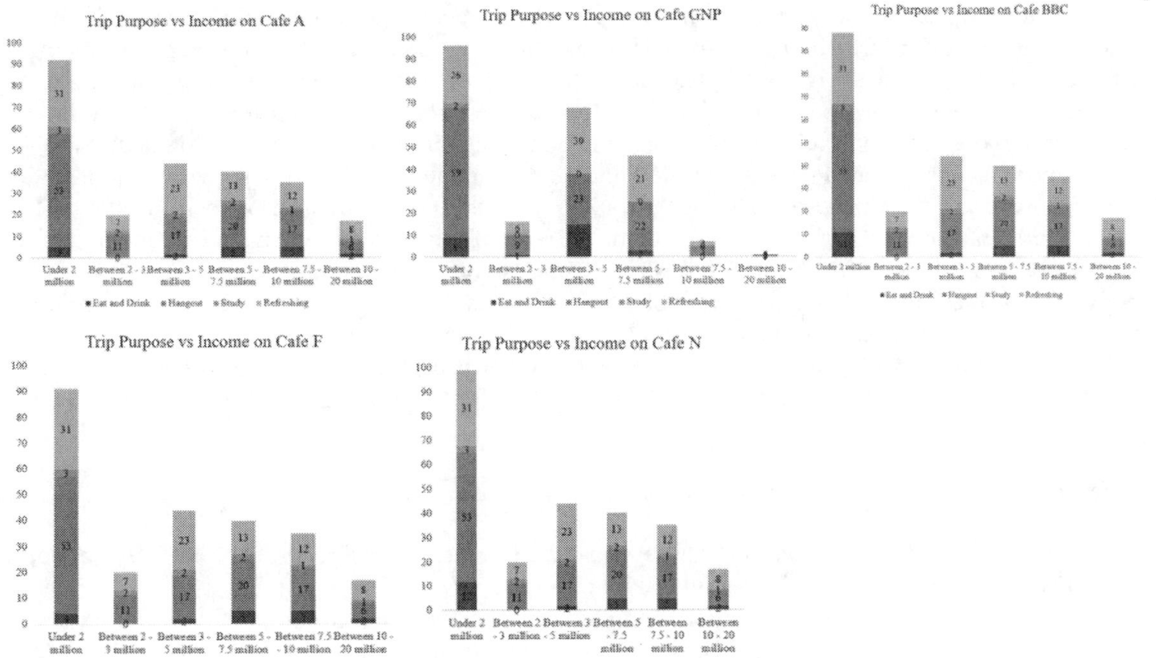

Figure 6. Trip Purpose vs Income

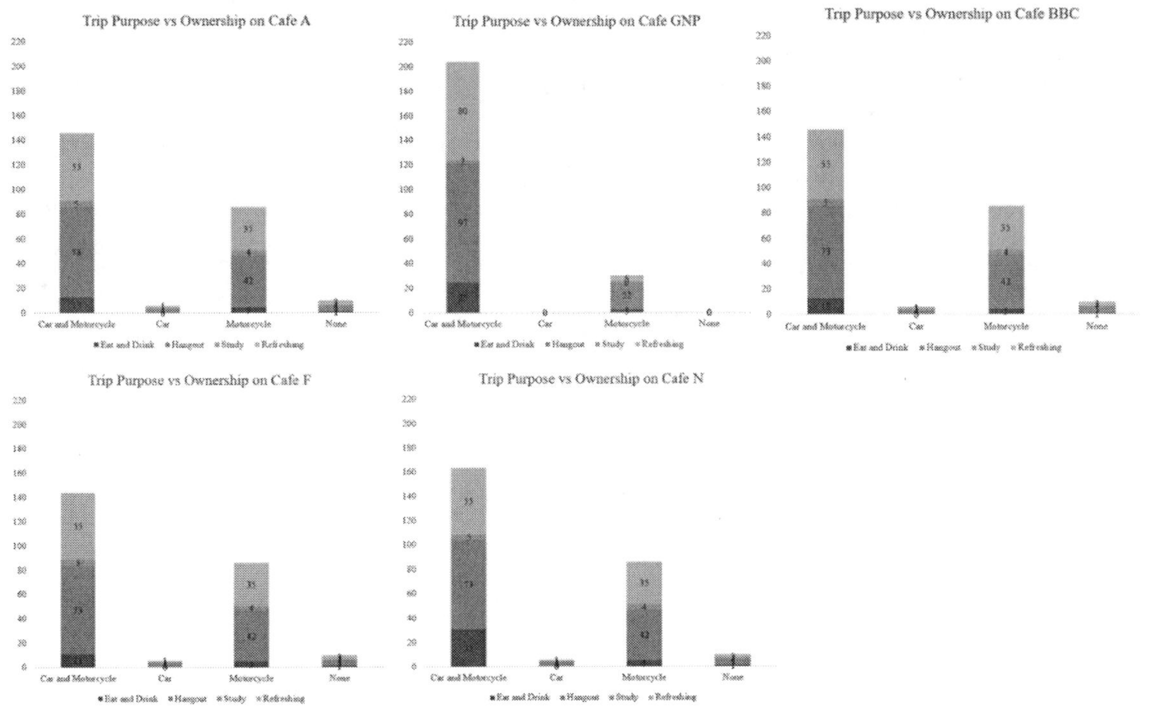

Figure 7. Trip Purpose vs Vehicles Ownership

Overall, the characteristics of responding from all café due to trip purpose with socio-demography were similar. It may be different depending on characteristics of urban societies that affect the trip demand, socio-demography, economy, and other factors.

6. Conclusions

In this study, trip preferences describe the travel demand according to the socio-demography of the modern café in Makassar. The results of this study show that hangout and refreshing were the most trip purpose and the least is study. The characteristics relation between trip purpose and social demography have similar from five modern café as samples. This study contributes to identifying the most trip purpose based on social-demography among the visitors of modern café in Makassar.

Furthermore, the characteristics of social-demography that related to trip purpose show the indication of people tend to café which are youth age 20 – 25 years old, men, students as a bachelor that income below 2 billion, and used car. Unfortunately, the purpose of this majority young age as students come to café for hangout with friends and refreshing with less of people choose to eat and drink, and to study. The availability of space for the public that is reachable from their home has been considered especially to hang out and refreshing.

The future research of this study can be extended to other trip preferences such as cost spend, time, and quality service of place that affect the production and attraction of travel demand in the urban area.

References

[1] Kuan P H 2017 *An Empirical Assessment on Customers' Preferences towards Coffee House* (Malaysia: Universiti Tunku Abdul Rahman)

[2] Kohansal M R, Firoozzare A 2013 *Applying Multinomial Logit Model for Determining Socio-Economic Factors Affecting Major Choice of Consumer in Food Purchasing: The Case of Mashhad* (Iran: J. Agr. Sci. Tech. 2013 Vol. 15: 1307-1317)

[3] Michael F 1995 *Transport planning and the human activity approach* (Journal of Transport Geography Vol 3 No.2 pp 105-116)

[4] Zhang, Y, Mohammadian A 2016 *An Explanatory Analysis of The Household Travel Behavior and Lifestyle Choices* (Elsevier) p 310-318

[5] Ellegard, Wilhemson 2004 *Home as a pocket of local order: everyday activities and the friction of* distance. (Swedish Society for Anthropology and Geography)

[6] Harvey J M 2017 *Time geography and space-time prism.* (The International Encyclopedia of Geography. DOI: 10.1002/9781118786352.wbieg0431)

[7] Dimas BED 2016 *The complexity and variability of individuals' activity-travel patterns in Indonesia.* Doctoral Thesis in Transport Science Stockholm (Sweden 2016)

[8] Widodo A J 2014 *Analisis Preferensi Pengunjung Kedai Kopi Terhadap Menu Kedai Kopi di Kota Semarang* in Bahasa. (Ekonomika, Fakultas Bisnis, Universitas Diponegoro)

[9] Rahman Q R 2013 *Studi Faktor-Faktor Berpengaruh Terhadap Frekuensi Perjalanan Berbelanja Ke Pasar Tradisional Berbasis Structual Equation Modeling (SEM)* in Bahasa. (Universitas Hasanuddin)

[10] Estika I 2017 *Lifestyle The Teenageres of City (The Study Of Visitors Kafe In Pekanbaru).* (JOM FISIP) 4(1), 1–15

[11] Herlyana E 2012 *Fenomena Coffee Shop Sebagai Gejala Gaya Hidup Baru Kaum Muda* in Bahasa. (THAQAFIYYAT) 13(1), 188–204

[12] Muhammad I R, Yoshinao O 2010 *Study on Mode Choice Model of Trip for Daily Household Logistic based on Binomial Logit Model* (Proceeding of T-LOG 2010)

[13] Muhammad I R et all 2013 *A Simultaneous Choice Model of Departure Time and Travel Mode on One-Day Shopping Travel based on Disutility Minimizing Model Approach* (Proceedings of the Eastern Asia Society for Transportation Studies) Vol.9 2013

[14] Muhammad I R et all 2013 *A Trip Pattern Choice Model of Shopping Travel Based on Consideration of Flexible Daily Time Constraint* (Proceedings of the Eastern Asia Society for Transportation Studies) Vol.8 2011

[15] Mirilovic M, Pejin I 2008 *Application of descriptive statistics in the analysis of experimental data* (Journal Veterinarski Glasnik) Vol 62 np. 1-2 pp 85-95

[16] Umamaheswari S, Bhuvaneswari R 2020 *Students' Preference and Satisfaction towards Restaurants in Chennai City* (International Journal of Advanced Science and Technology) Vol. 29, No. 5, (2020), pp. 2994 - 3001

Acknowledgments
The authors gratefully acknowledge the support provided by the Transportation Engineering System Laboratory of Civil Department Faculty of Engineering Universitas Hasanuddin.

Traffic management at intersection to minimize dispersion of air pollution

L Ambarwati[1] and A K Indriastuti[2,3]

[1] Dept. of Civil Engineering, Brawijaya University, Jl. M.T. Haryono 167, Malang, Indonesia
[2] Dept. of Civil Engineering, Diponegoro University, Jl. Prof. Soedharto, Semarang, Indonesia

[3] amelia@live.undip.ac.id

Abstract. One of the consequences of higher mobility is the increase in air pollution. The increase in traffic volume at intersections impacts delays and congestion, thus producing higher air pollution concentrations. This research aimed to identify intersection performance and analyze air quality at existing conditions, then propose traffic management scenarios that increase intersection performance and reduce air pollution at a time. This study was taken on Soekarno-Hatta – M.T. Haryono – D.I. Panjaitan intersection, in Malang.
The intersection performance was at the worst level of service (LOS F) for each approach from traffic analysis using the Indonesian Highway Capacity Manual. At this condition, the prediction of air pollutant parameters was out of standard level. The CO concentrate was lower than the standard level, while NO was higher than the standard level. Traffic management was proposed by controlling the movements at the intersection approaches and the number of phases at the intersection. The third alternative can improve intersection performance from F to C and decrease air pollution. The concentration reductions are about ±37.4% for NOx and ±61.3% for CO from the road median to the end of the road.
Keywords: Intersection performance, air pollution dispersion, traffic management

1. Introduction

Transportation is a considerable fuel consumption activity that results in vast amounts of air pollution and global warming. The growth of private vehicles increases the number of trips due to high mobility and air pollution due to fossil fuels. Transportation emitted 70% of urban air pollutants to ambient air [1]. CO gas is one of the pollutant parameters emitted from motor-vehicle emissions due to traffic congestion. CO gas in the human body will react with hemoglobin (Hb) in the blood and form CO_2Hb. CO concentrations of up to 2-5% will react to unusual responses to the five senses and influence the central nervous system [2].

Strategies to improve road capacity and reduce air pollution are essential in transport policies, and the strategies must consider integrating environmental aspects into traffic management [3]. A strategic traffic management scheme should balance the issues of road capacity, safety, and environmental health within the city. The changes in transport infrastructure, traffic regulation, speed limit, and fleet composition will impact the air quality and air pollution level [4]. A deliberate transportation system related to land use management, such as considering the intensification of public transport (PT) associated with proper urban structures, should be undertaken to increase accessibility and reduce the emission loads, thus enhancing the quality of the environment. In Surabaya, the improvement of the PT system can reduce ±25% of air pollutant parameters during peak hours [5]. Upgrading the public transport system combined with changes in the urban structure and environmental assessment considerations can also minimize urban sprawl [6].

There were numerous studies on transportation demand management (TDM) to reduce air pollution from motorized vehicles regarding transport strategies. Nejadkoorki et al. [7] suggested that urban restructuring, road network development, and changing traffic demands would reduce air pollution, CO2 emissions for significant roads in Norwich, in the UK. Early studies focused on vehicle structure and travel behavior to minimize air pollution, and they indicated the need to consider integrating urban development and transport systems to reduce air pollution. Previously, Badami et al. [8] found that two-wheeler vehicles (M2W) account for 60% of vehicle-kilometers (but only 16% of passenger-kilometers) in motorized passenger vehicles movement. This condition triggered the production of carbon monoxide, hydrocarbon, and particulate emissions, up to 30%–50%. M2W vehicles alone consumed about half of all gasoline throughout the country. This study also recognized that using some buses and other diesel vehicles emitted nitrogen oxides and sulfur dioxide. Furthermore, Badami [9] explained that technological measures related to vehicle and fuel technology, road capacity, and transport system management have essential roles in addressing air pollution and other transport impacts, nevertheless involving considerable financial and administrative resources.

Some studies showed that limiting the speed of 40 km/h on the highway can reduce air pollution emissions (NOx, CO2, and PM10). From the observation, NOx was reduced by 5.7%, CO2 by 0.5%, and PM10 by 3.2%). Meanwhile, with the prohibition of Heavy-Duty Vehicles (HDV), pollutant emissions can be reduced by 44% for NOx, 18% for CO2, and 20% for PM10. Another effort was the encouragement to use alternative transportation to reduce PM2.5 concentration and other air pollution exposure, thus lowering the health impacts. In addition, changes in travel behavior can also minimize the number of road traffic accidents [10]. Two scenarios were applied to reduce CO2 emissions from road traffic in two European cities (Basel and Rotterdam) and two Chinese cities (Xi'an and Suzhou). The scenarios reduced the private vehicle kilometers driven up to 10% on urban streets and introduced the 50% electric-powered private vehicle. The first and second scenarios reduced CO2 emissions up to 5% and 25%, respectively. Air pollution in the Chinese cities was 3 to 5 times higher than in the European cities in 2010 and 2020 [11].

As mentioned before, some studies have been conducted to reduce air pollution, but few considered the integration of traffic management to improve road network performance and reduce air pollution. Therefore, this study focuses mainly on traffic management at intersections, which will reduce congestion and impact reducing air emissions.

A TDM (transport demand management) strategy related to highway network priorities, especially at intersections, should reduce air pollution. This effort is applied in the city of Malang as a study area. Malang is the second biggest city in East Java Province - Indonesia, as a city of tourism and education and a connecting city.

The growth of motorized vehicles and trips increases the motorized vehicle emissions, the risk of road safety, and an unhealthy environment for humans [6]. Based on statistics data [12], there was an increase in the number of vehicles from 441,123 (2015) to 456,693 units (2016) in Malang. This condition will worsen air quality. With the high growth of private vehicles (motorcycles and cars), there are many movement conflicts on the highway network, particularly at the intersections.

Poor performance describes the imbalance between space and cycle time at the intersection for vehicle movement. Intersection performance can be improved by controlling traffic movements, adjusting cycle times with the number of vehicles and turning movements, and improving road geometry. These efforts also relate to improving air quality. Previous studies have not considered increasing intersection performance to reduce air pollution parameters. Air emission parameters at the intersection should be assessed on the interaction and management of the intersection to minimize delays and queue length, thus improving intersection performance (level of service, LOS). The study is aimed to identify the performance of a signalized intersection and analyze air pollutant parameters for the existing condition, then propose traffic management scenarios that increase intersection performance and reduce air pollution at a time.

2. Methods

2.1. Research Framework

The case study area is Malang City, consisting of five sub-districts and 57 villages (figure 1) with an area of 110 km² and 861,414 residents [12]. High traffic volumes load highway networks at this education, business, and tourism destination area, especially intersections. The traffic volume increase was also affected by the expansion of suburban housing development since the beginning of the 20th century. As a result, there are traffic congestions on highways and intersections, and delays and queues at intersections result in high air pollution.

Congestion and air quality have become significant problems in Central Business District (CBD) and high-activity areas such as education centers and tourism places. The expansion of CBD will grow disproportionately, and it may be doubled in size in the next twenty years. Rapid and uncontrolled growths have an impact on residents' mobility. Transportation infrastructure development lags, resulting in large-scale congestion, delays, and air pollution [5]. In the future, TDM strategy in the highway network should be managed by improving highway performances integrated with the environmental assessment to reduce significant congestion and balance with air quality and maximize accessibility.

This study focuses on the intersection with high queues and high traffic due to many activities in the road corridors that bond Soekarno-Hatta Street (northward, connecting this intersection to Surabaya), M.T. Haryono Street (westward, connecting to Batu), and D.I. Panjaitan Street (eastward, connecting to Malang CBD), as shown in figure 1. The intersection becomes one of the main access roads to Brawijaya University and Malang State Polytechnic, surrounded by residential and commercial areas along those streets.

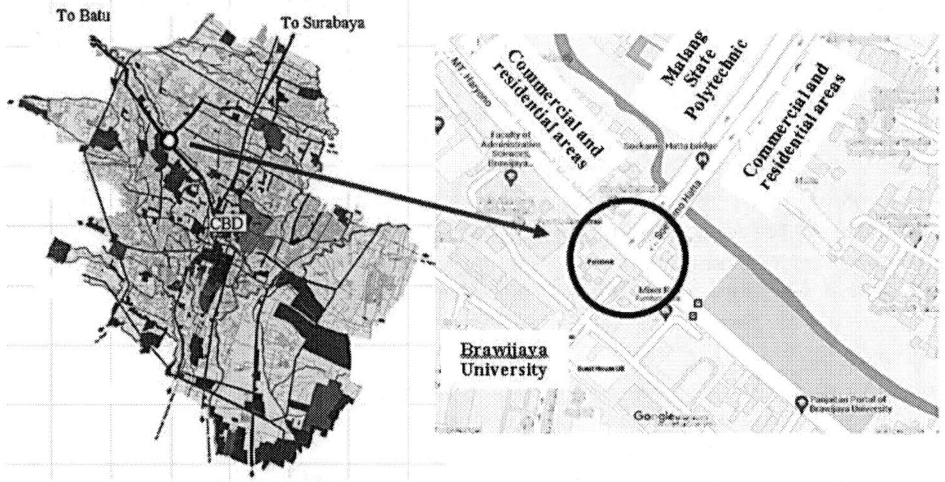

Figure 1. The study area (Malang City) and intersection location and its corridors.

Traffic volume, speed, and road geometry data were observed at the intersection. The vehicle emission and dispersion values were determined based on volume and speed data. The survey was conducted on Friday 3.00-9.00 p.m. and Monday during peak hours (06.00-12.00 a.m.) in 15-minute intervals. Secondary data were collected from the Environment Agency of Malang City.

The concept is to assess intersection performance and ambient concentration at the existing condition and some traffic management scenarios. The target is to reduce emission and dispersion of air pollution by improving intersection performance.

Two primary analyses defined in this study were intersection performance and ambient concentration. Intersection performance was analyzed using the Indonesian Highway Capacity Manual [13], and ambient concentrations were calculated based on vehicle speed [15], as seen in figure 2.

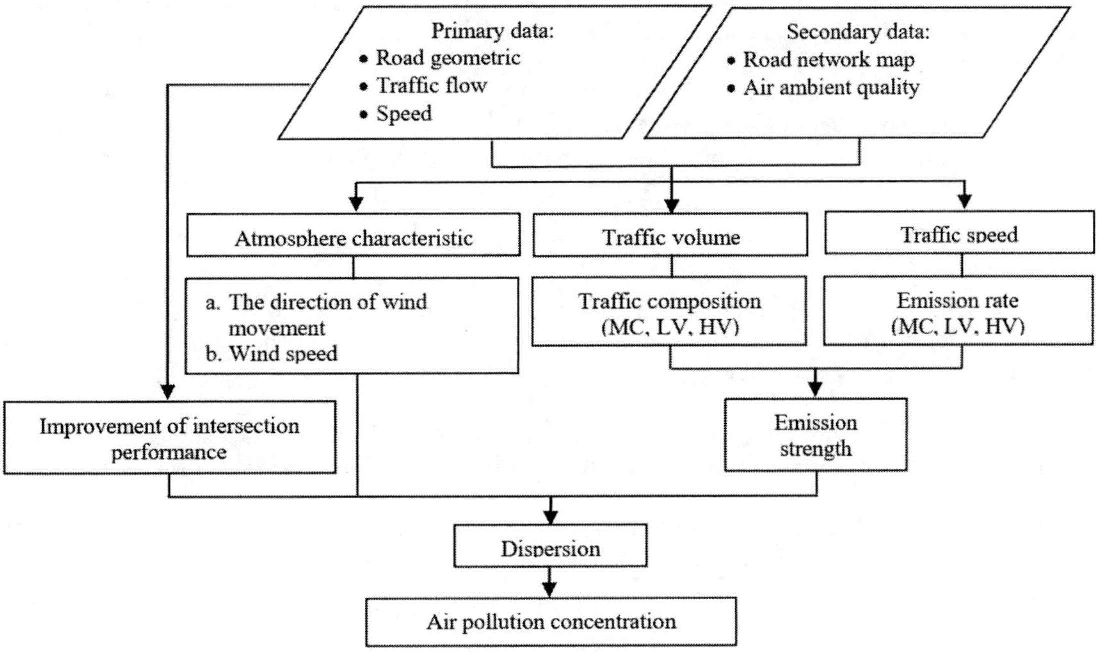

Figure 2. Research framework.

2.2 Assessment of Intersection Performance

The intersection performance especially with traffic signal is identified by analyzing degree of saturation, delays and queue lengths [13], which is calculated as follows:

$$DS = \frac{Q}{C} \quad (1)$$

$$C = \frac{S.g}{c} \quad (2)$$

$$Q_L = \frac{NQ_{max} \cdot 20}{W_{entry}} \quad (3)$$

$$DT_j = c.\frac{0{,}5.(1-GR)^2}{1-GR.DS} + \frac{NQ_1.3600}{C} \quad (4)$$

$$DG_j = (1-P_{SV}).P_T.6 + (P_{SV}.4) \quad (5)$$

$$D_j = DT_j + DG_j \quad (6)$$

$$D = D_j.Q \quad (7)$$

in which *DS* is the degree of saturation, *C* is the capacity (pcu/h), *Q* is the traffic flow (pcu/h), S is the saturation flow (pcu/h of green), *QL* is the queue length (m), NQ_{max} is the total queue (pcu), W_{-entry} is the entry width (m), *c* is the cycle time (s), *GR* the is the green ratio, NQ_1 is the number of queues remaining from the previous green phase (pcu), *Psv* is the proportion of stopped vehicles (%), *PT* is the proportion of vehicles turning at the approaches of intersection (%), *DTj* is the average traffic delay for approach *j* (s/pcu), *DGj* is the average geometric delay for approach *j* (s/pcu), *Dj* is the average delay (s/pcu), D is the total delay (s/pcu), and pcu stands for passenger car unit.

According to the Regulation of the Minister of Transportation [14], level of service (LOS) of intersection is classified into six level, namely LOS A (delay < 5 s/pcu), LOS B (delay: 5 – 15 s/pcu), LOS C (delay: 15 – 25 s/pcu), LOS D (delay: 25 – 40 s/pcu), LOS E (delay: 40 – 60 s/pcu), and LOS F (delay > 60 s/pcu). For intersection on secondary arterial and collector road, the minimum LOS is C.

2.3 Assessment of Emission Flow and Dispersion

Emission flow is estimated for each type of vehicle-based on the average spot speed at the intersection. The emission flow for each air pollutant parameter is analyzed by equations (8) and (9) [15].

$$q_{NOx} = 0.0005\,V^2 - 0.0656\,V + 3.6586 \tag{8}$$

$$q_{CO} = 867.92\,V^{-2.8648} \tag{9}$$

where V is average spot speed (km/h), q is emission flow (g/m).

Emission flow (q) is calculated to determine emission strength (Q) spread by the wind from the emission source to the observation point.

$$Q = n\,x\,q \tag{10}$$

in which Q is emission strength (g/s or g/s.m), n is vehicle volume in a second, q is emission flow (g/m).

Analysis of air pollutant concentrations uses air pollutant data sampling and line source method. These values inform the quality and dispersion of air pollutants [16]:

$$C(x,y,z) = \frac{Q}{\pi\,\mu\,\sigma y\,\sigma z}\left(\frac{-H^2}{2\,\sigma z^2}\right)^{\left(\frac{-y^2}{2\,\sigma y^2}\right)} \tag{11}$$

where C is pollutant concentration (g/m^3), Q is emission strength (g/s), H is the height of emission source (m), (x,y,z) is receptor coordinate (m), z = 1.5 m, y= 0, going straight to the point source, and $\sigma_y \approx 1$.

Improvement of intersection performance takes into account the dispersion of air pollution. This strategy is expected to be the best transport management to solve congestion at the intersection.

3. Results

3.1. Vehicle Speed

Observation of speed of each vehicle type (motorcycle/MC), car and minibus (light vehicle/LV), and bus and truck (heavy vehicle/HV) on each approach during 6 hours are shown in table 1. In general, the lowest speed occurs on the eastern approach at the intersection (D.I. Panjaitan St.).

Table 1. The average spot speed data (km/h).

Approach	MC	LV	HV
West (M.T. Haryono St.)	19.28	17.42	15.99
East (D.I. Panjaitan St.)	17.39	11.84	14.85
North (Soekarno-Hatta St.)	26.34	23.77	20.51

3.2. Traffic Performance at Intersection

From the counting survey on Monday 1 April 2019 at 06.00-12.00 a.m. and Friday 5 April 2019, at 3.00-9.00 p.m., the total traffic volume showed that the highest traffic volume (peak hour volume) occurred on Monday 07.05-08.05 a.m. At peak hours, the highest traffic volumes are 2,267 pcu/h, 1,918 pcu/h, and 33.8 pcu/h, respectively, for motorcycle (MC), light vehicle (LV), and heavy vehicle

(HV). At the intersection, the traffic light is set with a total cycle time of 87 seconds for the two-phase period, total time lost per cycle of 17 seconds, green time for each approach (north, east, and west), 45 seconds, and 25 seconds respectively.

Traffic performance at intersections is determined by road capacity, traffic flow, degree of saturation, delays, and queues. The intersection performance of each approach as a study area can be seen in table 2. The approach from the east side shows relatively poor performance (delay > 40 seconds/pcu). While, at the service levels of western and northern approaches, traffic jam occurs with the degree of saturation > 1, queue length > 1400 m, and delay > 600 s/pcu.

Table 2. Performance of each approach of intersection (existing condition).

Approach/ Approach type	Green phase period	Effective width (We)	Capacity (C)	Saturation flow (S)	Intersection flow ratio (IFR)	Cycle time (c)	Degree of Saturation (DS)	Queue length (Q_L)	Delay (D)
		m	pcu/h	pcu/h		s		m	s/pcu
North/ Protected	2	3.5	1106.44	2139.11	1.00	87	1.44	1417.1	612.78
East/ Opposite	1	6	1088.72	3788.75	0.34	87	0.87	175.00	43.99
West/ Opposite	1	4.2	639.85	2226.67	0.73	87	1.90	1786.7	913.10

At existing conditions, the intersection performances (level of service, LOS) are F, E, and F for North, East, and West approaches, respectively, which refer to unstable traffic flow conditions and congestion (high delay and queue length) [14].

3.3. Dispersion of air pollution at the existing condition

The concentration of each emission parameter is determined for each type of vehicle moving at the intersection. The air pollutant dispersion assessment model uses the line source model because the buildings around the intersection are relatively homogeneous (less than 10 meters). The Building Coverage Ratio (BCR/ ratio of the distance between buildings and width) is less than 0.3.

To calculate the air pollutant dispersion, values of emission flow (q) and emission strength (Q) are required. Calculations of emission flow (q) and emission strength (Q) use the formulas in equation (8), equation (9), and equation (10), which require spot speed and traffic volume for each type of vehicle at each intersection approach. The results are described in table 3 for NOx and table 4 for CO.

Table 3. Assessment of emission flow and emission strength of NOx (existing condition).

Vehicle type	Spot speed	q_{NOx}	Total vehicles		n_{NOx}	Q_{NOx}
	km/h	g/m	veh/h	pcu/s	pcu/s	g/s
MC	30.56	2.12	9,068	0.6297	0.3778	0.801
LV	26.89	2.26	1,918	0.5328	0.4475	1.01
HV	23.2	2.41	26	0.00361	0.0052	0.0126
					Σ Q_{NOx}	**1.82**

Table 4. Assessment of emission flow and emission strength of CO (existing condition).

Vehicle type	Spot speed	q_{CO}	Total vehicles		n_{CO}	Q_{CO}
	km/h	g/m	veh/h	pcu/s	pcu/s	g/s
MC	30.56	0.048	9,068	0.6297	0.3778	0.0182
LV	26.89	0.070	1,918	0.5328	0.4462	0.029
HV	23.2	0.106	26	0.00361	0.0070	0.0007
					Σ Q_{CO}	**0.049**

Emission flow for heavy vehicles has the highest value because of its low speed for both pollutant types, as shown in table 3 and table 4. The number of vehicles is calculated in passenger car unit/pcu per second to obtain the equivalent normalization of the passenger car unit for each air pollution parameter. For NOx parameters, the equivalent values for intermediate cities, such as Malang are 0.6 (MC), 0.84 (LV), and 1.45 (HV), respectively, as seen in table 3, while the equivalent values of CO parameter for MC, LV, and HV are 0.6, 0.8, 1.95, respectively (table 4). The larger total volume in pcu per second will produce a higher value of emission strength (Q). The greatest emission strength is air pollution from light vehicles (LV).

Calculation of pollutant concentration uses a linear source method based on pollutant emission at the intersection approaches. It is an infinite line where pollutants at the observed intersection have the same distance from the roadside with the same concentration. Calculation of pollutant concentration parameters requires the values of emission source height, receptor coordinates, the standard deviation of the Y-axis (σ_y), the Z-axis (σ_z), and the emission strength.

Emission strengths (Q) of NO_x and CO are 1.82 and 0.049 g/s, respectively. Pollutant concentrations for distances of 0, 2.5, 5, 7.5, 10, 20, 40, 80, 160 m from the road median are shown in table 5.

Table 5. NOx and CO concentration (existing condition).

Distance (X) m	C_{NOx} g/m³	C_{CO} g/m³	Distance (X) m	C_{NOx} g/m³	C_{CO} g/m³
0	0.015798	0.000307	20	0.002794	0.000054
2.5	0.012163	0.000237	40	0.000370	0.000007
5	0.009494	0.000185	80	1.13E-06	2.19E-08
7,5	0.008410	0.000164	160	3.59E-15	6.99E-17
10	0.006613	0.000129			

According to the Regulation of Governor of East Java [17], the standard value of C_{NOx} and C_{CO} are 2.26×10^{-3} and 9.25×10^{-6}. Table 5 explains that NOx concentrations are higher than standard values up to 20 m from the road median. The condition means that NOx concentrations still endanger human health on the right of way (ROW). Meanwhile, CO concentration is still below the standard value.

3.4. Assessment of Intersection Performance and Air Pollution Dispersion with Traffic Management

This study also analyses the difference in air pollution concentrations with traffic management to increase intersection performance. Traffic management is regulated by adjusting cycle time, developing road geometry for some approaches of intersection and vehicle movements.

Three alternatives planned are setting traffic lights at the intersection. The first alternative is determined by setting the change of a standard cycle time for the 3-phase period, which is each period for each approach with a total cycle time of 99 seconds for the 3-phase period, total lost time per cycle of 9 seconds, green time in each approach (north, east, and west) of 45, 20 and 25 seconds respectively. The second alternative is set by changing the decent cycle time (2-phase period) with the change of traffic flow and without, while the third alternative is planned by developing road geometry. The second alternative is set up with a total cycle time of 53 seconds for a 2-phase period, total lost time per cycle of 6 seconds, green time for each approach (north and east) of 27 and 20 seconds, respectively. The third alternative is to plan a similar condition of cycle time with the second alternative and two-phase period and widening the entry width of 7 m for the north and west approaches. All movement from the west must turn left for the second and third alternatives.

The first and second alternative is expected to protect the movement of vehicles at each intersection approach and reduce emission parameters. The third alternative is established to protect vehicle movement, improve intersection performance by improving road geometry, and reduce emission parameters.

Table 6. Assessment of intersection performance (the first alternative).

Approach	Green phase period	Effective width (We) m	Capacity (C) pcu/h	Saturation flow (S) pcu/h	Intersection flow ratio (IFR)	Cycle time (c) s	Degree of Saturation (DS)	Queue length (Q_L) m	Delay (D) s/pcu
North	3	3.5	972.32	2139.11	1	99	1.64	2182.86	802.3
East	2	6	765.40	3788.75	0.336	99	1.24	310.00	418.5
West	1	4.2	562.29	2226.67	0.732	99	2.16	2053.33	1045.2

The first alternative causes long queues and delays. This condition cannot be served by adjusting signalization at the intersection. This condition also impacts increasing emission parameters due to motorized vehicles. In this condition, the intersection performance is worse than the existing condition, as indicated by the degree of saturation of more than 1 for all intersection approaches. Queue length of more than 2 km and delay of more than 800 pcu/s for the north and west sides indicate unstable traffic flow conditions and congestion, as seen in table 6. It means the first alternative has not been appropriately realized to accommodate all movements due to additional periods of total phase (3-phase period).

The result of the second alternative can be seen in table 7. Using this scenario, the intersection performance is better to diminish traffic congestion. The delay is less than 25 s/pcu for east and west approaches of intersection, while the north approach has worse performance (delay >500s/pcu and degree saturation in LOS F) [14]. The third alternative is the best alternative to reduce traffic congestion. Queue length is less than 200 m, and delays less than 25 pcu/s refer to stable and fair traffic flow conditions where the operating speed is limited by traffic flow, as shown in table 8. The third alternative is expected to accommodate all movements at the intersection by improving road geometry, such as widening the entry width of the intersection.

Table 7. Assessment of intersection performance (the second alternative).

Approach	Green phase period	Effective width (We) m	Capacity (C) pcu/h	Saturation flow (S) pcu/h	Intersection flow ratio (IFR)	Cycle time (c) s	Degree of Saturation (DS)	Queue length (Q_L) m	Delay (D) s/pcu
North	2	3.5	972.32	2139.11	1	53	1.38	262.86	544.38
East	1	6	765.40	3788.75	0.336	53	0.63	140.00	24.34
West	1	4.2	562.29	2226.67	0.732	53	0.55	120	10.94

Table 8. Assessment of intersection performance (the third alternative).

Approach	Green phase period	Effective width (We) m	Capacity (C) pcu/h	Saturation flow (S) pcu/h	Intersection flow ratio (IFR)	Cycle time (c) s	Degree of Saturation (DS)	Queue length (Q_L) m	Delay (D) s/pcu
North	2	7	2310.24	4278.23	1	53	0.69	131.43	21.15
East	1	6	1515.50	3788.75	0.671	53	0.63	140.00	24.34
West	1	7	3711.12	3711.12	0.878	53	0.33	51.43	9.20

The three-phase period at the intersection (first alternative) results in low vehicle speeds of 21 km/h (MC), 18.68 km/h (LV), and 16.11 km/h (HV), respectively (see table 9 and table 10). With low vehicle speed passing at intersections, exhaust emissions are higher than the existing conditions.

Table 9. Assessment of emission flow and emission strength of NOx for all alternatives (scenarios).

Vehicle type	Existing Condition				First Alternative				Second Alternative			
	Spot speed km/h	q_{NOx} g/m	n_{NOx} pcu/s	Q_{NOx} g/s	Spot speed km/h	q_{NOx} g/m	n_{NOx} pcu/s	Q_{NOx} g/s	Spot speed km/h	q_{NOx} g/m	n_{NOx} pcu/s	Q_{NOx} g/s
MC	30.56	2.12	0.3778	0.801	21	2.5	0.3778	0.945	32.8	2.05	0.3023	0.618
LV	26.89	2.26	0.4475	1.01	18.68	2.61	0.4475	1.167	30.5	2.12	0.3580	0.760
HV	23.2	2.41	0.0052	0.0126	16.11	2.73	0.0052	0.0014	24.4	2.36	0.00419	0.01
			ΣQ_{NOx}	**1.82**			**ΣQ_{NOx}**	**2.13**			**ΣQ_{NOx}**	**1.39**

Vehicle type	Third alternative			
	Spot speed km/h	q_{NOx} g/m	n_{NOx} pcu/s	Q_{NOx} g/s
MC	40	1.83	0.2645	0.485
LV	40	1.83	0.31327	0.575
HV	30	2.14	0.00367	0.008
			ΣQ_{NOx}	**1.07**

Table 10. Assessment of emission flow and emission strength of CO for all scenarios

Vehicle type	Existing Condition				First Alternative				Second Alternative			
	Spot speed km/h	q_{CO} g/m	n_{CO} pcu/s	Q_{CO} g/s	Spot speed km/h	q_{CO} g/m	n_{CO} pcu/s	Q_{CO} g/s	Spot speed km/h	q_{CO} g/m	n_{CO} pcu/s	Q_{CO} g/s
MC	30.56	0.141	0.3778	0.0182	21	0.141	0.3778	0.053	32.8	0.04	0.3023	0.012
LV	26.89	0.198	0.4462	0.029	18.68	0.198	0.4462	0.084	30.5	0.049	0.3580	0.017
HV	23.2	0.302	0.0070	0.0007	16.11	0.302	0.0070	0.0021	24.4	0.092	0.004189	0.0005
			ΣQ_{CO}	**0.049**			**ΣQ_{CO}**	**0.14**			**ΣQ_{CO}**	**0.029**

Vehicle type	Third alternative			
	Spot speed km/h	q_{CO} g/m	n_{CO} pcu/s	Q_{CO} g/s
MC	40	0.022	0.2645	0.006
LV	40	0.022	0.2984	0.007
HV	30	0.051	0.004937	0.0003
			ΣQ_{CO}	**0.013**

These speeds produce q_{NOx} of 2.5, 2.61, 2.73 g/m, and q_{CO} of 0.141, 0.198, 0.302 g/m, respectively for MC, LV, and HV, as described in table 9 and table 10. This condition leads to an increase in emission concentrations. Using equation (11), the concentration of NOx and CO from the road median to the end of the road increases as follows: C_{NOx} ±41% and C_{CO} ±70.7%, compared to the existing condition. This means that the first alternative could not improve intersection performance and reduce emission parameters.

The second alternative with a two-phase period arrangement for the north and east approaches the intersection, and the vehicle's movement from the west approaches directly to the left. The setting of a two-phase period at the intersection results in low vehicle speeds of 32.8 km/h (MC), 30.5 km/h (LV), and 24.4 km/h (HV), respectively (see table 9 and table 10). With higher vehicle speed passing at intersections than the first alternative, exhaust emissions are lower than the existing conditions. These speeds produce q_{NOx} of 2.05, 2.12, 2.36 g/m, and q_{CO} of 0.04, 0.049, 0.092 g/m, respectively for MC, LV, and HV, as described in table 9 and table 10. This condition leads to a reduction in emission concentrations. Using equation (11), the concentration of NOx and CO from the road median to the end of the road is reduced as follows: C_{NOx} ±26% and C_{CO} ±43.8%, compared to the existing condition.

The third alternative is similar to the second alternative and the additional entry width for the north approach (7 m), which will accelerate vehicle speed. The speed assumptions for the third alternative are 40 km/h (MC), 40 km/h (LV), and 30 km/h (HV). At intersections, vehicles moving at high speed produce lower exhaust emissions than the existing conditions. The results are $qNOx$ of 1.83, 1.83, 2.14 g/m, and qCO of 0.022, 0.022, 0.051 g/m respectively for MC, LV, and HV as described in table 9 for NOx and table 10 for CO.

As explained in table 9 and table 10, the emission strength decreases emission concentration parameters, using equation (11). The concentration of NOx and CO from the road median to the end of the road are decreased as follows: C_{NOx} ±37.4% and C_{CO} ±61.3%, compared to the existing condition. Therefore, the third alternative is the best scheme to recommend minimizing congestion at the intersection and reducing emission parameters for NOx and CO. The third alternative can reduce queue length up to ± 60% of traffic volume and improve air quality up to ±50%. These results are in line with the study recommendation of Badami [8] that considers road capacity and management of transport systems to minimize air pollution and other transport impacts.

Table 9 and table 10 inform that the exhaust emissions of motorcycle (MC) and light vehicle (LV) are higher than other types of vehicles. Therefore, intersection conditions and geometry should be planned to increase the MC and LV speed.

4. Conclusions

The existing condition informs that the degree of saturation for the north, east, and west intersection approaches are 1.44, 0.87, and 1.9, respectively, identifying the LOS F, D, and F. The first alternative performance is LOS F for all approaches indicating unstable traffic flow conditions and traffic jams. With the modification of the two-phase period, the second alternative can improve the performance of east and west approaches of the intersection. The arrangement of the third alternative with the same conditions as the second alternative and widening the entry width of the road can significantly improve the performance of the intersection. The degree of saturation at the intersection decreases to 0.69, 0.63, and 0.33 for the north, east, and west approaches, indicating excellent and stable conditions.

From the results of air pollutant dispersion in the existing condition, the concentration of CO from the road median to the end of the road and 80 m from the road median is approximately 0.000354 g/m^3-1.899 g/m^3 below the quality standard. NOx concentrations range from 0.000679 g/m^3 to 0.0000429 g/m^3, higher than the standard value. At a distance of 40 meters from the road median, NOx has concentrations below the expected value.

The concentration of air pollutant parameters with the first alternative, C_{NOx} and C_{CO} will increase ±41% and ±70.7%, respectively, compared to the existing condition from the median to the end of the road (right of way/ROW). In comparison, the second alternative, set by planning a two-phase period, will decrease the emission concentration to C_{NOx} ±26% and C_{CO} ±43,8% from the road median to the end of the road. The third alternative is the same as the second alternative, and widening the entry width of the north approach of intersection and all vehicle movements from the west approach directly to the left will reduce emission concentration to C_{NOx} ±37.4% and C_{CO} ±61.3% from the road median to the end of the road. The second alternative is a better scheme to minimize congestion and improve traffic performance at the intersection and air pollutant concentration of CO and NOx.

In the long term, intersection performance can be improved by controlling the number of motorcycles and private cars and improving the performance of public transportation.

Acknowledgments
We would like to thank Mr. Hendi Bowoputro, Assistant Professor of the Department of Civil Engineering, Brawijaya University, for his assistance in collecting and processing data.

References

[1] Thomas L and Cousins W 1996 *The Compact City: A Sustainable Urban Form?,* ed Jenks M, Burton E and Williams K (Oxford: Oxford Brookes University) p 224

[2] Syahril S, Resosudarmo B P, and Tomo H S 2002 *Study on Air Quality in Jakarta, Indonesia: Future Trends, Health Impacts, Economic Value, and Policy Options* (Jakarta: Asian Development Bank)

[3] Armijaya H 2000 Application of environmental capacity in measurement highway capacity in Indonesia, *Proceeding of FSTPT III* (Yogyakarta: Universitas Gajahmada)

[4] Tang J, McNabola A and Misstear B 2020 The potential impacts of different traffic management strategies on air pollution and public health for a more sustainable city: a modeling case study from Dublin, Ireland, *Sustainable Cities and Society* (Amsterdam: Elsevier)

[5] Ambarwati L and Indriastuti A K 2019 Improvement of public transport to minimize air pollution in urban sprawl, *International Journal of Geomate* (Mie, Japan: The Geomate International Society), **17**, pp 43–50

[6] Ambarwati L, Verhaeghe R, van Arem B, Pel AJ 2016 The influence of integrated space-transport development strategies on air pollution in urban areas. *Transp. Res. Part D: Transp. Environ.* (USA: Elsevier) **44**, pp 134–46

[7] Nejadkoorki F, Nicholson K, Lake I, and Davies T 2008 An approach for modeling CO2 emissions from road traffic in urban areas. *Sci. Total Environ.* (Amsterdam: Elsevier), **406,** no 1-2, pp 269–78

[8] Badami M, Millo F and D'amato D D 2001 Experimental investigation on soot and NOx formation in a DI common rail diesel engine with pilot injection, *SAE Transactions* (New York: JSTOR), pp 663–74

[9] Badami M 2005 Transport and urban air pollution in India, *Environmental Management* (Switzerland: Springer Science+Business Media, Inc) **36**, No. 2, pp. 195–204

[10] Xia T et al. 2015 Traffic-related air pollution and health co-benefits of alternative transport in Adelaide, South Australia, *Environment International* (Amsterdam: Elsevier), **74**, pp 281–90

[11] Keuken M P, Jonkers S, Verhagen H L M, Perez L, Trüeb S, Okkerse W J and Sabel C E 2014 Impact on air quality of measures to reduce CO2 emissions from road traffic in Basel, Rotterdam, Xi'an and Suzhou. A*tmospheric Environment* (Amsterdam: Elsevier), **98**, pp 434–41

[12] Statistics Bureau of Malang City 2017 *The Figures of Malang City* (Malang: Statistic Bureau of Malang City)

[13] Directorate General of Highway 1997 Indonesian Highway Capacity Manual (Jakarta: Department of Public Works of Republic of Indonesia)

[14] Directorate General of Land Transportation 2015 Regulation of the Minister of Transportation of the Republic of Indonesia no PM 96/2015 about Guideline for Traffic Management and Traffic Engineering Implementation (Jakarta: Department of Transportation of Republic of Indonesia)

[15] Directorate General of Highway 1999 Technical Guideline no.017/T/BM/1999 about Procedure for Prediction of Micro-scale Air Pollution from Traffic, *Technical Report* (Jakarta: Department of Public Work of Republic Indonesia)

[16] Turner D B, 1969 *Workbook of Atmospheric Dispersion Estimates* (Florida: CRC Press)

[17] East Java Provincial Government 2009 Regulation of the Governor of East Java no 10/2009 about Ambient Air Quality Standards and Immediate Source Emissions in East Java (Surabaya: Regional Secretariat of East Java Province)

IOP Conf. Series: Earth and Environmental Science 1000 (2022) 012018 doi:10.1088/1755-1315/1000/1/012018

Test of mindful motorcycling as a psychological intervention to increase awareness of riding

M P Dewi [1,2], **M I Sulthoni**[1,3], **B C Puspitaningrum** [1,4] **A N Kusumastuti** [1,5] **A Marissa**[1,6] **H Prabowo**[1,7]
Faculty of Psychology, Gunadarma University, Depok, West Java Indonesia[1]

mahargyantari@staff.gunadarma.ac.id[2]
ihsan.sulthony@gmail.com[3]
bellacintia@staff.gunadarma.ac.id[4]
astri@staff.gunadarma.ac.id[5]
aski@staff.gunadarma.ac.id[6]
hendroprabowo@staff.gunadarma.ac.id[7]

Abstract. The purpose of this study was to test mindful motorcycling interventions to raise awareness of driving on motorcyclists. Mixed method research is conducted with qualitative research followed by quantitative experiment research. Both of these methods result in increased awareness in motorcyclists.

Keywords – Mindfulness, Awareness, Motorcyclist.

1. Introduction

About 200 million motorcycles, including mopeds, motor scooters, motorized bicycles, and other powered two and three-wheelers, are in use worldwide or about 33 motorcycles per 1000 people [1]. Indonesia is in the top five or fourth in the world category, after India, China, and Japan [2]. In 2018 Indonesia was the first number of motorcycles in ASEAN with 106.6 million followed by Vietnam (58.1 million), Thailand (21 million), and Malaysia (13.7 million) [3].

In the COVID-19 era, the global motorcycles market was dropped 14% or losing 9 million units from the previous year in 2020 [4]. This decrease in the number of global motorcycles did not occur in Indonesia, wherein in 2020 the number of motorcycles reached 136 million [5] or increased compared to the previous two years, in 2018 (106 million) and 2019 (112 million) [6]. The number of motorcycles is 136 million is equal to 50% of the population of 266.9 million in 2019 [7]. One consequence of the increase in the number of these motorcycles is the number of traffic accidents [8]. According To Naci, Chisholm, and Baker, about 180,000 and more motorcycle riders were killed in road crashes each year around the world [9]. Table 1 below is data on the increase in the number of accidents, in general, included four- or two-wheeled vehicles, in Indonesia 2017-2019 [10].

According to Kirono [11], motorcycles are the biggest contributor to traffic accidents (64%). Every month there are at least 7,000 traffic accidents. Kirono [11] also details some of the deviant behavior of motorcycle users in Indonesia: do not use a helmet, no discipline on the left lane, go against the flow, use the pedestrian bridge, speeding and using an open tub (three-wheeled motorcycle). Similarly, Sundari [12] added that the deviant behavior in adolescents is to cut markers in the form of solid white lines, riding without a helmet, and running red lights.

Table 1. Number of Accidents and Killed, 2017-2019

	2017	2018	2019
Number of Accident (Case)	104,327	109,215	116,411
Number of Killed (Person)	30,694	29,472	25,671

Source: BPS-Statistics Indonesia [10]

Suraji, Cakrawala, Tjahjono and Effendy [13] found several indicators of human factors in motorcycle accidents, namely lack of discipline, speed, emotions, and lack of concentration. Meanwhile, Marsaid, Hidayat, and Ahsan [14] found human factors in motorcycle accidents that are disorderly, high speed, tired, sleepy, careless, and unskilled. Similarly, Watson, Tunnicliff, White, Schonfeld, and Wishart [15] also found that human factors which contribute to many crashes are excessive speed for the conditions, the presence of alcohol and/or other drugs, as well as decision, perception, and/or handling errors. Watson et al. [15] added that young people are generally more likely to speed and engage in risk-taking behavior than older people and this is particularly true for young males. University students as young people tend to exhibit various forms of reckless behavior, characterized by sensation-seeking and risk-taking. Risk perception, risk-taking, and crash involvement among young people rider, particularly males, has received considerable research attention [16]. So, a human factor is an important thing to study; even though the rider is the main actor in the driving activity, riding is not an isolated activity. It takes place in a wider context in which the driver constantly interacts with his or her immediate environment and the vehicle [17].

To prevent road traffic deaths and injuries, WHO [18] recommends some interventions such as managing speed, reducing drink-driving, increasing motorcycle helmet use, increasing seat-belt use, increasing child restraint use, reducing distracted driving, and reducing drug-driving. Porchia, Baldasseroni, Dellisanti, Lorini, and Bonaccorsi assess the effectiveness of two interventions to prevent road traffic accidents: the introduction of graduated driver licensing (GDL) and the interventions to improve pedestrian and cyclist visibility. They find that both of the intervention seems to be effective, but needed to measure long-term effects in further examinations [19].

Young, Koppel, Stephens, Osborne, Chambers, and Hassed recommend a mindfulness intervention that potentially reduces driver engagement in multiple distracting activities. [20]. And then, Prabowo, Sulthoni, and Dewi [21] developed a community intervention called Mindful Motorcycling. This program is based on means that mindfulness means paying attention in a particular way: on purpose, in the present moment, and nonjudgmentally [22]. The purpose of this program is to improve safety riding on motorcyclists [21].

Initially, mindfulness was developed by Jon Kabat-Zinn in 1979, called MBSR (mindfulness-based stress reduction) program at Massachusetts university to treat the chronically ill [23]. Programs based on MBSR and similar models have been widely adopted in schools, prisons, hospitals, veterans' centers, and other environments [24].

The definitions themselves were then developed by other scholars. Mindfulness means paying attention in a particular way: on purpose, in the present moment, and nonjudgmentally [22]. The short definition of mindfulness is (1) awareness, (2) of present experience, (3) with acceptance [25]. Hahn [26] defined mindfulness as keeping one's consciousness alive to the present reality. Germer [27] defined mindfulness as an awareness of present experience with acceptance. From some of the definitions above, it can be concluded that mindfulness is related to awareness, paying attention, present moment, acceptance, and nonjudgmentally. In its development, mindfulness also can be applied in daily activities such as mindful eating (eg. Jordan et al [28]), mindful walking (eg. Teut et al. [29]), mindful workplace [30], and mindful driving (eg. [31]).

There are several research results, discussions, and recommendations from scholars which point to the importance of mindfulness for the motorcyclist, with sometimes different terms but with similar meanings, although these studies lead more to drive a car. From a personality trait perspective, conscientiousness or carefulness has a stronger direct effect on the driving behavior and accident risk (eg. [32], [3]), relation of lower conscientiousness and violation (eg. Miles & Johnson [34]). On the contrary, Kerr [35] proposed a new term "the driving without attention mode". He sees the main characteristic of this state as the loss of awareness due to automatizing processes of perception induced by a highly predictable visual scene. Brown [36] uses a descriptive definition of what he calls "driving without awareness" which assumes that drivers are oblivious to impending collisions.

Driving is a multitasking activity that requires drivers to manage their attention between various driving and non-driving-related tasks. For instance, during driving, a driver not only focuses his or her attention on the driving task but at the same time is aware of what is happening around them. This involves making a judgment about other road users' actions so that they can anticipate happenings on the road [31]. This is an inattention phenomenon, have some similarity to an individual with less mindful, or demonstrating mindlessness. According to Brown and Ryan [37], a "mindless" person tends to be less attentive and aware of the present moment. Langer added: "When in a mindless state, an individual operates much like a robot; thoughts, emotions, and behaviors (hereafter just behaviors) are determined by 'programmed' routines based on distinctions and associations learned in the past" [38]. In driving, Segal, Teasdale, and Williams [39] added that when driving on a familiar route, of suddenly realizing that one has been driving for miles "on automatic pilot," unaware of the road or other vehicles, preoccupied with planning future activities or ruminating on a current concern. Contrary, mindful driving is associated with being fully in the present moment, consciously aware of sights, sounds, thoughts, smell, and body sen4sations as they arise.

Kass and VanWormer [40] found that mindfulness and concentration levels were both significantly related to situation awareness for driving. Mindfulness training also has a high impact on actual driving performance over time by improving drivers' awareness of their environment and enabling them to block out distractions and quickly identify hazards. From a total of 309 drivers who responded via an online questionnaire, Stephens, Koppel, Young, Chambers, and Hassed [41] found that mindfulness had negative relationships with driving anger and aggressive driving.

Some of the findings and arguments above, in fact, are for car drivers. Even though there are differences between car drivers and motorcycle riders. Motorcycles and cars may share the road, but riding a motorcycle and driving a car are very different experiences. Driving often is more destination-oriented, while riding can be a full-sensory experience in itself. Every time a rider gets on a motorcycle, the motorcyclist needs to channel different kinds of focus and concentration [42]. Shahar, Poulter, Clarke, and Crundall [43] made an experiment and found that real-life riders however reported the scenarios as more dangerous than real-life drivers, suggesting that their specific motorcycle experience influenced their criterion for danger.

2. Methods

This research was conducted during lecture hours on campus and involved several post-graduate psychology students. This research is mixed methods research, a study combining both qualitative and quantitative aspects to understand the phenomenon [44]. A mixed-method study also incorporates both qualitative and quantitative methods of data collection and analysis in a single study. This study enables a policy researcher to understand complex phenomena qualitatively as well as to explain the phenomena through numbers, charts, and basic statistical analyses [45].

According to Palinkas, Aarons, Horwitz, Chamberlain, Hurlburt, and Landsverk, there are three elements namely structure, function, and process. From the structure of the element, this research is categorized into qual → QUAN, a sequential collection, and analysis of mixed methods, starting with qualitative data, for the primary purpose of hypothesis testing. From the function of the element, the study is a convergence that uses both types of methods to answer the same question, either through comparison of results to test whether they reach the same conclusion (triangulation). In the process of elements, this research is included in the embed, namely conducting complementary research, a qualitative study of the implementation process embedded in experimental research [46].

2.1. Qualitative Research

The purpose of this study was to qualitatively describe the participants' experience after practicing Mindful Motorcycling intervention. Participants in the qualitative research involved 26 psychology students (9 doctoral students and 17 master students) of Gunadarma University and a motorcyclist. Before the study, the researchers developed a script in a written manner that is a mindfulness intervention for motorcyclists to increase awareness of riding.

Here are the stages of the intervention.

First, a participant gets psychoeducation in the form of a lecture about mindful motorcycling to promote safe riding. Psychoeducation consists of definitions of mindfulness and mindlessness, and how to improve motorcyclists to be more mindful.

Second, participants were asked to listen to Mindful Motorcycling's instructions which were also a trial for the authors. The script contains mindful riding instructions (which are based on the concept of the present moment and non-judgmental), which begin with turning on the motorcycle engine from home, then driving consciously on the road, and the ends with arriving at the destination of campus. During the instruction, the participants only imagine when riding a motorcycle in the class. In this phase, Mindful Motorcycling scripts were also developed based on input from participants.

Third, the participants are asked to do Mindful Motorcycling, a kind of 'waking meditation' based on the instruction the next day. They start to ride motorcycles from home, then ride on the streets and end up on campus; all of this is done mindfully. After arriving at campus, they were asked to write down their experiences in riding.

Data derived from notes for motorcyclists are analyzed qualitatively with thematic analysis. Thematic analysis (TA) is a method to identify, organize and provide information about thematic patterns in a data set systematically. By focusing on the meaning of a data set, TA enables the researcher to see and understand collective or shared meanings and experiences.

Identifying unique and idiosyncratic themes and experiences that can only be found in a single piece of data is not the focus of TA. Therefore, this method is a way to identify and understand the similarities in the way a topic is spoken or written [47].

2.2. Quantitative Experimental Research

The research experiments to test Mindful Motorcycling interventions to raise awareness of riding. Mindful Motorcycling is an intervention program developed by Prabowo, Dewi, and Sulthoni [21], to be given to motorcyclists, to increase awareness of riding. This intervention has five sessions: Mindful Motorcycling Psychoeducation, Deep Breathing Exercises, Mindful Eating Exercises, Mindful Motorcycling Exercises, and Mindful Motorcycling Feedback. Meanwhile, awareness of riding is a state of awareness in the motorcyclist and focus attention on the goals that occur based on his experience present in certain situations, as well as focusing attention in a certain way such as the current goal, and without judging. Researchers used a 15-item MAAS (mindful attention awareness scale) to measure awareness of driving on a motorcyclist from Brown and Ryan that had been modified. This scale has a 6-point scale was 1=*almost always,* 2=*very frequently,* 3=*somewhat frequently,* 4=*somewhat infrequently,* 5=*very infrequently,* and 6=*almost never* [37]. The reliability of this scale is obtained Alpha coefficient as wide as 0.948.

This experimental study uses Single Case ABA Design. This design has three phases, namely baseline (initial condition), treatment (intervention), and baseline (final condition) [48]. The participant of this study is a motorcyclist, D (initial name), male, a master student of psychology, and has been willing to participate in research activities for ten days. Data collected from measurements through a MAAS scale consists of 4 data in the baseline phase (initial condition), 3 data in the treatment phase (intervention), and 3 data in the baseline phase (final condition).

The experimental procedure consists of three phases. In *Baseline Phase I,* participants are required to fill the MAAS for four consecutive days, to obtain a relatively stable score. In the *Intervention Phase,* participants received Mindful Motorcycling Psychoeducation and Deep Breathing Exercises interventions on the first day of the intervention phase. Then, continued with the intervention of Mindful Eating Exercises and Mindful Motorcycling Exercises on the second day of the intervention phase and the Intervention of Mindful Motorcycling Feedback on the third day of the intervention phase. During the three-day phase of this intervention, participants remained measured with MAAS. In the *Baseline Phase II,* participants were asked to fill out MAAS for three consecutive days without any intervention. The experiment was conducted on campus and during the experiment, a participant was asked to ride his motorcycles, from home to campus and from campus to home, for 10 days. A participant was also asked to practice Mindful Motorcycling when riding his motorcycle, especially in the intervention phase. Data from ten days of MAAS score analyzed with visual analysis with the aspect of average [48], trend, variability, and immediate effect [49]. Interviews about the riding experience were also conducted with participants after the experiment was completed.

3. Results

3.1. Results: Qualitative Research

The experience of students after doing Mindful Motorcycling, in fact, they have a variety of features. When practicing mindful motorcycling meditation in class, two students recognized themselves immediately as a type of step on the gas (*tancap gas*) and a red light hater on the traffic light. Five features with some experience after the student write down their experiences are presented below.

1. *Present moment*: e.g. no need to hurry, awareness of speed of the motorcycle which slowed down to 20 km/h, and feeling anxious because it is late but then can accept.
2. *From judgmental to nonjudgmental*: e.g. traffic light makes upset and then becomes neutral, from "oh red light again" to "oh yes it's a red light, just wait". When riding on the highway there is a public transportation that stops suddenly, so it is possible for only a shortstop, and continue the journey without blaming the public transportation driver.
3. *Beginner's mind*: e.g. feels like a new environment, apparently some buildings have been ignored, feeling driving with a motorcycle is more than tired, it turns out that the road is quite far and there are potholes.
4. *From mindlessness to mindfulness*: e.g. realize driving while listening to music is not mindful; awareness that riding a motorcycle without safety equipment, such as helmets, jackets, shoes, makes the rider not mindful.
5. *Sensations*:
   a. Hearing: hear the sound of the horn, hear the sound of animals (goats, birds, and cows), feel the sound of the motor brake when it stops.
   b. Touch and kinesthetic: feel the heat of the motor engine, feel the vibration of the motor engine, feel the wind on the face, feel the soft seat, and feel the sweat on the back, feel the heat of the sun, feel the wet clothes exposed to rain, and feel the dust that comes alive.
   c. Smelling: the smell of car perfume, the smell of vehicle smoke, the smell of vehicle fumes, and the smell of food when passing food stalls.

3.2. Results: Quantitative Experimental Research

The results of visual analysis are presented in the image below.

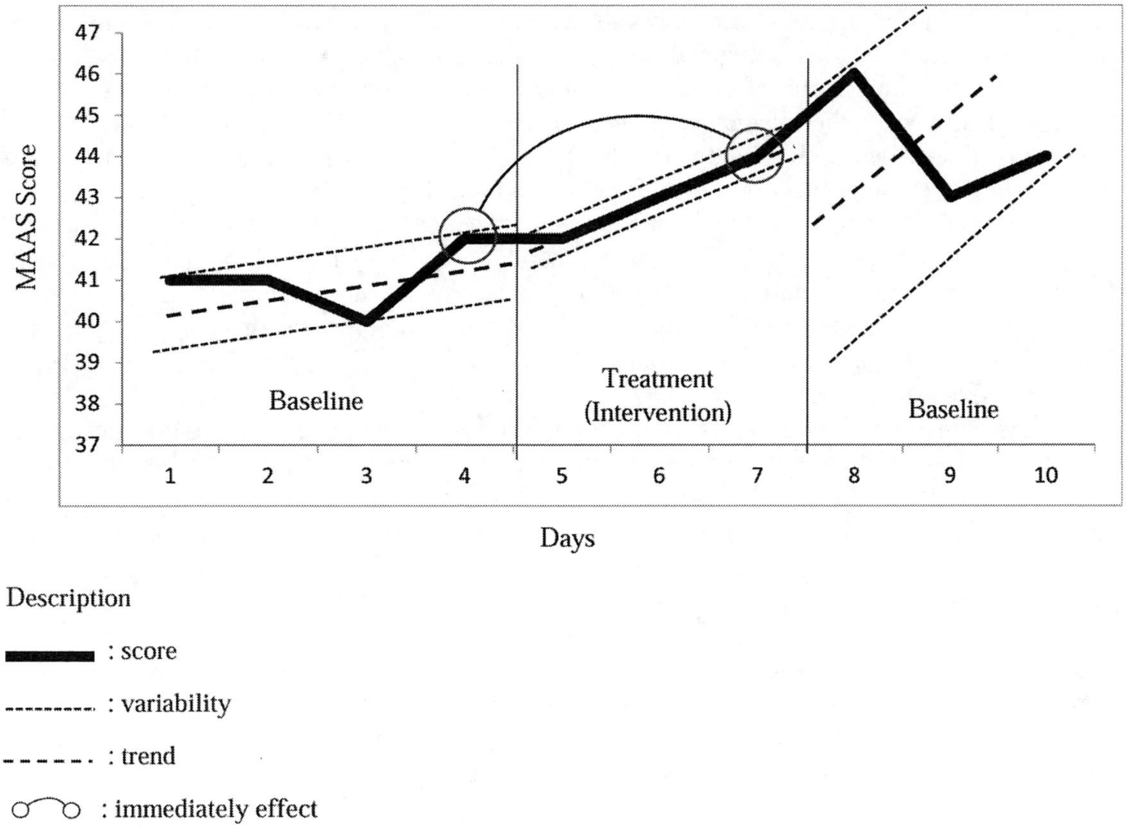

Figure 1. Visual Analysis

Based on visual analysis, there is a tendency to increase the average between phases, where the baseline phase I (Mean=41), followed by the treatment phase (Mean=43) and the baseline phase II (Mean=47). Based on variability and trend, there is an increase from baseline phase I to treatment phase, and there is a decrease from treatment phase to baseline phase II. Aspects of immediate effect were found on the fourth day of baseline phase I to the third day of the treatment phase. All aspects of this analysis showed an increased tendency to riding awareness in participants.

The interview after the experiment showed that the way D ride is not mindful so he had an accident that caused him only to focus on the destination with late conditions. After the intervention, D felt more relaxed and surrendered whatever happened during the trip. D also became more attentive to the situation on the street by seeing the changes of each building along the way.

4. Discussion

This research is preliminary in the form of developing mindful motorcycling manuscripts, then tested into simple field experiments on several students. In both of the methods, there is increased awareness in motorcyclists after getting Mindful Motorcycling intervention However, the results generally support Kabat-Zinn's [22] proposal on attitudes as the foundation of mindfulness being, especially present moment, nonjudgmental, and beginner's mind. Specifically, the results of this study also support the opinion of Segal, Teasdale, and Williams [39] that "mindful driving" is associated with being fully present in the present moment, consciously aware of sights, sounds, thoughts, smells, and body sensations as they arise.

This research focuses more on mindful riding (for motorcycles) whose scientific literature is still scarce because most studies focus more on mindful driving (for cars). Some of the results of previous studies below are about mindful driving which is used to discuss mindful riding. There are two aspects of mindfulness related to mindfulness in driving, mindfulness as a trait and mindfulness as a treatment or intervention. As a trait, mindfulness is a construct that may aid understanding of the relationship between drivers' intentions and behavior [31]. Mindfulness trait is associated with decreased engagement in problematic driving behaviors including errors, lapses, willful violations of road rules, aggressive driving, and phone use. Mindfulness is also associated with reduced anxious driving behaviors and reduced negative thoughts while driving [50].

As a treatment, mindfulness training may greatly impact actual driving performance over time by improving drivers' awareness of their environment and enabling them to block out distractions ([40]; [52]) and to quickly identify hazards [40]. Mindfulness also has a role in helping to explain speeding behavior in school zones [31]. Abdul Hanan [51] found that mindfulness, a construct rarely used in road safety before, directly influenced Australian drivers' intention to comply, while habit influenced intention to comply in Malaysia. Mindfulness was also negatively related to each self-reported aberrant driving behavior, with the strongest relationships being between mindfulness meditation and driving-related lapses and errors. Participants who practice mindfulness meditation had significantly fewer crashes in the past two years and reported significantly fewer driving-related violations and lapses compared to participants who did not practice mindfulness meditation [52].

The results of this study support Reynaud and Navarro [53] who found that one session of mindfulness meditation practices can have a positive influence on driving performance. Or Koppel et al. [54] found that mindfulness-based intervention can improve road safety through meta-analysis study.

5. Recommendation

Mindful Motorcycling interventions can increase motorcyclist awareness in a university setting. We recommend developing these interventions in communities other than students in the university such as employees or police. For further research is recommended to research with similar interventions on four-wheeled vehicles.

References

[1] Adachi, S 2006 Fuel cell-powered motorcycles *Journal-Society of Automotive Engineers of Japan.* ***60*(1)** p 90-93
[2] Worldmapper. (2002). Discover the new world mapper. http://archive.worldmapper.org/display.php?selected=31
[3] ASEAN Stats. Total number of registered motorcycles (in thousand). https://data.aseanstats.org/indicator/ASE.TRP.ROD.B.011

[4] MCD Team. Global Motorcycles Market lost 9 million sales in 2020. https://www.motorcyclesdata.com/2021/04/08/world-motorcycles-market/

[5] Jumlah Kendaraan Bermotor Menurut Provinsi dan Jenis Kendaraan (unit), 2020 https://www.bps.go.id/indikator/indikator/view_data_pub/0000/api_pub/V2w4dFkwdFNLNU5mSE95Und2UDRMQT09/da_10/1

[6] BPS-Statistics Indonesia 2020 Perkembangan Jumlah Kendaraan Bermotor Menurut Jenis (Unit), 2017-2019. https://www.bps.go.id/indicator/17/57/1/jumlah-kendaraan-bermotor.html

[7] BPS-Statistics Indonesia 2019 (Statistik Indonesia 2019)

[8] Narelle Haworth & Peter Rowden 2012. Applicability of Learner Driver Research to Learner Motorcyclists. In Lisa Dorn & Mark Sullman. (Eds.). *Advances in traffic psychology: Human factors in road and rail transport* (Ashgate Publishing Limited, Surrey)

[9] Naci, H, Chisholm, D, Baker, T.D 2009 Distribution of road traffic deaths by road user group: A global comparison. *Injury Prevention,* **15** p 55–9

[10] BPS-Statistics Indonesia. 2020 (Land Transportation Statistics 2019)

[11] Kirono, C 2013 Mewujudkan keselamatan jalan oleh pengendara sepeda motor melalui pembenahan di sektor hilir. Kakorlantas Polri. Retrieved from: http://www.aisi.or.id/fileadmin/user_upload/Download/03.Kakorlantas.pdf

[12] Sundari, N. P 2009 *Perilaku pengendara sepeda motor pada remaja terhadap risiko kecelakaan lalu lintas* (Thesis, Universitas Airlangga)

[13] Suraji, A, Cakrawala, M, Tjahjono, N, Effendy, S. B 2010 Indikator faktor manusia terhadap kecelakaan sepeda motor. *Jurnal Transportasi,* ***10*(2)** p 125-134

[14] Marsaid, M., Hidayat, M., & Ahsan, A 2013 Faktor yang berhubungan dengan kejadian kecelakaan lalu lintas pada pengendara sepeda motor di wilayah Polres Kabupaten Malang *Jurnal Ilmu Keperawatan,* **1(2)** p 98-112

[15] Watson, B. C, Tunnicliff, D. J, White, K. M, Schonfeld, C. C, & Wishart, D. E 2007 *Psychological and social factors influencing, motorcycle rider intentions and behaviour. Centre for Accident Research and Road Safety (CARRS-Q)* (Queensland University of Technology)

[16] Glendon, A.I 2011 Neuroscience and young drivers. In B.E. Porter. (Ed.). *Handbook of traffic psychology* (London: Academic Press) Chapter 9 p 109 – 125

[17] Oppenheim, I., & Shinar, D 2011 Human factors and ergonomics. In B.E. Porter. (Ed.). *Handbook of traffic psychology* (London: Academic Press) Chapter 15 p 193 - 211

[18] WHO 2018 Global status report on road safety 2018 (Geneva : World Health Organization)

[19] Porchia, B. R., Baldasseroni, A., Dellisanti, C., Lorini, C., & Bonaccorsi, G 2014 Effectiveness of two interventions in preventing traffic accidents: a systematic review. *Ann Ig,* **26(1)** p 63-75

[20] Young, K. L., Koppel, S., Stephens, A. N., Osborne, R., Chambers, R., & Hassed, C 2019 Mindfulness predicts driver engagement in distracting activities. *Mindfulness* **10(5)** p 913-922

[21] Prabowo, H., Sulthoni, M. I., & Dewi, M. P 2020 The Meaning of Membership in Motorcycle Community in the Campus. In *2nd International Symposium on Transportation Studies in Developing Countries (ISTSDC 2019)* (Atlantis Press) pp. 67-71

[22] Kabat-Zinn, J 1994 *Full catastrophe living: Using the wisdom of your body and mind to face stress, pain, and illness* (New York: Delta)

[23] Goleman, D 2003 *Healing emotions: Conversations with the Dalai Lama on mindfulness, emotions, and health* (New York: Shambhala publications)

[24] Ergas, O 2014 Mindfulness in education at the intersection of science, religion, and healing. *Critical Studies in Education,* ***55*(1)** pp 58-72

[25] Morgan, W.D., & Morgan, S.T 2005 Cultivating attention and empathy. In G. Germer, R. Siegel and P. Fulton. (Eds.) *Mindfulness and psychotherapy* (New York: Guilford) pp 73-80

[26] Hanh, T. N 1991 *The miracle of mindfulness* (London: Rider)

[27] Germer, G 2005 What is mindfulness? In G. Germer, R. Siegel and P. Fulton. (Eds.). *Mindfulness and psychotherapy* (New York: Guilford) pp1-27

[28] Jordan, C. H., Wang, W., Donatoni, L., Meier, B. P 2014 Mindful eating: Trait and state mindfulness predict healthier eating behavior. *Personality and Individual Differences* **68** p 107-111

[29] Teut, M., Roesner, E. J., Ortiz, M., Reese, F., Binting, S., Roll, S., & Brinkhaus, B 2013 Mindful walking in psychologically distressed individuals: A randomized controlled trial. *Evidence-Based Complementary and Alternative Medicine* (2013) p 1 - 7

[30] Chaskalson, M 2011 *The mindful workplace: Developing resilient individuals and resonant organizations with MBSR* (New York: John Wiley & Sons)

[31] Abdul Hanan, S., King, M. J., & Lewis, I. M 2012 The role of mindfulness in an extended TPB framework to understand drivers' speeding intentions in school zones. In *5th International Conference on Traffic and Transport Psychology,* 29-31 August (2012) Groningen, the Netherlands

[32] Arthur Jr, W., & Graziano, W. G 1996 The five-factor model, conscientiousness, and driving accident involvement. *Journal of Personality* **64(3)** p 593-618

[33] Sümer, N., Lajunen, T., & Özkan, T 2005 Big five personality traits as the distal predictors of road accident. *Traffic and Transport Psychology: Theory and Application* **215** p 215-227

[34] Miles, D. E., & Johnson, G. L 2003 Aggressive driving behaviors: are there psychological and attitudinal predictors?. *Transportation Research Part F: Traffic Psychology and Behaviour* **6(2)** p 147-161

[35] Kerr, J. S 1991 Driving without attention mode (DWAM): a formalisation of inattentive states while driving. In A.G. Gale, I.D. Brown, C.H. Haslegrave, I. Moorhead, S.P. & Taylor, S.P. (Eds.). *Vision in vehicles III* (Amsterdam: Elsevier) pp 473-479

[36] Brown, I. D 1991 Highway hypnosis: implications for road safety researchers and practitioners. In A.G. Gale, I.D. Brown, C.H. Haslegrave, I. Moorhead, & S.P. Taylor, S.P. (Eds.). *Vision in vehicles III* (Amsterdam: Elsevier) pp 459-466

[37] Brown, K. W., & Ryan, R. M 2003 The benefits of being present: Mindfulness and its role in psychological well-being *Journal of Personality and Social Psychology* **84(4) p** 822-848

[38] Haigh, E. A., Moore, M. T., Kashdan, T. B., & Fresco, D. M 2011 Examination of the factor structure and concurrent validity of the Langer Mindfulness/Mindlessness Scale *Assessment* **18(1)** p 11-26

[39] Segal, Z. V., Teasdale, J. D., & Williams, J. M. G 2004 Mindfulness-Based Cognitive Therapy: Theoretical rationale and empirical status. In S. C. Hayes, V. M. Follette, & M.

M. Linehan (Eds.). *Mindfulness and acceptance: Expanding the cognitive-behavioral tradition* (New York: Guilford Press) pp 45-65

[40] Kass, S. J., VanWormer, L. A., Mikulas, W. L., Legan, S., & Bumgarner, D 2011 Effects of mindfulness training on simulated driving: Preliminary results. *Mindfulness* **2(4)** p 236-241

[41] Stephens, A. N., Koppel, S., Young, K. L., Chambers, R., & Hassed, C 2018 Associations between self-reported mindfulness, driving anger and aggressive driving. *Transportation Research part F: Traffic Psychology and Behaviour* ***56*** p 149-155

[42] Nevada Department of Public Safety 2015 The difference between riding and driving. https://lasvegassun.com/native/ndps/2015/sep/13/difference-between-riding-and-driving/

[43] Shahar, A., Poulter, D., Clarke, D., & Crundall, D 2010 Motorcyclists' and car drivers' responses to hazards. *Transportation research part F: Traffic Psychology and Behaviour* **13(4)** p 243-254

[44] Gary R. VandenBos 2007 APA Dictionary of Psychology (Washington, DC. American Psychological Association)

[45] Creswell, J. W 1999 Mixed-method research: Introduction and application. In *Handbook of educational policy* (Academic Press) pp 455-472

[46] Palinkas, L. A., Aarons, G. A., Horwitz, S., Chamberlain, P., Hurlburt, M., & Landsverk, J 2011 Mixed method designs in implementation research. *Administration and Policy in Mental Health and Mental Health Services Research* **38(1)** p 44-53

[47] Braun, V., & Clarke, V 2012 Thematic analysis. In H. Cooper, P. M. Camic, D. L. Long, A. T. Panter, D. Rindskopf, & K. J. Sher (Eds.), *APA handbook of research methods in psychology, Research designs: Quantitative, qualitative, neuropsychological, and biological* Vol 2 (American Psychological Association) pp 57–71 https://doi.org/10.1037/13620-004

[48] Sunanto, J., Takeuchi, K., & Nakata, H 2005 Pengantar penelitan dengan subjek tunggal. (Tsukuba: Center for Research on International Cooperation in Educational Development University of Tsukuba)

[49] Kratochwill, T. R., Hitchcock, J., Horner, R. H., Levin, J. R., Odom, S. L., Rindskopf, D. M., Shadish, W. R 2010 What Works Clearinghouse: Single Case Design Technical Documentation. http://ies.ed.gov/ncee/wwc/pdf/wwc_scd.pdf.

[50] Murphy, G., & Matvienko-Sikar, K 2019Trait mindfulness & self-reported driving behavior *Personality and individual differences* **147** p 250-255

[51] Abdul Hanan, S 2014 *An application of an extended theory of planned behaviour to understand drivers' compliance with the school zones speed limit in Australia and Malaysia* (Doctoral dissertation, Queensland University of Technology)

[52] Koppel, S., Stephens, A. N., Young, K. L., Hua, P., Chambers, R., & Hassed, C 2018 What is the relationship between self-reported aberrant driving behaviors, mindfulness, and self-reported crashes and infringements? *Traffic Injury Prevention* **19(5)** p 480-487

[53] Reynaud, E., & Navarro, J 2019 Is Mindfulness Helping the Brain to Drive? Insights From Behavioral Data and Future Directions for Research. In Hasan Ayaz, Frédéric Dehais, (Eds.) *Neuroergonomics* (Academic Press) pp 93-97 https://doi.org/10.1016/B978-0-12-811926-6.00015-4

[54] Koppel, S., Bugeja, L., Hua, P., Osborne, R., Stephens, A. N., Young, K. L., Stephensa, A.N., Younga, K.L., Chambers, R. & Hassed, C. 2019 Do mindfulness interventions improve road safety? A systematic review *Accident Analysis & Prevention* **123** p 88-98

IOP Conf. Series: Earth and Environmental Science 1000 (2022) 012019 doi:10.1088/1755-1315/1000/1/012019

Impact of Overloading Vehicle towards the Level of Service on Freeway Segment (Case Study: JORR KM 27 to KM 23)

Herlin Sugari

Civil and Environmental Engineering Department, Universitas Indonesia

Andyka Kusuma

Civil and Environmental Engineering Department, Universitas Indonesia

Robby Yudo Purnomo

Civil and Environmental Engineering Department, Universitas Indonesia

andyka.k@ui.ac.id

Abstract. The congestion problem that occurs on the road is one of the indicators to determine the level of service. Approximately 20% of all traffic congestion is due to the existence of shockwave jams or phantom jams. One of the factors causing the shock wave phenomenon is the speed differences between heavy vehicles and light vehicles (Garber & Hoel, 2009). On the other hand, the Over Dimension and Over Loading (ODOL) Vehicle worsened the situation by reducing operational speed due to the exceeding load. Indonesia Traffic Police stated that throughout 2019 there were 136.470 vehicles out of 1.376.956 offences that were ODOL vehicles. This research aims to identify the effect of overloading vehicles and the volume of heavy vehicles on creating shock wave phenomenon that led to the lower level of service. Microsimulation modelling is carried out to obtain the resulting level of service from heavy vehicles volume using the primary data from the data collection. The result shows that the large volume of heavy vehicles exacerbated by the presence of ODOL vehicles can cause a temporary change in road speed and lead to a decreased level of service.

1. Introduction

Level of Service (LOS) captures the traffic performance on a particular road segment. High traffic may result in traffic congestion that associate with a lower level of service. In an urban area, traffic congestion is an everyday phenomenon. However, approximately 20% of all traffic congestion occurrence is known as a phantom (Suijs, et al., 2014). This congestion is not caused by clear reasons such as traffic accidents but by minor causes of the driver's limited reaction time. This driver's little reaction time cause speed disruption, which affects the speed of the vehicle behind it.

One of the factors causing the shock wave phenomenon is the significant speed difference between heavy vehicles and light vehicles, whereas heavy vehicles are highly correlated with low speed (Garber & Hoel, 2009). Aghabayk et al. (2012) found that the headway between two consecutive heavy vehicles generates the longest headway compared to the other type of vehicle interaction. Moreover, the reaction time between two successive heavy vehicles was also higher (2 seconds). This condition is exacerbated by the high number of heavy vehicles forced to carry more load exceeding the allowable load limit. The speed gap between vehicles not only trigger traffic congestion but also increase the probability of traffic

IOP Conf. Series: Earth and Environmental Science 1000 (2022) 012019 doi:10.1088/1755-1315/1000/1/012019

accident occurrence, particularly the involvement of over-dimension and overloading vehicle (ODOL). Safety is an issue on the overloaded truck, Jasamarga toll road operator shows that approximately more than 56% accident while it only holds 18.23% share along Jakarta-Cikampek toll road segment by October 2020. Furthermore, ODOL vehicles offences on the toll road are still relatively high, at 47% until March 2020. Tjahjono & Setiawan (2019) stated that the increasing volume heavy vehicles accompanied by a significant number of ODOL vehicles would have a negative impact on the speed and travel time of road users on traffic flow. Similarly, Wang et al., (2018)'s research also expresses that overloaded vehicle have a significant negative impact on traffic flow condition. The increasing number of overload vehicles will result from a reduce the overall vehicle average speed and, at the same time, increase the congestion time. Therefore, this research aims to determine the influence of heavy vehicles' speed, especially ODOL vehicles, on Indonesia's freeway segment performance.

2. Theoretical Background

The three main elements of traffic flow's theory are speed, volume, and density. These elements are used to analyse traffic conditions to be used to plan, design, and evaluate traffic conditions. Ability to understand, research, and relate the relationship between three main elements can be used to evaluate the traffic condition in the past and predict the future situation (Institute of Transportation Engineering, 2016).

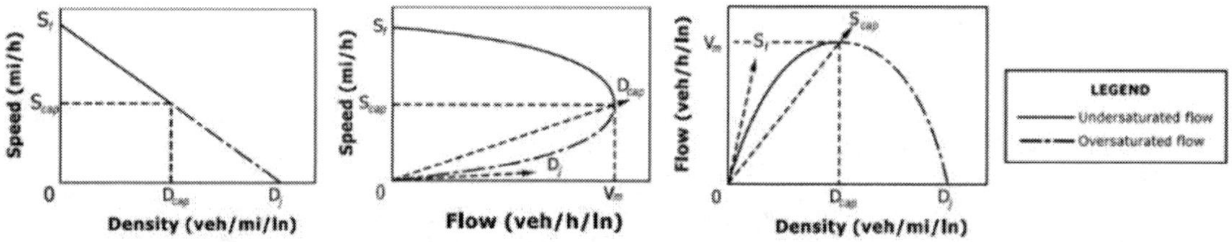

Figure 1. Relationship between volume, speed, and density

Garber & Hoel (2009) reveal the shock wave phenomenon where this phenomenon appears due to a temporary speed reduction on a road segment. For example, a truck enters a road segment at time t1 and travels at a slower speed than vehicles behind it. The truck travels for some time and leaves the road segment at time t2. If traffic condition prevents the vehicles behind it from passing the truck, the shock wave will be formed behind the truck. At time t1, the vehicles behind the truck will slow down, and the density behind the truck will increase. The movement of the truck and the vehicles behind it is presented in the figure below.

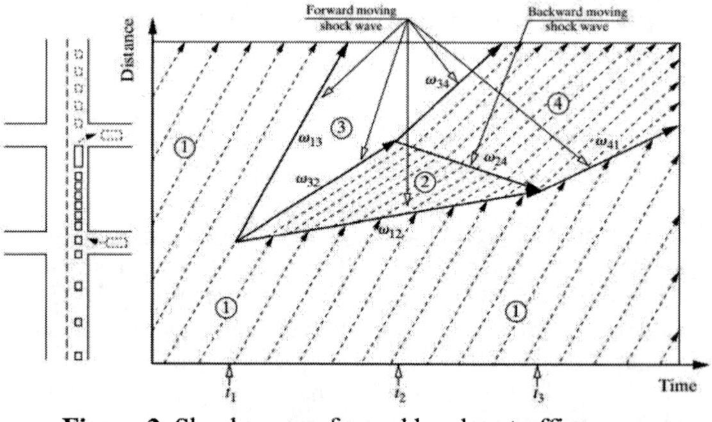

Figure 2. Shock waves formed by slow traffic

LOS was introduced to measure how effective planning, design, and operation of a road segment is. It measures the road segment service effectiveness by providing scale A to F based on traffic criteria on the road segment. According to Transportation Research Board (2010), road segment LOS's determination is heavily associated with road density. Although speed is a primary concern of drivers related to service quality, it would be challenging to describe LOS using speed since it remains constant up to flow rates 1.000 to 1.800 pc/hour/lane, depending on the free-flow speed. Density describes the proximity to other vehicles and is related to the freedom to manoeuvre within the traffic stream. LOS A – C is a condition in which the vehicle speed is at free-flow speed, and the vehicle can still manoeuvre, even though on LOS C, the speed of the vehicle decreases and freedom for manoeuvre is limited. While LOS D – F is a condition of road section that has reduced speed and increased density. On LOS D – F, traffic disruptions are easily absorbed so that they create queues easily. The vehicles are restricted to manoeuvre due to lines.

Garber & Hoel (2009) mentions 2 (two) classifications of mathematical representation of traffic flow characteristics, namely macroscopic model and microscopic model. The macroscopic model approach observes the overall vehicle on a road segment. In contrast, the microscopic model observes individual vehicles and the between vehicles on the traffic system. Based on the previous statement, the microscopic approach is more suitable for understanding the impact of heavy vehicles on the traffic stream. Sefarini (2009), study and simulated the speed and traffic flow relationships using two microscopic model theories namely the car-following model and kinetic energy model. Car following model can analyses speed and traffic flow based on road segment traffic density. The model found that vehicles move at maximum speed until it reaches a critical density, and then the vehicle speed will decrease until the vehicle completely stops when it reaches maximum density. While traffic flow will increase linearly until a critical density reaches a maximum condition, the traffic flow will decrease until it reaches zero at the maximum density condition.

3. Methodology

The problem identification arises as the number of vehicles at Jakarta Outer Ring Road Section S started increasing and forming a long queue during morning rush hour. Additionally, the corresponding road segment is one of the alternative routes to the port. Therefore, there is a high number of heavy vehicles, particularly loaded logistic trucks, that passes the road. The mixed traffic between heavy vehicles and passenger cars results in the speed reduction of the passenger cars and long queue across the road segment. In this research, the authors hypothesize that the high number of heavy vehicles create a phantom jam on the road section due to the speed gap between vehicles and generate the traffic queue along the road segment.

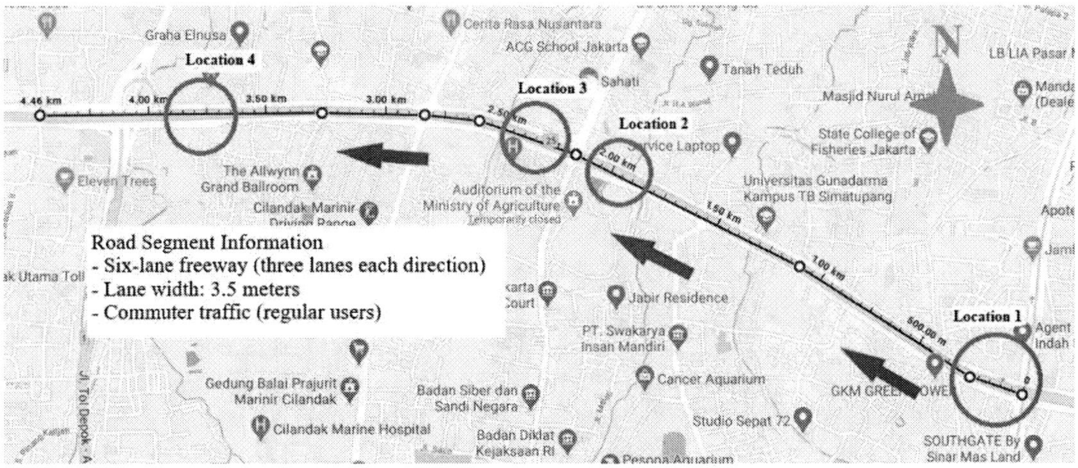

Figure 3. Review Point Location

The Jakarta Outer Ring Road location, which is used as the survey and model location, can be seen in Figure *3*. Location 1 – 4 are the review point locations for the analysis process. Location selection is based on the existing conditions of the site. Location 1 is the location where the vehicle volume data survey was taken. Location 2 and location 3 are close because that section is an underpass where location 2 is the entry to the underpass and location 3 is the exit part of the underpass. While location 4 is part of the flyover, which is located between on ramp and off-ramp. The road section is a freeway segment with an operating speed limit of 60 – 80 km/hour. The modelling process will use the road from east to west (one-way only) where this road segment is one of the alternative routes to port.

The research requires primary data collection from the road segment during morning rush hour on a weekday. The data collection utilizes video recording of the traffic flow condition for 3 hours. To capture the whole road segment, the video is taken from the pedestrian crossing bridge. The author would conduct the traffic count based on the video recording and determine the average spot speed on the road segment.

As stated in the previous chapter, the research will focus on the implementation of the microscopic approach. Therefore, the author will utilize PTV VISSIM as the main tool to simulate the traffic stream. During the modelling process, there will be several simulations based on the various speeds of heavy vehicles. The volume of heavy vehicles will be grouped based on classification on Survey Guidelines Pd. T-10-2004-B. Regarding traffic volume, the model would adopt the empirical result from Tjahjono & Setiawan (2019), where the heavy traffic volume is 1.14%. The study was held on interurban toll road; meanwhile the current paper adopts this approach for developing the analysis in the Jakarta Outer Ring Road toll road.

4. Result and Analysis

4.1. Data Collection

The survey was carried out on April 26th, 2021, at 06.00 – 09.00 WIB, which is morning rush hour. From the survey process, the highest traffic volume is 5283 pcu/hour therefore, peak hour could be at 06.45 – 07.45. Meanwhile, the result of the spot speed survey can be seen in Figure *4*.

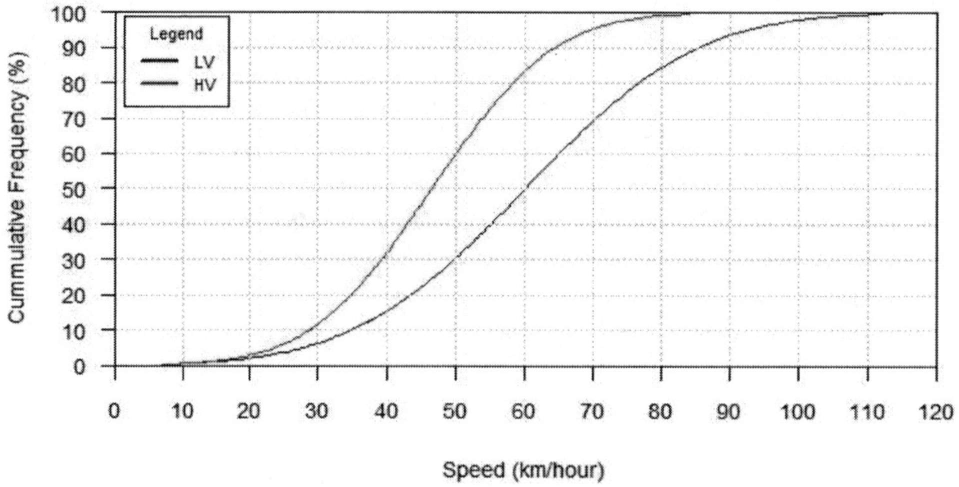

Figure 4. Cumulative frequency distribution of a road section

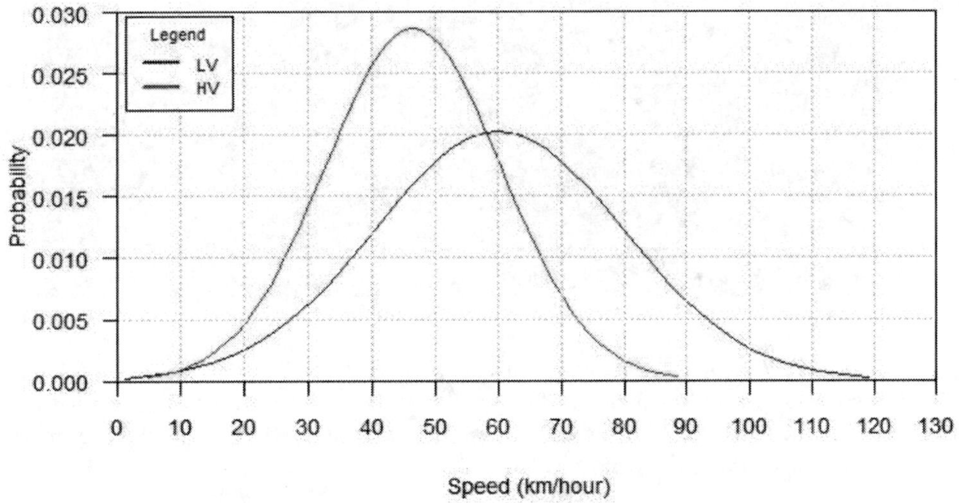

Figure 5. Probability Distribution of vehicle speed

Figure *4* demonstrates the speed distribution from the data collection. Light vehicles line (LV) is distributed to the right of the heavy vehicles line (HV), which indicates that the speed of light vehicles is faster than heavy vehicles. From Figure *4*, vehicles that are driving their vehicles outside the toll road speed limit range (60 – 80 km/hour). For the light vehicles, there are 14.44% vehicles are driving above the speed limit and 46.67% vehicles driving below the speed limit. Meanwhile, for heavy vehicles, there are 0.56% vehicles are driving above the speed limit and 83.06% of vehicles driving below the speed limit. In general, 72.36% of vehicles do not drive at the toll road speed limit. Figure *5* shows the speed distribution of the measured data. The peak of HV is higher than LV, which shows that the HV has lower speed variation or quite uniform distribution. On the opposite, LV have higher speed variation. It can be seen from the graph that peak of HV is at a probability of 0.029, while the peak of LV has a probability of 0.02. This is because the peak of the curve is the mean value of vehicle speed. So that the mean speed of heavy vehicles has a higher probability than the light vehicles. According to the previous statement, the mean speed of light vehicles has a low probability value due to the higher speed variation. From the observation, this phenomenon occurs due to LV is considered to have a higher free-flow speed. Therefore, the vehicles may move freely at high speed during empty roads or reduce the speed during congestion. However, HV has a lower free-flow speed; even when the road is empty, HV may not be able to accelerate more during dense traffic.

4.2. Simulation and Result

The simulation focuses on the variation of heavy vehicles volume scenario on the road section, particularly in the increasing the number of heavy. The simulation consists of two scenarios: the road section forbids the existence of ODOL vehicles, and the road section allows the ODOL vehicles. Based on the data collection, heavy vehicles hold a 15.79% share in traffic, including 1.14% ODOL based on the empirical data. Variation share of heavy vehicle scenario is carried out by increasing the percentage of heavy vehicles by approximately 5%. The percentage of heavy vehicles is got on iteration process with increasing the volume of heavy vehicles and ODOL vehicle every increasing 5% and fit the peak hour volume by 5283 pcu/hour. So that from this iteration, the numbers 15.79%, 20.39%, 25.27%, 30.10%, 35.26%, 40.03%, 45.09%, and 50.03% are generated for road performance analysis of the increase in the percentage of heavy vehicles.

Figure 6. Road Segment Model

The simulation is executed for 2 hours with data taken as a data in of period time of 1 hour after 30 minutes of the warm-up period (when the data is in peak hour condition). The input for simulation includes vehicle volume data from the survey every 15 minutes and vehicle speed in Figure *4*. The result of the simulation is presented in the following graph.

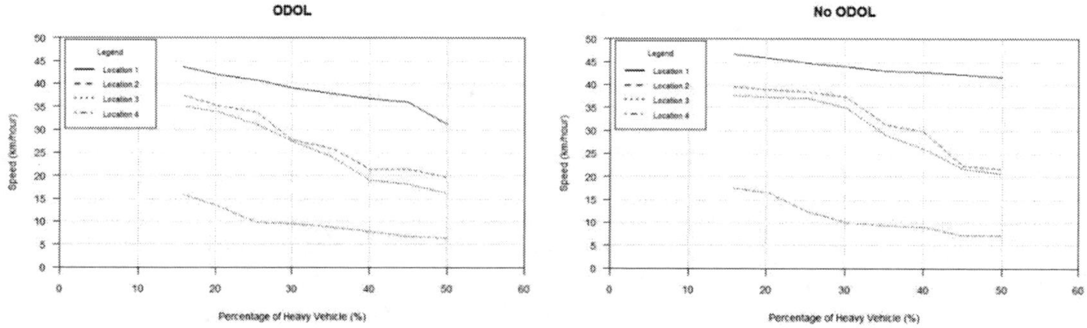

Figure 7. Relationship between percentage of heavy vehicles and speed

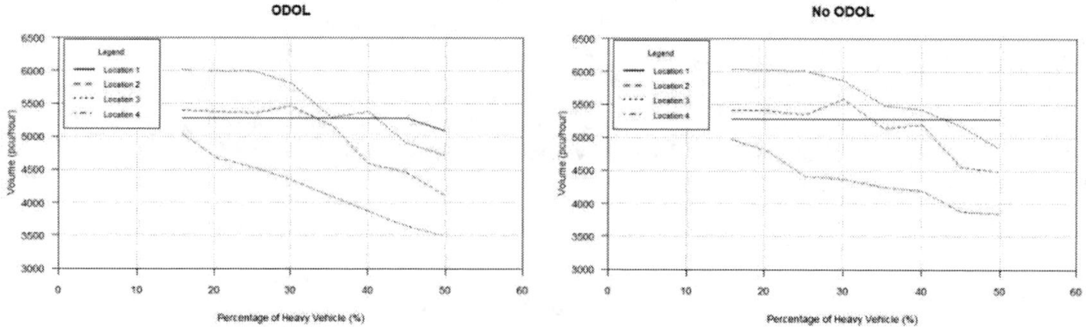

Figure 8. Relationship between percentage of heavy vehicles and volume

The fluctuation of heavy vehicles on a road section is heavily affecting the road section performance. Based on the spot speed survey, around 83.06% of the heavy vehicles are below the toll road speed limit of 60 km/hour. This causes the speed of vehicles on road sections under the toll road speed limit. Moreover, this condition will worsen on the simulation process because the process will have a scenario when the percentage of heavy vehicles increases. The line in Figure *7* shows that the decreasing speed at all locations is in tune with the increasing percentage of heavy vehicles. Meanwhile, the line on Figure *8* tends slightly decreasing when increasing percentage of heavy vehicle. This is consistent with the theory characteristics of traffic flow, especially relation between volume and speed graph that state if speed decreases and volume also decreases, then a road section is indicated on the congested area (can be seen in Figure *9*).

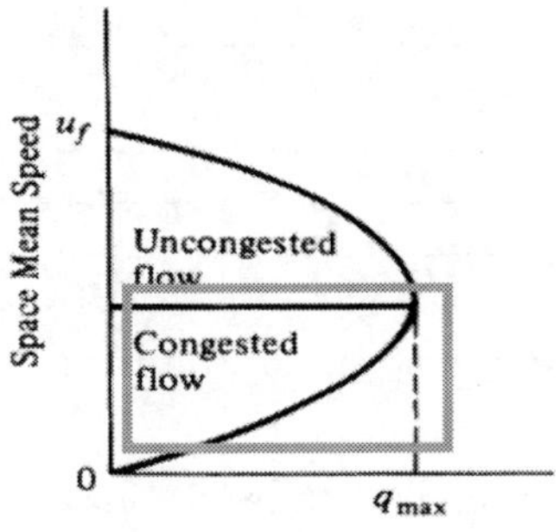

Figure 9. Congested Area

In Figure 7, location 1 and location 2 have a higher speed than location 3 and 4. In this case, the effect of road geometric also affects truck performance. Location 1 is a descending section of the flyover while the location 2 and 3 are underpass section. Location 2 is a sloping descent from flyover, and location 3 is a sloping ascent. Location 4 is a climbing section of the flyover. Due to geometry design, locations 1 and 2 tend to be downward while locations 3 and 4 are climbing sections that generally reduces the vehicle's speed. The same graph shows that location 4 is a worse performance road section than another location because location 4 is located between on ramp and off-ramp before weaving section area that may require driver to decreasing speed to avoid the crash with another vehicle when changing lane. The decrease in truck performance affects road performance that can be seen in the following table.

Table 1. Level of service data simulation results in condition there are ODOL vehicles

% HV	Time	Location 1	Location 2	Location 3	Location 4
15,79%	06.45 – 07.00	A	A	A	A
	07.00 – 07.15	A	A	A	D
	07.15 – 07.30	A	A	A	E
	07.30 – 07.45	A	A	A	F
20,39%	06.45 – 07.00	A	A	A	A
	07.00 – 07.15	A	A	A	E
	07.15 – 07.30	A	A	A	F
	07.30 – 07.45	A	A	A	F
25,27%	06.45 – 07.00	A	A	A	A
	07.00 – 07.15	A	A	A	F
	07.15 – 07.30	A	A	A	F
	07.30 – 07.45	A	A	A	F
30,10%	06.45 – 07.00	A	A	A	B
	07.00 – 07.15	A	A	C	F
	07.15 – 07.30	A	A	B	F
	07.30 – 07.45	A	B	A	F
35,26%	06.45 – 07.00	A	A	A	B
	07.00 – 07.15	A	A	C	F
	07.15 – 07.30	A	A	B	F
	07.30 – 07.45	A	D	B	F
40,03%	06.45 – 07.00	A	A	A	C
	07.00 – 07.15	A	A	B	F
	07.15 – 07.30	A	C	C	F
	07.30 – 07.45	A	F	F	F
45,09%	06.45 – 07.00	A	A	A	D
	07.00 – 07.15	A	A	C	F

% HV	Time	Location 1	Location 2	Location 3	Location 4
	07.15 – 07.30	A	D	C	F
	07.30 – 07.45	A	F	F	F
50,03%	06.45 – 07.00	A	A	A	D
	07.00 – 07.15	A	A	C	F
	07.15 – 07.30	A	D	C	F
	07.30 – 07.45	C	F	F	F

Table 2. Level of service data simulation results in condition without ODOL vehicle

% HV	Time	Location 1	Location 2	Location 3	Location 4
15,79%	06.45 – 07.00	A	A	A	A
	07.00 – 07.15	A	A	A	C
	07.15 – 07.30	A	A	A	F
	07.30 – 07.45	A	A	A	F
20,39%	06.45 – 07.00	A	A	A	A
	07.00 – 07.15	A	A	A	E
	07.15 – 07.30	A	A	A	F
	07.30 – 07.45	A	A	A	F
25,27%	06.45 – 07.00	A	A	A	A
	07.00 – 07.15	A	A	A	E
	07.15 – 07.30	A	A	A	F
	07.30 – 07.45	A	A	A	F
30,10%	06.45 – 07.00	A	A	A	A
	07.00 – 07.15	A	A	A	F
	07.15 – 07.30	A	A	A	F
	07.30 – 07.45	A	A	A	F
35,26%	06.45 – 07.00	A	A	A	B
	07.00 – 07.15	A	A	A	F
	07.15 – 07.30	A	A	A	F
	07.30 – 07.45	A	D	F	F
40,03%	06.45 – 07.00	A	A	A	B
	07.00 – 07.15	A	A	A	F
	07.15 – 07.30	A	A	C	F
	07.30 – 07.45	A	E	F	F
45,09%	06.45 – 07.00	A	A	A	D
	07.00 – 07.15	A	A	A	F
	07.15 – 07.30	A	D	D	F
	07.30 – 07.45	A	F	F	F
50,03%	06.45 – 07.00	A	A	A	D
	07.00 – 07.15	A	A	A	F
	07.15 – 07.30	A	F	D	F
	07.30 – 07.45	A	F	F	F

Table 1 and Table 2 show that the greater the percentage volume of the heavy vehicles, the worse level of service. This can be seen at location 4 with a tendency of LOS F and going upstream accompanied by the greater percentage of heavy vehicles, the level of service tends to decrease. The comparison of these two conditions can also be seen from the speed comparison in Figure *7*. Figure *7* shows the simulation result of two conditions when there are ODOL vehicles and no ODOL vehicles. Figure *7* measures that the road without ODOL vehicles would have 16.75% higher average speed than to the road section with ODOL vehicles. This shows that the larger percentage of heavy vehicles can result a large decreasing vehicle speed. This condition is aggravated by ODOL vehicles that contribute to the longer delay because the operational speed of ODOL vehicles is lower than the general heavy vehicles. In some comparison level of service, even in conditions without ODOL vehicles, obtained a higher LOS in that condition than there were no ODOL vehicles. So can be said that the lower percentage of heavy vehicles can minimize the phenomenon of shockwave or phantom jam. The simulation result is consistent with the theory that said when a road section tends to have a normal traffic flow and great density, then the speed of vehicles gradually decreases to pass through the congestion area. The point that having congestion and this operational speed reduction will spread to the upstream so that the congestion queue will be longer. This can be seen on the LOS table (Table 1 and Table 2) that from location 4 to the upstream and along with the increasing the percentage of heavy vehicles, location with LOS F or congested condition will spread longer to the upstream. High density and the formation of queues are an indication of poor road performance. In Tables 1 and 2, the performance of road segments in LOS D – F will form the queue due to disruption caused by heavy vehicles. Based on theory, the formation of queue and high density will make the vehicle restricted to manoeuvre.

5. Conclusion

From the modelling and simulation process, the operational speed of heavy vehicles that lower than the light vehicle can cause temporary speed reduction on a traffic flow. The greater proportion of heavy vehicles, then the worse performance of road network. ODOL vehicles that have weight more than the general heavy vehicles can make the condition worst. So, a road section with ODOL vehicles on it will have a worse level of service and low operational speed. In addition, the geometric condition of the road can cause the performance of heavy vehicles to decrease and disrupt the road segment (as happened at Locations 3 and 4). It can be concluded that vehicle performance is very low because the speed of 83.06% of heavy vehicles on the road segment is below the toll road speed limit (60 km/hour). The performance of the low speed of heavy vehicles results in disruption that can be absorbed and creates queueing. This causes the performance of the road segment to be at LOS D – F. The poor performance of heavy vehicles, especially loaded trucks in Indonesia, has poor road network performance. This is supported by the fact that truck technology quality in Indonesia is still lagging. The design of the road segment is also still in favour of passenger vehicles (light vehicles). Therefore, the critical length of the designed road segment and the volume of heavy vehicles must be considered in road design planning. In addition, the toll road operating speed limit needs to be differentiated between heavy vehicles and light vehicles. From the results of this study, it was found that a great number of heavy vehicles could not reach the speed limit toll road.

References

[1] Aghabayk, K., Sarvi, M. & Young, W., 2012. Understanding the Dynamics of Heavy Vehicle Interactions in Car-Following. *Journal of Transportation Engineering,* 138(12), pp. 1468-1475.
[2] Garber, N. J. & Hoel, L. A., 2009. *Traffic & Highway Engineering.* 4th ed. Toronto: Ceangage Learning.
[3] Institute of Transportation Engineering, 2016. *Traffic Engineering Handbook.* 7th ed. Canada: John Wiley & Sons, Inc., Hoboken, New Jersey.
[4] PTV Group, 2020. *PTV Vissim First Steps Tutorial.* Karlsruhe: PTV AG.
[5] Safarini, D., 2009. *Kajian Model Mikroskopik dan Model Kinetik Lalu Lintas Kendaraan dan Simulasinya,* Bogor: Sekolah Pascasarjana Institut Pertanian Bogor.
[6] Suijs, L., Wismans, L., Krol, L. & Berkum, E. v., 2014. Phantom jam avoidance through in-car speed advice. *ELSEVIER.*
[7] Tjahjono, T. & Setiawan, D., 2019. *Dampak Kendaraan Overloading Terhadap Kinerja Lalu Lintas Jalan Tol Jakarta - Cikampek.* Depok, s.n.
[8] Transportation Research Board, 2010. *Highway Capacity Manual.* Washington DC: National

Academy of Sciences.
[9] Wang, X., Zhao, P. & Tao, Y., 2018. Evaluating Impacts of Overloaded Heavy Vehicles on Freeway Traffic Condition by a Novel Multi-Class Traffic Flow Model. *Sustainability.*

IOP Conf. Series: Earth and Environmental Science 1000 (2022) 012020 doi:10.1088/1755-1315/1000/1/012020

Determination of Junction Geometrical Design for Pedestrian and Bicycle Movement (Case Study): Duren Sawit

Muhammad Ariel Pratama[1], Tri Tjahjono[1]

[1]Department of Civil and Environmental Engineering, Universitas Indonesia, East Java 16424, Indonesia

marielpratama@gmail.com

Abstract. East Jakarta has the highest amount of traffic accident than other cities in Jakarta for the last few years, indicating the need of traffic improvement on their safety, particularly for active mobility. Various projects have been implemented in Jakarta to improve its serviceability for pedestrian and bicycle user to drive the habit of active mobility. However, they still not have been implemented in Jakarta as a whole. This paper aims to do traffic improvement on a particular unsafe intersection in East Jakarta. Intersection itself is chosen as pedestrian and bicycle user are the most vulnerable when using it. Through comparative study cases, this paper is expected to determine appropriate junction geometrical designs that improve its safety for pedestrian and bicycle movement, while maintaining its performance, such as its capacity, degree of saturation, and delay. The study shows that junction geometrical improvement with several adjustments can improves its serviceability for active mobility.

1. Introduction

1.1. Background

Institute of Transportation Development Policy (ITDP) has developed a five-year (2017-2022) implementation guide, including pedestrian facilities planning and upgrade. This plan aims to drive the use of active transportation mode in Jakarta, focusing on non-motorized transportation strategy and policy development. It aligns with Indonesia's commitment to reduce CO_2 emission, especially in the transportation sector, thereby achieving green mobility in the long run. Therefore, the capability to support active mobility needs to be prioritized in the transportation sector.

East Jakarta had a total of 1,361 traffic accidents from 2019 to 2020, which is the highest compared to other areas in Jakarta (Achrianto, 2020). Meanwhile, transportation infrastructure categorized as the most prone to an accident is intersection because many parties move in this particular space (Achrianto, 2020). An intersection in Duren Sawit, a part of East Jakarta, is chosen for the study. One of the significant factors that led to its selection is the lack of traffic signal, which endangers pedestrians and cyclists, thereby minimizing the potential to drive active mobility in the area. Furthermore, as the intersection is located near residential areas and public transportation, it links transportation users' first and last miles, which supposed to act as the driving factor for active mobility.

Therefore, this study focuses on improving the intersection performance in the chosen location. Additionally, the accommodation of pedestrians and cyclists as the means of active transportation mode acts as a determinant for improvement.

1.2. *Objective and Limitation*

This study aims to simulate improvement scenarios for the chosen intersection and determine the best one to be implemented. The scenarios include existing/do-nothing scenarios, traffic light installation, limited land acquisition, and full-blown land acquisition.

The study area intersection is located in Duren Sawit, specifically where Teratai Putih Raya Road and Nusa Indah road meet. Furthermore, due to limited time and resources, the traffic light installation used a fixed-time signal.

2. Literature Review

2.1. *Intersection*

According to Road Safety International, an intersection is a critical location of a road network in terms of capacity, level of service, and safety. In a non-signalized intersection, the safety of road users is at higher risk as they must compete for space and time. The non-signalized intersection has a higher risk of collisions, as it can only be avoided assuming the vehicle movement is separated by time. Geometric safety is an essential starting point in designing intersections for traffic control.

The Webster method is commonly used in designing traffic lights because its sequence is composed of red, red/amber, amber, and green (Webster, 1996). The red and amber periods are set at 2 and 3 seconds, respectively. The combination between them is green phases called inter green period, which gives time to shift the traffic to move into the net green phase (Webster, 1996).

The general shape of the intersection is suggested to be T-shaped or crossroad, with the junctions perpendicular to each other. One of its geometrical aspects is the right or left turning lane in Indonesia. The existence of a left turning lane is recommended for every intersection, except there are prohibitions with adequate capacity, and a two-way lane with a design speed of less than 40 km/hour, and a design volume of less than 200 vehicles/hour. In grading the traffic performance of an intersection, the capacity and delay are calculated. Capacity is the maximum value of a vehicle accommodated by the junction. Delay is the time loss of vehicle movement due to traffic light, while the degree of saturation is also considered to monitor the capacity of the road based on the incoming vehicle.

2.2. *Intervisibility*

Junction intervisibility is defined as the area bounded by measurements from a distance of 2.5 m behind the stop-line extending across the full carriageway width for each arm. It represents the visible area from the vehicle user's perspective.

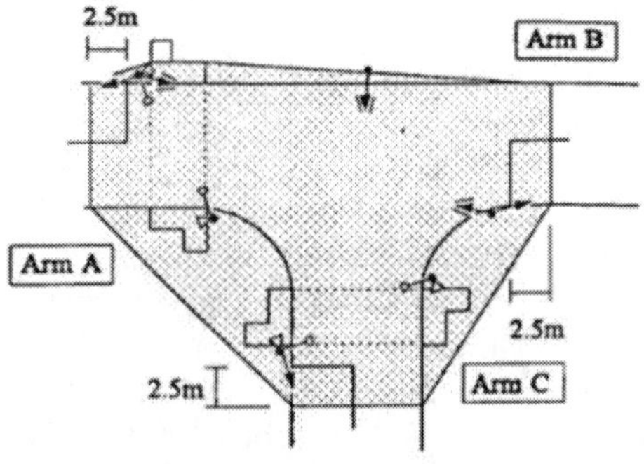

Figure 1. Junction Intervisibility

2.3. *Intersection Safety Improvement*

The illegal and unsafe behavior of pedestrians occurs frequently and represents one of the significant factors in traffic accidents (Wang, 2011). Pedestrian non-compliance rates are found to be proportionate with the increase of cycle times at signalized intersections. An increase in the waiting time is the major reason for pedestrian non-compliance to traffic signals (Marisamynathan, 2014). Therefore, it is very important to provide sufficient time for pedestrians to pass a crossing at a signalized intersection (Onelcin & Alver, 2017).

2.4. *Bicycle Lane*

Bicycle lane facilitates movement on streets at a minimum width of 1.5 meters against a curb or adjacent to a parking lane (FHWA, 2019). However, the inability to apply the minimum width in a road lane provides an unmarked lane. Bicycle users' level of comfort is higher with the provision of a striped area. Therefore, an unmarked lane in the form of a striped area is used to improve the bicycle level of service for streets. This area has a width of 0.6 m and above without markings or signals that denote it is specifically for bikes. The London Cycling Design standards recommended a minimum cycle lane of 2 meters. Therefore, it has a higher priority in the traffic flow.

Bicycle lanes are always located at intersections and on both sides of the road on two-way streets. However, it needs to be separated from other lanes by curbs because bicycle users need to adapt to motorized vehicles periodically. Additionally, two-way bike lanes on one side of the street are not recommended as they create a hazardous condition for bicycle users.

2.5. *TRANSYT Software*

TRANSYT is an offline software for determining and studying optimum fixed time and coordinated traffic signal timings on roads with average traffic flow (Binning, 2009). It is a macroscopic software package for designing, evaluating, and modeling everything from single isolated road junctions to large mixed-signal and priority-controlled traffic networks.

3. Data Source and Method

3.1. *Data Source*

The data collection process was carried out in the morning at 08.00-09.00 WIB. The survey consists of the traffic volume, flow direction, geometrical condition, and the average pedestrian crossing time. The chosen intersection is located in Duren Sawit as shown in figure 2.

Figure 2. Intersection Location

3.2. *Method*

This study modeled 4 scenarios using TRANSYT Software based on the Webster method. Each scenario has an additional improvement, thereby leading to changes in value of delay and capacity.

Furthermore, the scenarios are compared based on the traffic performance and factors affecting each improvement, such as intervisibility, pedestrian and cyclist accommodation, traffic conflict management, and the associated efforts.

3.2.1. Do-Nothing. In this scenario, the existing condition of the intersection was processed to determine the maximum throughput value using data obtained from the Highway Capacity Manual of non-signalized intersections in Indonesia.

3.2.2. Scenario 1/Optimum Traffic Light Installation. In this scenario, phases and optimum cycle time are applied to the intersection. This scenario also consider the average pedestrian crossing time, which contributes to the cycling process.

3.2.3. Scenario 2/Limited Land Acquisition. This scenario was carried out by applying the geometrical improvement that affected the road width. It also considered the possible geometric improvement based on the site condition using the left turning lane in the east approach, which also has the highest peak hour value of PCU. Other than that, it also applied bicycle lane in the form of 1-meter striped lane to minimize the risk of affecting the road's traffic performance and maintaining the standard bicycle lane at the same time.

3.2.4. Scenario 3/Full Blown Land Acquisition. In this scenario, geometrical improvement was applied to all left turning lanes on all junctions without regard to land ownership or space limitation. In addition, bicycle variations are considered by developing lanes widths of 1 meter like Scenario 2.

Table 1 consists of scenarios codes used to provide concise and readable calculations for bicycle and pedestrian lanes.

Table 1. Scenario Code

Scenario		Scenario Code
Do-Nothing		DN
Scenario 1: Optimal Traffic Light Setting		SC1
Scenario 2:		
Limited Acquisition Geometrical	2.1: Dedicated Left Turn	SC2.1
Improvement	2.2: Dedicated Left Turn + Bike Lane	SC2.2
Scenario 3:		
Full Blown Geometrical	3.1: Dedicated Left Turn	SC3.1
Improvement	3.2: Dedicated Left Turn + Bike Lane	SC3.2

4. Data Results

4.1. Geometrical Aspect of The Existing Condition

Based on observation, the traffic flow could move to all directions due to its two-way characteristics. The approaches located in the North and South, as well as the East and West have width sizes of 5.42 m and 4.65 m, respectively.

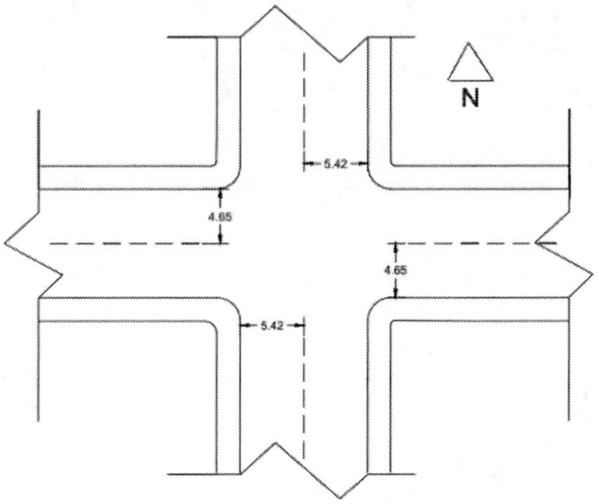

Figure 3. Site Layout of the Existing Intersection

4.2. Traffic Counting Data

Table 2 shows the result of traffic counting. The hourly peak hour is divided into 3 categories, namely non-signalized, signalized, and signalized with dedicated turn according to varying passenger car unit (PCU) of a motorcycle with its values of 0.5, 0.4, and 0.3, respectively. The signalized and dedicated left-turn values are calculated as preparation for the scenarios of the improvement made.

Table 2. Hourly Passenger Car Unit of Traffic Counting

Approach Code	Toward	Q1 hour		
		Non signalized (PCU)	Signalized (PCU)	Signalized (Dedicated Left Lane) (PCU)
	East	70.9	61.5	42.7
	West	89.7	75.8	-
North	South	69.6	59.9	-
	South	72	61	40
	North	72.3	61.7	-
East	West	736.5	604.4	-
	West	69	64.2	54.6
	East	47	40.8	-
South	North	154.4	134.9	-
	North	28	23.8	15.4
	South	41.5	35	-
West	East	39.5	34.4	-

4.3. Average Pedestrian Crossing Time

Table 3 shows the number of pedestrians crossing the intersection during the observation period and the average time needed to carry out this process. The table shows varying time differences for each period as the hindrance mainly came from the non-signalized characteristic of the intersection. For the modeling process in a traffic light setting, red is indicated for 8 seconds to provide an average accommodating time for pedestrians crossing the road.

Table 3. Average Pedestrian Crossing Time

Period	Amount	Average Needed Time (Second)
8.00-8.15	5	4.8
8.15-8.30	14	5.4
8.30-8.45	9	5.7
8.45-9.00	17	5.6
9.00-9.15	15	6.4
9.15-9.30	13	6.1
9.30-9.45	12	5.8
9.45-10.00	5	5.7

5. Discussion

5.1. Changes between scenarios

The calculated number of passenger car units is inputted to the TRANSYT Software to determine its capacity value and delay. The degree of saturation is calculated by dividing the capacity with passenger car units at peak hours. Meanwhile, the number of phases and cycle time is adapted according to the existing traffic counting data.

The change of scenarios is compared to SC1 as the Do-Nothing/Existing scenario has a non signalized characteristic. Therefore, theoretically, the variables are likely to be higher in quality and would only be affected by lane width and traffic volume, with a higher capacity and a lower degree of saturation and delay. However, based on the site observation, the non-signalized characteristic coupled with the drivers' behavior crossing the intersection tends to cause heavy traffic jams and congestion in peak hours, thereby invalidating the result of the capacity, degree of saturation, and delay time. The visualization of all scenarios is shown in Figures 4 to 8.

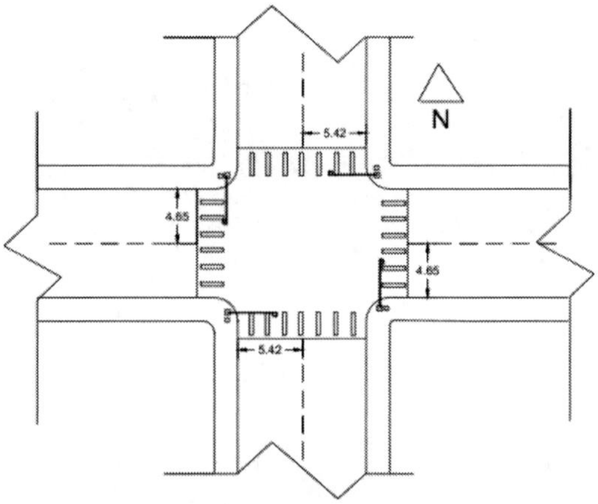

Figure 4. Site Layout of the SC1

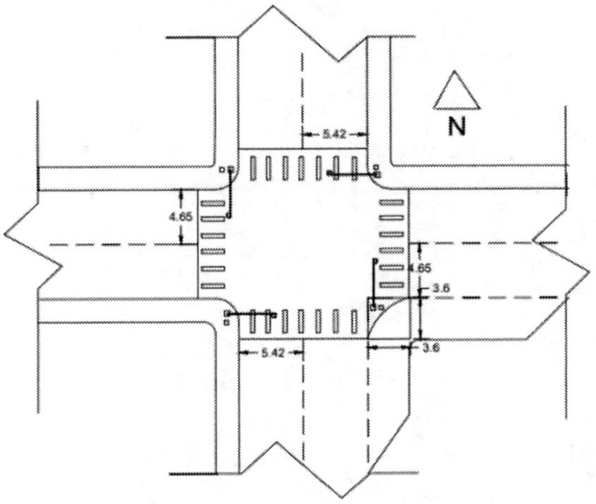

Figure 5. Site Layout of the SC2.1

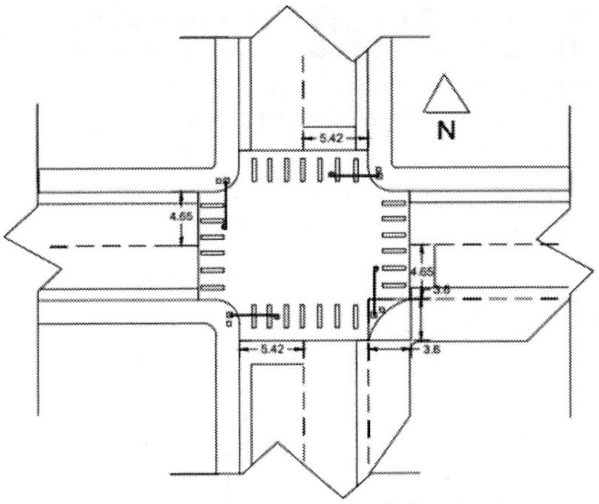

Figure 6. Site Layout of the SC2.2

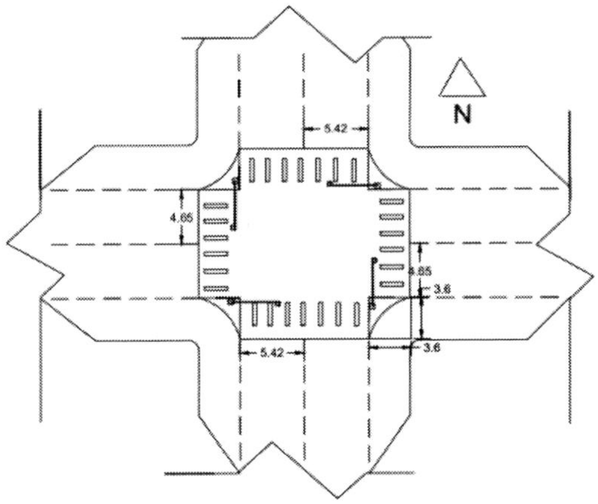

Figure 7. Site Layout of the SC3.1

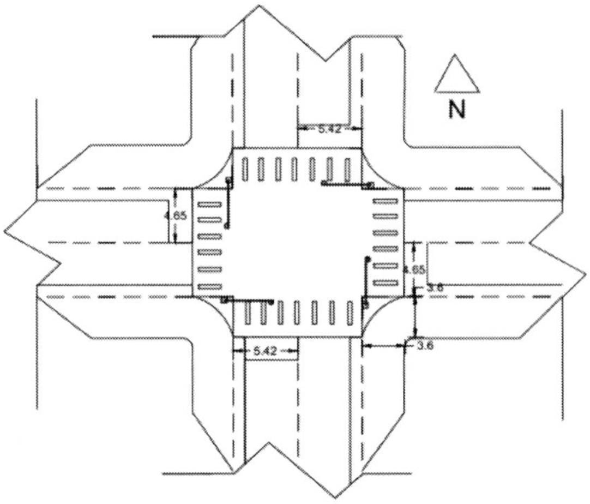

Figure 8. Site Layout of the SC3.2

5.1.1. Capacity. Table 4 shows the total capacity comparison between each scenario, whereby DN is only based on the lane width. Therefore, the percentage comparison is based on SC1 as the control sample, DN associated with the lane width tends to have a higher capacity than a signalized intersection. Furthermore, the addition of a bicycle lane is likely to reduce the road capacity of the existing lane width.

Table 4. Capacity Comparison between Scenarios

Scenario Code	Capacity (PCU/Hour)	% Changes
DN	11,200.02	-
SC1	1,746.03	100%
SC2.1	1,746.03	-
SC2.2	1,430.99	-18%
SC3.1	1,746.03	-
SC3.2	1,430.99	-18%

5.1.2. Degree of Saturation. Table 5 shows the average degree of saturation comparison between each scenario. It should be noted that the DN's degree of saturation was not affected by cycle time and total loss time, which has a lower value than the signalized scenarios. Therefore, the percentage comparison is also based on SC1 as the control sample. It could be observed that the geometrical improvement could lower the degree of saturation, which is increased by adding a bicycle lane. However, all values are acceptable because they are lower than 0.9.

Table 5. Degree of Saturation Comparison between Scenarios

Scenario Code	Average Degree of Saturation	% Changes
DN	0.13	-
SC1	0.72	100%
SC2.1	0.69	-3%
SC2.2	0.84	18%
SC3.1	0.52	-28%
SC3.2	0.65	-10%

5.1.3. Delay. Table 6 shows the total delay comparison between each scenario, which has the same characteristic as previous ones. The DN scenario has a more significantly lower value than others due to its non-signalized characteristic. Therefore, the percentage comparison is also based on SC1 as the control sample with a geometrical improvement used to lower the delay and increase the bicycle lane.

Table 6. Delay Comparison between Scenarios

Scenario Code	Delay (PCU-Hour/Hour)	% Changes
DN	0.4	-
SC1	627.8	100%
SC2.1	606.2	-3%
SC2.2	616.8	2%
SC3.1	514.6	-18%
SC3.2	525.1	-16%

5.2. Determination of Junction Design

5.2.1. Intervisibility. The intervisibility of the non-signalized junction is limited due to the lack of a fixed stopping line. Therefore, the intervisibility is adapted on the signalized scenarios with the full blown ones consisting of relatively better intervisibility as the sides of each junction are designed to be a part of the intersection. Similarly, SC2.1 and SC2.2 have better intervisibility than 1, as shown in figure 9.

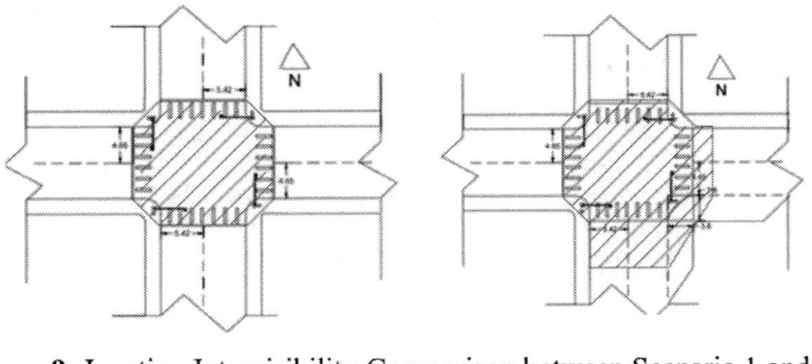

Figure 9. Junction Intervisibility Comparison between Scenario 1 and 2.1

5.2.2. Pedestrian and Cyclist Accommodation. The signalized intersections scenario is used to accommodate the pedestrian crossing the road, while the bike lane is for bike users. In addition, there would also be a traffic light specifically for cyclists, with the green time-synchronized with a motorized vehicle. The addition of bike lanes on the optimum cycle time automatically accommodates pedestrians. This is possible because the optimum cycle time also includes the time for pedestrians to cross the road. For the bicycle movement accommodation, existing lane space is carried out to maximize the limited space in the intersection. As stated previously, the implementation of the lane would be 1 meter for all junctions. The use of these width values leads to an overall motorized lane width of 4.42 meters and 3.65 meters. Therefore, they still exceed the standard motorized vehicle lane value, which is 3 meters.

Figure 10. Typical Cycling Lane in Utrecht

Figure 11. Standard Cycle Traffic Light

5.2.3. Traffic Conflict Management. The potential traffic conflict can be significantly reduced by applying the optimum traffic light. The conflicts found on the junction come from its non-signalized characteristic due to the lack of a systematized method or time for the vehicle users to move from one junction to another. Aside from that, they cannot safely accommodate pedestrian crossing between the sideways, thereby increasing the potential traffic conflict.

Figure 12. Traffic Conflict in The Junction

5.2.4. Effort Needed. Effort represents the feasibility of the scenarios to be applied to the existing site condition. SC1 is expected to have a relatively minimum cost because the effort is limited to installing the traffic light. The scenarios with the limited land acquisition are expected to have a higher effort initialized outside the road. The scenarios with full-blown land acquisition have more significant effort when applied because they pay no attention to the space limitation and constriction. The addition of the bike lane does not have a high cost, as it is only added to the existing road.

5.3. Chosen Junction Design

Table 7 shows the summary of the junction determination based on scenarios comparison. The "-" symbol means that the factors are incomparable because they are undetermined. The traffic performance of the existing/do-nothing scenario cannot be compared to the calculation of capacity, degree of saturation, and delay, which are limited to the traffic volume and lane width value. For SC3.1 and SC3.2, the effort needed was not determined due to the numerous obstructions that are ignored in the analysis process.

Based on the comparison, it is observed that SC2.2, which uses a limited land acquisition with the addition of a bicycle lane, is the best type of scenario. This is because it accommodates both pedestrian and bicycle users while maintaining the effort needed and its traffic performance.

IOP Conf. Series: Earth and Environmental Science 1000 (2022) 012020 doi:10.1088/1755-1315/1000/1/012020

Table 7. Comparison Summary of the Scenarios' Performance

Scenario	Capacity Improvement	Degree of Saturation	Delay Reduction	Intervisibility	Pedestrian Accommodation	Bicycle User Accommodation	Traffic Conflict Management	Effort Needed
DN	-	-	-	✗	✗	✗	✗	-
SC1	✓	✓	✓	✓	✓	✗	✓	✓
SC2.1	✓	✓	✓	✓	✓	✗	✓	✓
SC2.2	✓	✓	✓	✓	✓	✓	✓	✓
SC3.1	✓	✓	✓	✓	✓	✗	✓	-
SC3.2	✓	✓	✓	✓	✓	✓	✓	-

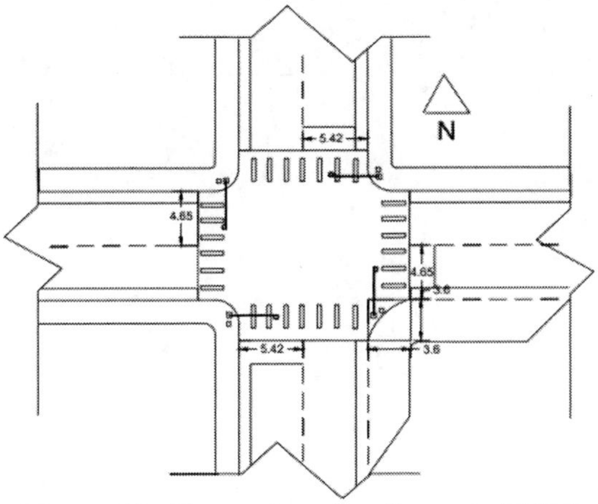

Figure 13. Chosen Junction Scenario/SC2.2

6. Conclusion and Recommendation

The intersection's traffic performance is possible to be improved by increasing the geometrical aspects using TRANSYT Software. Meanwhile, the pedestrian and bicycle user aspects can be improved by adding their respective facilities. This process is also used to decrease geometrical aspects until the value is accepted while improving the intersection condition to be pedestrian and bicycle user friendly. In addition, the installation of a traffic light is an adequate solution for motorized vehicle movement. Therefore, SC2.2 was chosen as the best due to its ability to accommodate pedestrians and bicycle users while improving the motorized vehicle's performance. The balance between those parties provided a win-win solution for all road users while driving active mobility activity in that area, thereby reducing CO_2 emissions.

This result is recommended as one of the bases for junction geometrical design determination, particularly for active mobility, as well as for similar conditions with the chosen location. Further studies need to prioritize active mobility accommodation compared to motorized vehicles at junctions.

Acknowledgments

The authors would like to acknowledge the Transportation Laboratory of Universitas Indonesia for providing the use of TRANSYT Software. This study was supported by PUTI grant number NKB-3663/UN2.RST/HKP.05.00/2020 from Universitas Indonesia.

References

[1] Institution of Transportation Development Policy. 2019. *Jakarta NMT Vission and Design Guideline*. Jakarta.

[2] Achrianto, T. 2020. Head of the Resort Police Accident Unit.
[3] Webster, F V. 1996. *Traffic Signals.* London: H.M.SO.
[4] King, M R C. 2014. Real Urban Intersection Design. *Institute of Transportation Engineers Journal*, **29.**
[5] Wang, et al. 2011. Crossing Behaviors of Pedestrians at Signalized Intersections Observational Study and Survey in China. *Transportation Research Record Journal of The Transportation Research Board*, **65-73.**
[6] Marisamynathan, et al. 2014. Study on Pedestrian Crossing Behavior at Signalized Intersections. *Journal of Traffic and Transportation Engineering Vol. 1* (2).
[7] Transport for London. 2016. *London Cycling Design Standards.* London
[8] Onelcin P. & Alver Y. 2017. The Crossing Speed and Safety Margin of Pedestrians at Signalized Intersections. *Transportation Research Procedia 22*, **3-12.**
[9] Federal Highway Administration. 2019. Bicycle Lanes. *Bicycle and Pedestrian Transportation.* California: U.S. Department of Transportation.
[10] Binning, G B. 2009. *TRANSYST 13 User Guide.* Crowthorne: TRL Software.

Behavior Model Analysis of Pedestrians and Cyclists Mode Selection Base on Active Transportation on Universitas Jember Tegalboto Campus

S Sulistyono[1], W Kriswardhana[1], J B Arianto[2]

[1] Civil Engineering Study Program, Universitas Jember, Jember-68121, East Java, Indonesia
[2] Civil Engineering Undergraduate Study Program, Universitas Jember, Jember-68121, East Java, Indonesia

Corresponding author: sonya.sulistyono@unej.ac.id

Abstract. The University of Jember as one of the campuses that have a high traffic volume is trying to realize a "Green Campus" through the "Ring the Bell" program. However, this vision has not been implemented optimally because there are still many campus residents who do not use active modes of transportation (walking & cycling) even though sidewalk facilities are available. This indicates that the behavioral preferences for choosing active transportation modes for the residents of the Jember University campus are still unclear. Therefore, this study aims to analyze the behavioral model of pedestrian and cyclists mode selection based on active transportation at the Tegalboto Campus, Jember University. The primary data collection of residents' preferences was obtained through the TPB (Theory Of Planned Behavior) questionnaire. SEM model (Structural Equation Model) was applied in the behavioral analysis process to determine the interaction between the independent variables of TPB as a whole. The results of behavioral modeling show that intention is the variable that most influences the behavior of campus residents in using active transportation modes, while attitude is the variable that most influences intentions than subjective norms and perceptions of behavioral control.
Keywords. Pedestrian, SEM, TPB, Active Transportation

1. Introduction

The World Health Organization revealed that the rate of traffic growth in urban areas in Indonesia is increasing rapidly by 15% per year. The Central Statistics Agency in 2020 also noted that the traffic volume was dominated by motorcycles, which was 137.7 million units [1]. The increase in the activity of these modes of transportation, especially on vehicles that are not environmentally friendly, is one of the factors for the emergence of bad impacts in the form of air pollution. [2] Emphasizes that 70% of the population living in urban areas in Indonesia experience air pollution problems due to the dominance of motor vehicle emissions in 2020. The application of sustainable and environmentally friendly active transportation modes can be a recommendation for efforts to overcome air pollution problems.

The results of a review of several studies show that people who use active transportation can be more productive than users of passive transportation [3]. The important role of active transportation triggers the emergence of various theories/research on the consideration of factors that encourage the choice of active transportation modes to school/campus. The results of research in Helsinki, Finland show that if the distance traveled is less than 1 km, then 97.2% of students choose to walk or bike to school. This percentage does not apply in the selection of active transportation modes in Indonesia, because the choice of mode of travel to school/campus is strongly influenced by ability, freedom, and willingness to walk/bicycle [4].

The University of Jember as one of the campuses that have a high traffic volume is trying to realize a "Green Campus" to ensure the health of campus residents [5]. "Ring the Bell", which is a bicycle ride program to campus, is one of the efforts that have been made to support the "Green Campus". A preliminary survey on mode choice at the University of Jember showed that 78.9% of students chose to use a motorbike, while 21.1% of students walked on campus. This percentage shows that there are still many campus residents who have not used active modes of transportation (walking and cycling). Identification of the behavior of choosing active transportation modes for campus residents is still very much needed to support the "Green Campus" program, so this study aims to analyze the behavioral model of choosing pedestrians and cyclists based on active transportation on the Tegalboto Campus, Jember University.

2. Method

2.1. Research sites

The study site is located in the Tegalboto Campus, Jember University. The survey of the existing condition of pedestrian and cyclist facilities was carried out by referring to the division of 19 zones (according to the code in Figure 1). The basis for determining the zone is divided into roads leading to each faculty and strategic buildings [6].

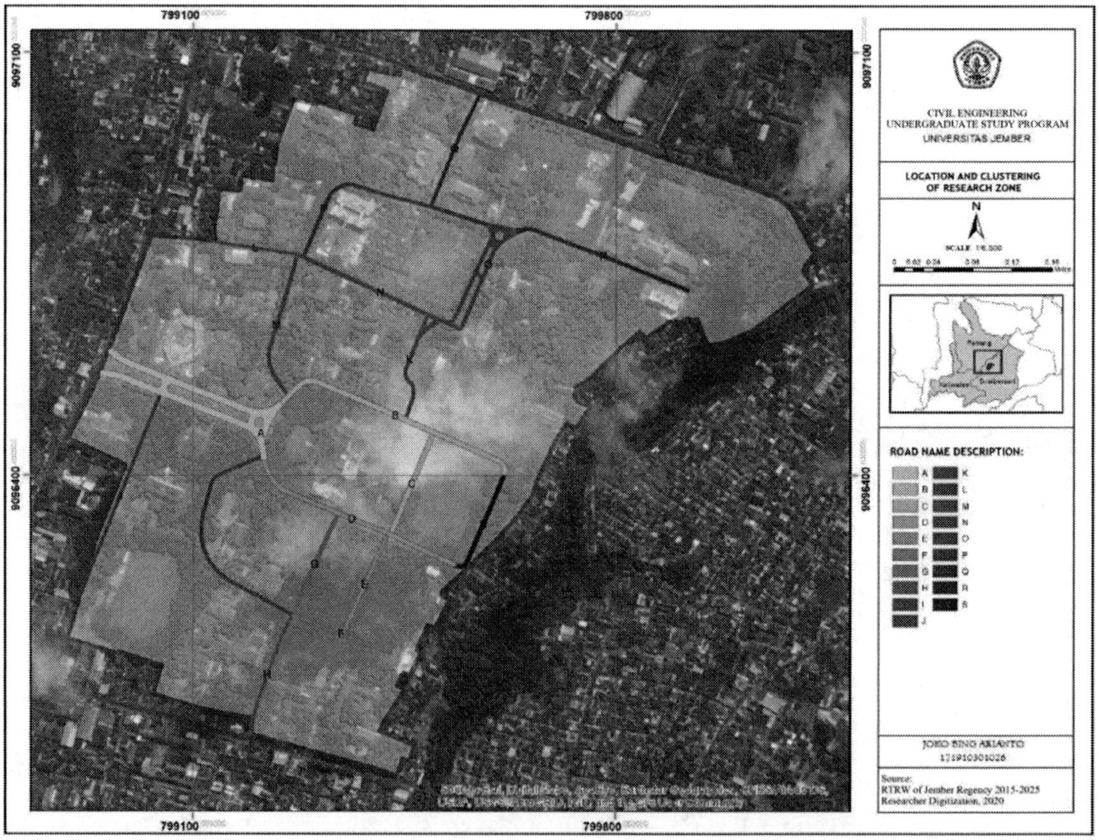

Figure 1. Location and clustering of research zone

2.2. Research stage

The stages of research carried out in this study are described in the flow chart as follows:

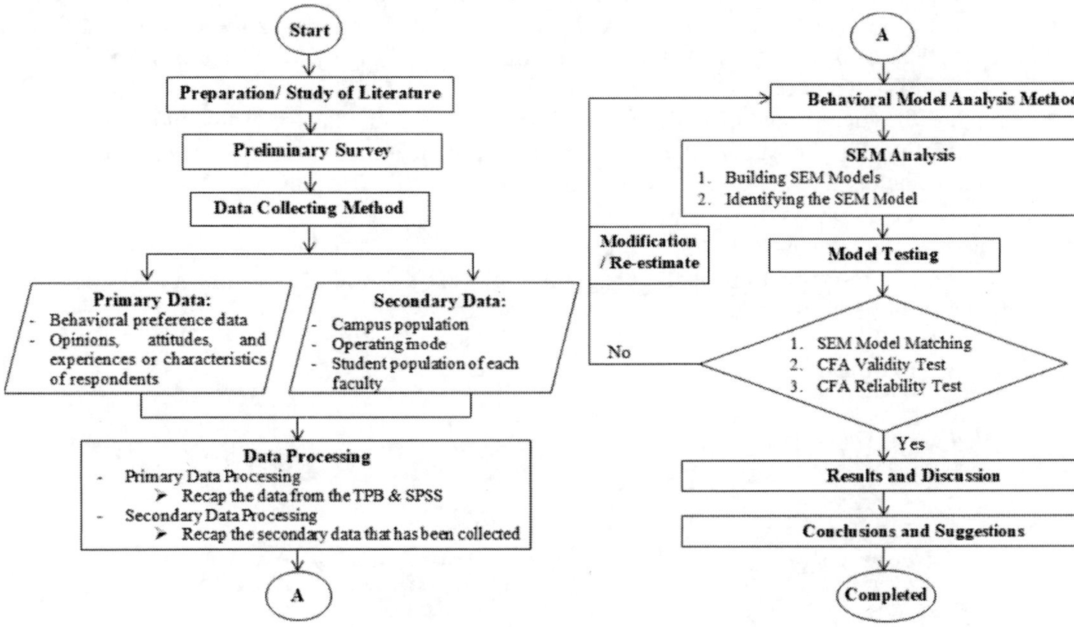

Figure 2. Research flow chart

2.3. Data collecting method

Primary data was obtained from a questionnaire on campus residents' behavioral preferences for the selection of active transportation modes. The data needed include opinions, attitudes, and experiences or characteristics of someone who is the subject of research (respondents). Secondary data is obtained from relevant sources and agencies which will then be processed directly by the researcher. The secondary data needed in this study include the total population of campus residents, the number of student populations for each faculty, the existing modes operating in the Tegalboto Campus area of the University of Jember. The sample was selected based on the proportionate stratified random sampling method and the Slovin formula to determine the minimum number of samples [7].

2.4. Behavioral model analysis method

The analysis of factors and behavior in this study is supported by a statistical processing aid program using LISREL software. SEM model (Structural Equation Model) was applied to determine the interaction between the independent variables of TPB as a whole [8]. The stages of SEM analysis refer to the SEM modeling guidelines [9]:

1. Building SEM models
   The SEM model process to be built must be based on relevant theories, and supported by the results of previous studies.
2. Identifying the SEM Model
   The identification of the SEM model is done by calculating the degree of freedom from the SEM model. The steps to get the value of degrees of freedom are as follows:
   a. Import data from excel file (xls).
   b. Create PRELIS (psf) files from excel files (xls).
   c. Change the variable to ordinal.

d. Create a SIMPLIS (spl) file for the measurement model using the syntax.
3. Model Testing
The stages in the SEM model testing process are as follows:
a. Matching the overall SEM model with the sample data by testing the p-value, GFI, and AGFI. The fit of the model to the data applies if the p-value is 0.05; the GFI value is 0.9; 0.8≤AGFI<0.9 and others.
b. Testing the measurement model with CFA (Confirmatory Factor Analysis) to determine the relationship between latent variables and indicators. validity test requirements (t loading factors 2; SLF 0.70 or 0.50), reliability test (CR or Construct Reliability 0.70; ve or variance extracted 0.50).
4. Modification/Re-estimate
Modification or re-estimation of the program applies if there are indicators that do not meet the model testing requirements.

3. Results and Discussion

3.1.1. Respondents overview

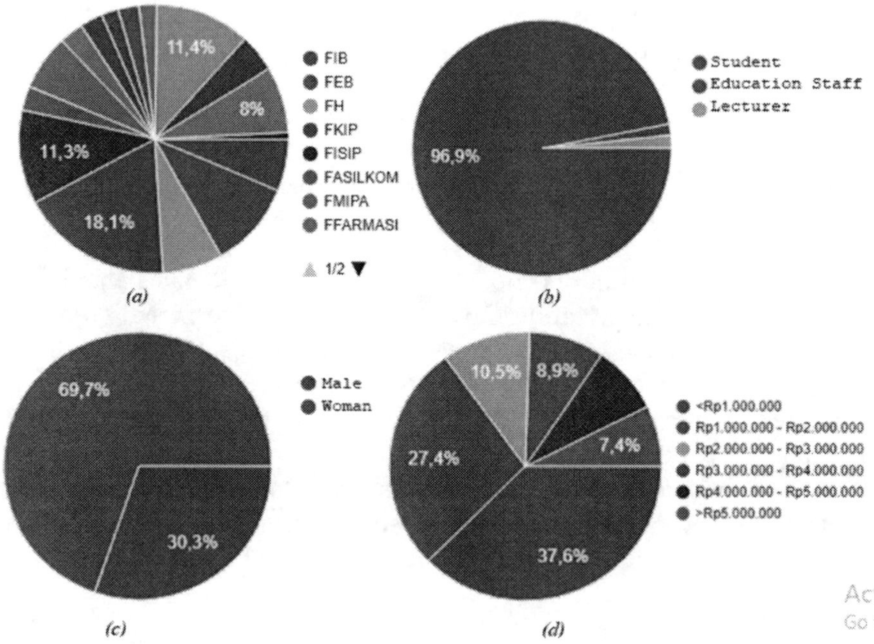

(a) Faculties/ work units; (b) Status of respondents; (c) Gender; (d) Income

Figure 3. Recapitulation diagram of the general characteristics of respondents

A total of 96.9% of respondents were students, while the remaining 1.7% were lecturers and 1.4% were education staff. This percentage has met the requirements of proportionate stratified random sampling because each sample of each respondent's status has exceeded the minimum limit of 396 respondents obtained from the slovin formula. The Faculty of Teacher Training and Education (FKIP) Universitas Jember is the faculty/work unit that fills the most questionnaires with a percentage of 18.1%, while 11.4% of respondents are from the Faculty of Engineering (FT), and 11.3% of respondents are from the Faculty of Engineering. Social and Political Sciences (FISIP). The percentage of 69.7% of the total respondents was dominated by women with a total of 37.6% on average having an income of fewer than one million rupiahs (<Rp. 1,000,000).

3.2. *Data processing*
Primary data obtained from distributing questionnaires through google forms were then processed using the Confirmatory Factor Analysis (CFA)-the second-order method by applying for the LISREL 8.8 aid program.

3.3. *Variable specification for model specification/ model building*
This process is the stage of preparing the initial structural equation model before starting the estimation analysis. The development of this model uses the reference of several similar studies, namely [8, 4]. The specifications of the measurement model used in this study include:

1. Latent variables: AT, SN, PBC, IN, BE.
2. Variables observed: AT1-AT10, SN1-SN12, PBC1-PBC12, IN1-IN12, and BE1-BE6.
3. Relationship between latent variables and observed variables: AT1-AT10 are indicators/observable variables from AT, SN1-SN12 are indicators/observable variables from SN, PBC1-PBC12 are indicators/observable variables from PBC, IN1-IN12 are indicators/observed variables of IN, BE1-BE6 are indicators/observable variables of BE.

3.4. *Test the quality of the questionnaire data*
The data from the TPB online questionnaire survey that had been collected was first tested for validity to determine whether or not the data on the questions in a questionnaire was valid. The indicator of data validity is the Pearson correlation value > r table at a significance of 5% (df = n-2 = 978-2 = 976). The results through the SPSS program show that the Pearson correlation value of all variables is > r table (0.063), so it can be concluded that the variables AT, SN, PBC, IN, and BE are valid. The reliability test was carried out after the questionnaire data met the validity test requirements. The questionnaire data indicator is said to be reliable, that is if the alpha value is > 0.7.

Reliability Statistics

Cronbach's Alpha	N of Items
.718	10

(a)

Reliability Statistics

Cronbach's Alpha	N of Items
.802	12

(b))

Reliability Statistics

Cronbach's Alpha	N of Items
.753	12

(c)

Reliability Statistics

Cronbach's Alpha	N of Items
.767	12

(d)

Reliability Statistics

Cronbach's Alpha	N of Items
.796	6

(e)

(a) Reliability AT; (b) Reliability SN; (c) Reliability PBC; (d) Reliability IN; (e) *Reliability* BE

Figure 4. Output reliability statistics for all variables

Figure 4 shows that all variables have Cronbach's alpha value > 0.7, so the questionnaire data is reliable.

One-Sample Kolmogorov-Smirnov Test

		Unstandardized Residual
N		978
Normal Parameters[a]	Mean	.0000000
	Std. Deviation	2.94688288
Most Extreme Differences	Absolute	.021
	Positive	.017
	Negative	-.021
Kolmogorov-Smirnov Z		.672
Asymp. Sig. (2-tailed)		.757

a. Test distribution is Normal.

Figure 5. Kolmogorov-Smirnov significance value for the whole variable

IOP Conf. Series: Earth and Environmental Science 1000 (2022) 012021 doi:10.1088/1755-1315/1000/1/012021

The normality test used in this study uses the Kolmogorov-Smirnov normality test which is part of the classical assumption test. Figure 5 shows that the Kolmogorov-Smirnov significance value is 0.757 (> 0.05) so that the residual value is normally distributed and there is no need for outliers.

3.5. Building and identifying SEM models

Building the SEM model must adapt to the concept of the theory of planned behavior as the basis for the assumptions of the hypotheses which include [8]:

1. Attitude has a positive influence on intention.
2. Subjective norm (subjective norm) has a positive influence on the intention (intention).
3. Behavioral control (perceived behavioral control) has a positive influence on intentions.
4. The intention has a positive influence on behavior (behaviors).

The quality-tested questionnaire data is then processed in the SPSS auxiliary program so that the data format becomes spv and sav for further import into the LISREL 8.8 application as PRELIS data. The PRELIS data that has been prepared is then converted into an ordinal type. The next process is to build the syntax as shown in Figure 8, then proceed with the running process to get the path diagram and printed output.

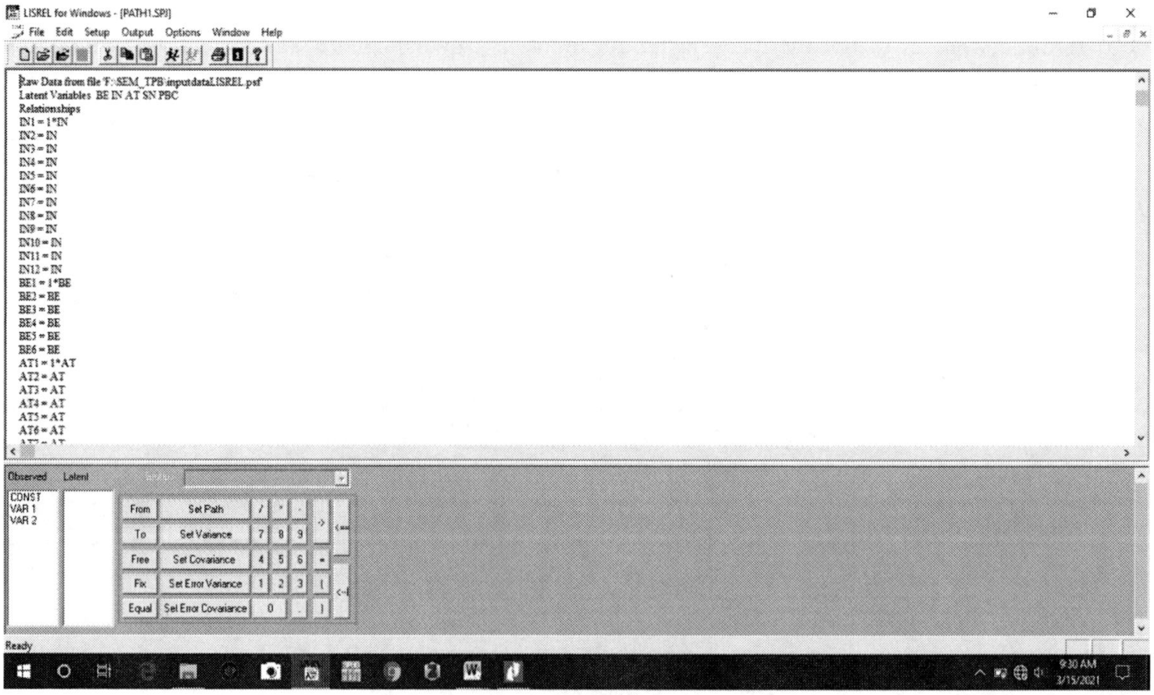

Figure 6. Layer *syntax*

3.5.1. Initial estimation of the SEM model. The initial estimation analysis focuses on the results of the measurement equations and ensures several aspects that need to be checked, namely: error variances, t-values, and standardized loading factors [9].

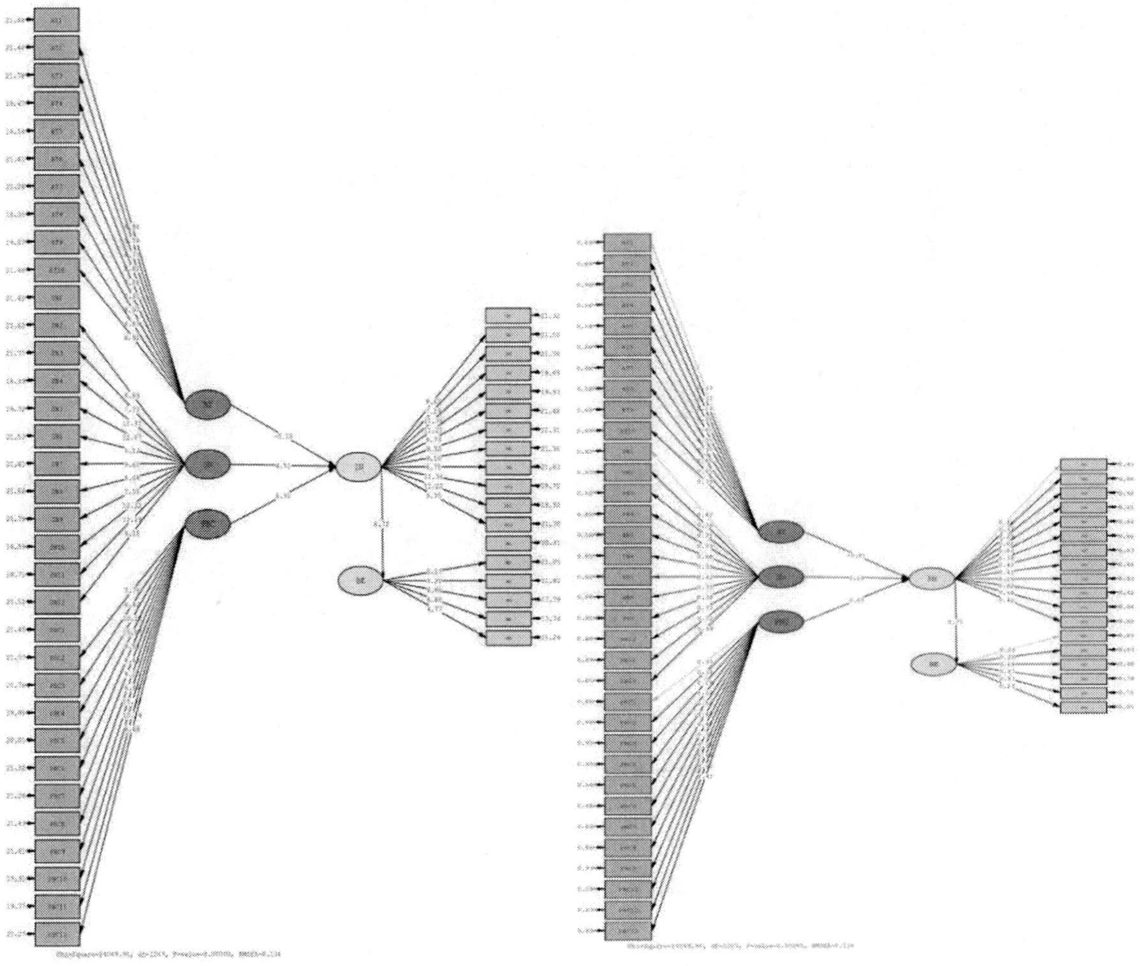

(a) t-values before model respecification (b) SLF before model respecification

Figure 7. t-values and SLF (standardized solution) before respecifying the model

The results of the initial estimation analysis show that there is one aspect that is not met from the model, namely the SLF value on several observed variables that do not meet the required range limit. [9] Stating that if a discrepancy is found in the results of the SLF output, then the observed variables that do not meet must be removed from the model, and further re-specification of the model is carried out by utilizing the LISREL output, namely, the modification indices suggest section.

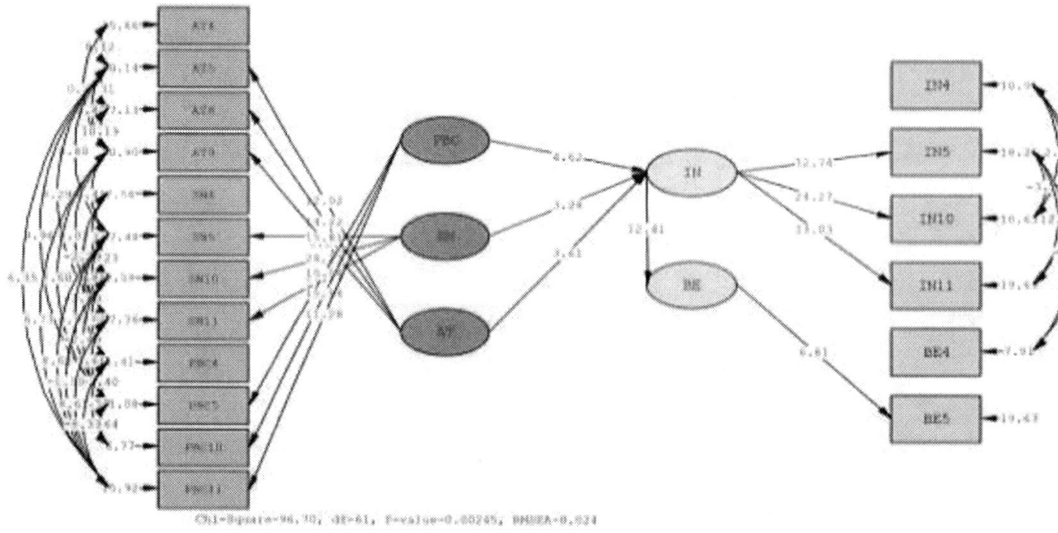

Figure 8. t-values after the model specification

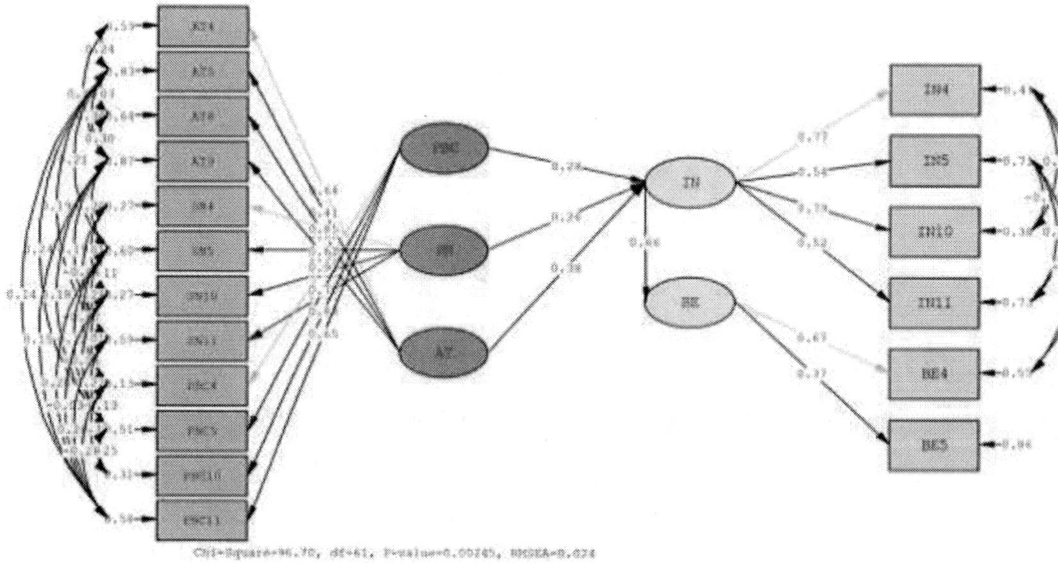

Figure 9. Standardized solution after the model specification

Figures 8 and 9 are SIMPLIS outputs from the model after re-specification. The printed output shows that there are no negative error variances, the t-values of the estimated loading factor > 1.96, the standardized loading factors (SLF) at the LISREL output all meet the range > 0.5 or > 0.7 except for the variable value. observed BE5. This figure is indeed below the required standard, but in [10] it allows the standard factor load value with a value below 0.5 with a note that it is still in the range > 0.3 [9]. Therefore, it is concluded that the factor load estimation results from the respecified model are good.

3.5.2. Test the overall fit of the SEM model. The overall fittest of the model was carried out based on the SIMPLIS printed output containing the Goodness of Fit (GOF) to determine the overall level of fit of the model. Table 1 shows 14 indicators with good fit and 1 chi-square indicator does not match well, so it can be concluded that the overall fit of the model is good.

Table 1. GOF test results SEM model

GIF Size	Target Match Rate	Target Match Rate	Target Match Rate
Chi-square (x2) P > 0.05	Chi-square (x2) The smaller. the better. P > 0.05	X2 = 96.70 P = 0.0025	Not good
NCP Interval	Small value Narrow intervals	NCP = 35.70 12.82 ; 66.51	Good
RMSEA P (Close fit)	RMSEA ≤ 0.08 P≥0.50	0.024 P = 1	Good
ECVI	Small value and Close to ECVI Saturated	M* = 0.32 S* = 0.35 I* = 18.96	Good
AIC	Small value and close to AIC Saturated	M* = 316.70 S* = 342.00 I* = 18525.61	Good
CAIC	Small value and close to CAIC Saturated	M* = 964.11 S* = 1348.42 I* = 18631.55	Good
NFI	NFI ≥ 0.90	0.99	Good
NNFI	NNFI ≥ 0.90	1.00	Good
CFI	CFI ≥ 0.90	1.00	Good
GFI	GFI ≥ 0.90	0.99	Good
AGFI	AGFI ≥ 0.90	0.97	Good
IFI	IFI ≥ 0.90	1.00	Good
RFI	RFI ≥ 0.90	0.99	Good
CN	CN ≥ 200	907.22	Good
RMR	Standardized RMR ≤ 0.05	0.022	Good

3.5.3. Test the validity of the SEM model. The next stage after the model is declared to have a good fit is to test the validity of the model. This test is carried out to determine whether or not an existing measurement model is valid.

Table 2. Result of validity test AT, SN, PBC

Laten → Observed	AT		SN		PBC		Result validity
	SLF*	Nilai-t	SLF*	Nilai-t	SLF*	Nilai-t	
AT4	0.82	**	-	-	-	-	Good
AT5	0.55	12.02	-	-	-	-	Good
AT8	0.78	14.22	-	-	-	-	Good
AT9	0.47	8.81	-	-	-	-	Good
SN4	-	-	1.06	**	-	-	Good
SN5	-	-	0.79	15.81	-	-	Good
SN10	-	-	1.05	28.23	-	-	Good
SN11	-	-	0.79	16.84	-	-	Good
PBC4	-	-	-	-	1.16	**	Good
PBC5	-	-	-	-	0.90	15.54	Good
PBC10	-	-	-	-	1.05	15.94	Good

PBC11	-	-	-	-	0.82	11.28	Good

Table 3. Result of validity test IN, BE

Var.Laten → Var. Observed	IN		BE		Result validity
	SLF*	Nilai-t	SLF*	Nilai-t	
IN4	0.95	**	-	-	Good
IN5	0.68	12.74	-	-	Good
IN10	0.97	24.27	-	-	Good
IN11	0.65	13.03	-	-	Good
BE4	-	-	0.82	**	Good
BE5	-	-	0.43	6.81	Good

Remark:
*SLF = Standardized Loading Factors.
Target SLF ≥ 0.70 or 0.50 (allowed ≥ 0,30), Value target t≥ 2
** = Set by default by LISREL, t-value not estimated.

Tables 2 and 3 show that all t-values of variable loading factors are 2, and standardized loading factors are 0.5 or 0.7. Variables AT9 and BE5 are said to meet even though the SLF value is below 0.5, because [10] allows the standard factor load value with a value below 0.5 with a note that it is still in the range >0.3 [9]. Therefore, it is concluded that the factor load of the latent and observable variables in the model is significant and has good validity.

3.5.4. SEM model reliability test. This test is carried out by determining the values of the CR (Construct Reliability) and VE (Variance Extracted) models. The reliability test used the printed output on the completely standardized solution section: LAMBDA-Y, LAMBDA X, THETA-EPSILON, and THETA-DELTA.

Table 4. Model reliability test results

Variable	CR	VE	Reliability Results
AT	0,808≥0,70	0,525≥0,50	Good
SN	0,887≥0,70	0,673≥0,50	Good
PBC	0,910≥0,70	0,674≥0,50	Good
IN	0,829≥0,70	0,552≥0,50	Good
BE	0,743 ≥0,70	0,614≥0,50	Good

The recapitulation of the reliability calculation results in table 4 shows that all variables have a construct reliability value of 0.70 and variance extracted 0.50, it can be concluded that the reliability of the measurement model (construct) is good.

3.6. Identification of behavioral factors for choosing active transportation modes

The results that were reviewed after the CFA-2nd order analysis process in the LISREL auxiliary program were the following structural equations:

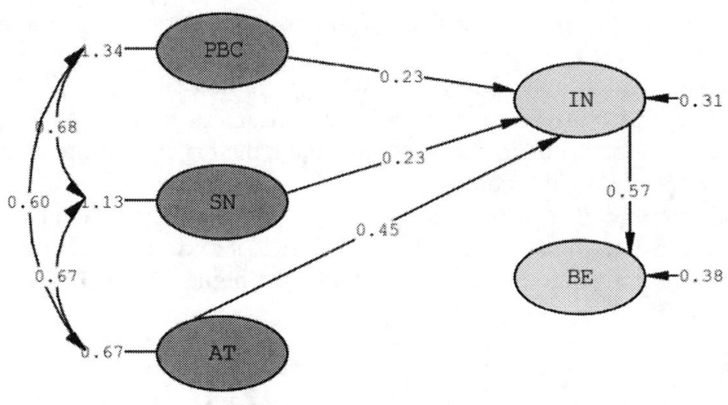

Figure 10. Structural model estimates after model respecification

Structural equation 1:

$$BE = 0.57*IN, \text{Errorvar.} = 0.38 \ , R^2 = 0.44 \quad (1)$$

Structural equation 2:

$$IN = 0.23*PBC + 0.23*SN + 0.45*AT, \text{Errorvar.} = 0.31 \ , R^2 = 0.66 \quad (2)$$

Figure 10 and the above equation show that the path coefficients of the latent variables PBC, SN, and AT are positive for the latent variable IN. The path coefficient of the latent variable IN is positive for the latent variable BE. These results indicate that the model analysis is in accordance with the hypothesis.

BETA

	IN	BE
IN	- -	- -
BE	0.66	- -

GAMMA

	PBC	SN	AT
IN	0.28	0.26	0.38
BE	- -	- -	- -

Figure 11. *Printed output* BETA and GAMMA

The BETA section interprets that IN (intentions) has the greatest direct influence on BE (behavior) which is 0.66. Figure 4.25 of the GAMMA section also shows that the AT variable (attitude) has the largest contribution (0.38) in influencing intention, compared to the PBC (0.28) and SN (0.26) variables. The following is an interpretation of the meaning of the results of the BETA and GAMMA scores:

1. The intention is the biggest variable in influencing the behavior of the residents of the University of Jember in using active transportation modes. This also means that the greater the intention, the greater the behavior of the residents of the University of Jember in using active transportation.
2. Attitude is the variable that has the greatest influence on the intentions of the residents of the University of Jember in using active transportation modes. Attitude variables do not directly affect the behavior of residents, but these results indicate that the better the understanding of

attitudes or perceptions of the residents of the University of Jember, the greater the intention to use active transportation modes.

3. Behavioral control is the second variable that determines whether or not the residents of Jember University intend to use active transportation modes. This means that the easier it is and the higher the freedom of campus residents in choosing the mode, the higher the intention of campus residents to use active transportation modes.
4. Subjective norm is the third variable that determines whether the residents of Jember University intend to use active transportation modes. This shows that the more support and advice from campus residents to use active modes of transportation, the higher the intention of residents to use these modes.

4. Conclusions

The results of the study on the analysis of the behavior of choosing active transportation modes on residents of the Jember Tegalboto University Campus show that: intention is the largest variable in influencing behavior, while attitude is the variable that has the greatest influence on intention. The greater the intention, the greater the behavior of the residents of the University of Jember in using active transportation. The better the understanding of the attitudes or perceptions of the residents of the University of Jember, the greater the intention to use active transportation modes.

References

[1] Kusumastutie, N. S. 2019. Studi pendahuluan: perilaku berkendara anak di bawah umur ditinjau dari theory of planned behavior. *Jurnal Keselamatan Transportasi Jalan (Indonesian Journal of Road Safety)*, 6(2): 110–119.

[2] Kusminingrum, N., & Gunawan, G. 2008. Polusi udara akibat aktivitas kendaraan bermotor di jalan perkotaan Pulau Jawa dan Bali. *Pusat Litbang Jalan Dan Jembatan*. 1(1): 1-13.

[3] Schauder, S. A., & Foley, M. C. 2015. The relationship between active transportation and health. *Journal of Transport & Health*. *2*(3): 343–349.

[4] Siahaan, P. A., Tjahjono, T., & Guritnaningsih. 2020. Understanding the behavior of elementary student's school travel mode choice based on active transportation. *Mekanikal, Infrastruktur dan Teknik Industri*. 1(1): 1-9.

[5] duta.co. 2019. Kampanyekan Go Green pada Mahasiswa Baru Unej. Detik.co Kantor Berita Religius-Nasionalis.https://duta.co/kampanyekan-go-green-pada-mahasiswa-baru-unej. [Diakses pada 8 November 2020].

[6] Ramadhan, M. A., Pratama, G. N. I. P., & Hidayah, R. 2018. Penataan sistem jalur pejalan kaki di Universitas Negeri Yogyakarta. *INERSIA*. 14(1): 101-117.

[7] Kriswardhana, W., dan Widyastuti, H. 2015. Probabilitas Perpindahan Moda Dari Bus Ke Kereta Api Dalam Rencana Re-Aktivasi Jalur Kereta Api Jember-Panarukan. *Seminar Nasional XI - 2015 Teknik Sipil ITS Inovasi Teknik Sipil Dalam Pengelolaan Sumber Daya Air Dan Kemaritiman Menghadapi Masyarakat Ekonomi ASEAN*: 1-8.

[8] Ajzen, I. (1991). The theory of planned behavior. *Organizational Behavior and Human Decision Processes*. 50(2): 179–211.

[9] Wijayanto, S. H. 2008. Structural Equation Modeling Dengan Lisrel 8.8 Konsep Dan Tutorial (1st ed.). Yogyakarta: GRAHA ILMU.

[10] Igbaria, M., Zinatelli, N., Gragg, P. & Cavaye, A. L. M. (1997). Personal computing acceptance factors in small firms: a structural equation model. MIS Quarterly, 279–305.

Microscopic Analysis of the Transportation Modes and Movement of Pedestrians in Dukuh Atas Transit-Oriented Development Area Using PTV Viswalk

R Ivan Adwitiya[1], R Jachrizal Sumabrata[2]

[1] Civil and Environmental Engineering Department, Faculty of Engineering, Universitas Indonesia, Depok, Indonesia

ivan.adwitiya@ui.ac.id [1], rjs@eng.ui.ac.id [2]

Abstract. DKI Jakarta is experiencing several economic obstacles as observed in the prevalence of traffic congestion which has prompted the government to build the first transit-oriented development (TOD) area in the city. The first is the TOD Dukuh Atas as indicated by the current integration of 4 modes of transportation as well as the ongoing construction of Dukuh Atas LRT Station in an area outside the existing TOD. This is to integrate the access through the use of a multipurpose Skyride. Therefore, this research was conducted to analyze the level of service (LOS) for the pedestrians in the existing and ultimate areas using the PTV Viswalk software. The LOS was simulated in the Dukuh Atas TOD Area in the form of the Dukuh Atas JPM based on two scenarios. Scenario 1 is 25% people leaving and 75% entering through the LRT series while Scenario 2 is 50% entering and 50% leaving. The results showed a very bad level of service, LOS F, in several areas for Scenario 2 and this means there is a need for improvement. Therefore, the proposed suggestions were simulated and the minimum LOS produced for all the access was category C.

1. Introduction

Indonesia is the fourth most populous country in the world with a density of 151 people per km^2 (Worldometers, 2020). Moreover, DKI Jakarta, as the capital city, has the highest population with 10.57 million people (Inter-Census Population Survey, 2020). This leads to traffic congestion which has a significant negative impact on the economic growth of the country as indicated by a loss of 65 billion Rupiah per year (World Bank, 2019). Therefore, an efficient public transportation system in the form of a Transit Oriented Development-based Area (TOD) was implemented in DKI Jakarta due to its administrative and economic importance in order to overcome existing congestion and serve the needs of the commuters.

Dukuh Atas is the first TOD point developed by the government as indicated by the 4 existing modes of transportation and the ongoing addition of another in the form of LRT. This new addition is planned not to be integrated into the existing Dukuh Atas TOD area and this means a Multipurpose Crossing Bridge is expected to be constructed to provide integrated access. Moreover, the construction of the LRT Station is certainly in line with the development of the Dukuh Atas TOD area towards reducing the congestion in DKI Jakarta. Therefore, it is necessary to analyze this plan in order to avoid implementation problems and ensure that it has the ability to fulfill the purpose and original goal for which it is designed.

2. Literature Review

2.1. Transit-Oriented Development

This concept was defined by Jabodebek Transportation Management Institution as a development area which integrates the urban spatial design to unite people, activities, buildings, and public spaces through easy connectivity by walking, cycling, and closeness to transportation services. Dukuh Atas is one of the central areas of activity located at the center of DKI Jakarta and is planned to have a TOD area of 146 Ha with 5 integrated modes of transportation. It is important to note that this area currently has 4 modes of transportation and 1 other, LRT, which is under construction is not in the existing Dukuh Atas TOD area and this means a Multipurpose Crossing Bridge is expected to be constructed to provide integrated access.

2.2. Pedestrian Level of Service (LOS)

This is an analytical concept developed in The Highway Capacity Manual (HCM) by the New York Transportation Research Board (TRB) which used as an industry-standard analysis for the flow of different modes of transportation. Moreover, the HCM uses the LOS concept as a qualitative indicator to explain the vehicle operating conditions and pedestrian flow based on certain service scales such as speed and travel time, mobility, traffic disruption, comfort, and convenience.

Table 1. Pedestrian Level of Service on Walkways

Level of Service (LOS)	Pedestrian Space (m^2/pedestrian)	Pedestrian Flow (pedestrian/minute/meter)
A	>5,6	<16
B	3,7 – 5,6	16 – 23
C	2,2 – 3,7	23 – 33
D	1,4 – 2,2	33 – 49
E	0,75 – 1,4	49 - 75
F	<0,75	>75

The HCM method is normally used to analyze the level of pedestrian service based on the pedestrian flow and space. The pedestrian flow which combines the speed, density, and volume of pedestrians is equivalent to the flow of vehicles. Moreover, the LOS is classified into 6 categories based on the comfort provided in the road segmentation with the highest is LOS A and the lowest is LOS F.

Table 2. Pedestrian Level of Service on Stairs

Level of Service (LOS)	Pedestrian Space (m^2/pedestrian)
A	>1,858
B	1,858 – 1,393
C	0,929 – 1,393
D	0,65 – 0,929
E	0,371 – 0,65
F	<0,371

The level of service for pedestrians on walkways and stairs is certainly different due to the difference in the safety hazards and energy expenditure required (Fruin, 1971). Therefore, the classification based on stairs is indicated in Table 2.

2.3. Validation

The modeling according to Makridakis et al. (1982) showed that the prediction error can be determined based on the root mean square value, root mean square error or root mean square deviation.

Therefore, the RMSE is a verification method in determining the accuracy of the estimation results by finding the average square of the error. It is important to note that a low RMSE value indicates the results are close to the real situation.

$$RMSE(\%) = \frac{\sqrt{\frac{1}{n}\sum_{t=1}^{n}(At - Ft)^2}}{\frac{1}{n}\sum_{t=1}^{n} At} \times 100\%$$

Where:
N = Amount of data
At = Actual data
Ft = Simulation Data

An RMSE value below 10% means the model is accepted, while the value above 10% indicates the model is rejected and needs to be reviewed.

3. Data

This study was conducted to analyze the Dukuh Atas LRT Station integrated into the other 4 modes of public transportation in the Dukuh Atas TOD area and the special focus was on pedestrian access. Several stages were involved with the first being the identification of the problem as well as the review of the literature to be used as the basis for the study. This was followed by the determination of the best method to be applied in order to ensure effective analysis and the next stage was the collection of secondary data on the layout of the existing TOD in Dukuh Atas and the Multipurpose Crossing Bridge Atas while the movement of the people in the area was used as the primary data. It is important to note that the data collected from the Dukuh Atas TOD Area were later used for simulation in PTV Viswalk and the output was the walking behavior applied to model the ultimate condition of the area and also to plan the Multipurpose Crossing Bridge. Meanwhile, the ultimate location was modeled using the data on the JPM Dukuh Atas layout.

The final stage was the analysis of the results obtained from modeling the ultimate condition plan for the Dukuh Atas TOD Area to determine the level of service for the intermodal pedestrian integration access since the LRT Station has started operation. However, an effective and efficient pedestrian access proposal was made for the planning scenario considered not to be feasible.

4. Results and Discussion

4.1. Validation

The first step was to determine the density of the existing condition through a survey of the traffic on the pedestrian access segments in the Dukuh Atas TOD Area at a predetermined one hour which was between 07.00 AM and 08.00 AM as well as 5.30 PM and 6.30 PM considered to be the peak hours with the highest traffic. It is important to note that the survey was conducted during the prevalence of the COVID-19 pandemic and this possibly caused a reduction in the number of pedestrians when compared to the period before the pandemic. The survey showed that the evening peak hours have more pedestrians with a total of 3434 people on the 3 different segments while the density is presented in the following table.

Table 3. Density for Each Segments

Segment	Density (m^2/pedestrian)			
	Time Interval 0-900 Sec	Time Interval 900-1800 Sec	Time Interval 1800-2700 Sec	Time Interval 2700-3600 Sec

Pedestrian Access Kendal	0,064	0,052	0,05	0,054
Pedestrian Access Sudirman	0,064	0,073	0,055	0,07
Pedestrian Access Tanjung Karang	0,063	0,069	0,057	0,066

The determination of the density value for each segment was followed by the evaluation of the errors in the data presented for the building layout of the existing Dukuh Atas TOD Area through the use of Viswalk software. The pedestrian movement in the 3 segments was observed and the highest volume and density were compared with the walking behaviors recorded in the modeling simulation of the Dukuh Atas TOD Area, default behaviors available in the PTV Viswalk application, findings from the "Analysis of the Effect of Development of the Transit Area on Pedestrians at Ploris Plawad" by Gari Mauramdha (2019), results of the "Analysis of Pedestrian Movement Due to Operation of the Cibubur LRT Station" by Wiby Adhitya Prayoga (2019), and those recorded in the experiment to have the smallest RMSE value for the density recorded using observation data or direct surveys.

Table 4. Used Walking Behavior Parameter

	Walking Behavior				
Parameter	Default	Wiby	Gari	Iteration 1	Last Iteration
Tau	0,4	0,4	0,4	0,4	0,4
ReactToN	8	7	8	7	7
ASocIso	2,72	1,5	2,72	1,5	1,5
BSocIso	0,2	0,2	0,2	0,2	0,2
Lambda	0,176	0,1	0,176	0,12	0,1
ASocMean	0,4	0,5	0,6	0,55	0,55
BSocMean	2,8	1,5	1,6	1,6	1,5
VD	3	3	3	3	3
Noise	1,2	0,5	1,2	0,9	0,9
Side Preference	None	Left	None	None	None

The walking behavior in each of the segments was also compared based on the RMSE values as indicated in the following table.

Table 5. RMSE Value for Each Used Walking Behavior

RMSE Comparison Each Walking Behavior					
Segments	RMSE Value (%)				
	Default	Wiby	Gari	Iteration 1	Last Iteration
Pedestrian Access Kendal	4,399	4,503	4,207	4,232	4,342
Pedestrian Access Sudirman	8,973	8,181	7,852	7,882	7,693
Pedestrian Access Tanjung Karang	6,194	5,893	5,562	5,332	5,185
SUM	19,566	18,577	17,622	17,446	17,220

The findings showed that the trial-and-error last iteration conducted had the smallest SUM value of RMSE and this means it was applied for the Multipurpose Cross Bridge modeling.

4.2. Multipurpose Crossing Bridge in Dukuh Atas

A Multipurpose or Integrated Crossing Bridge is a pedestrian bridge designed to be constructed to integrate the Dukuh Atas LRT Station into the existing Dukuh Atas TOD Area on the opposite side of the station with both sides cut-off by the Ciliwung River. Moreover, the route from the bridge is to precisely connect the pedestrian area around Sudirman Commuter Line Station with the LRT Station *Concourse Level* to ensure the bridge passes the Commuter Line railway and the Ciliwung River at a free elevation of 5,5 meters and approximately 265 meters length for the 1st-floor route. The design is for the pedestrian access to have 2 floors which are to function as a route for pedestrians crossing over the Ciliwung River and as retail areas for *Food and Beverage* as well as to later provide a space for the *Tawang Pandang area* which is to be used as a recreation area and a *River Deck* such as the one on the Bostanil Bridge in Turkey.

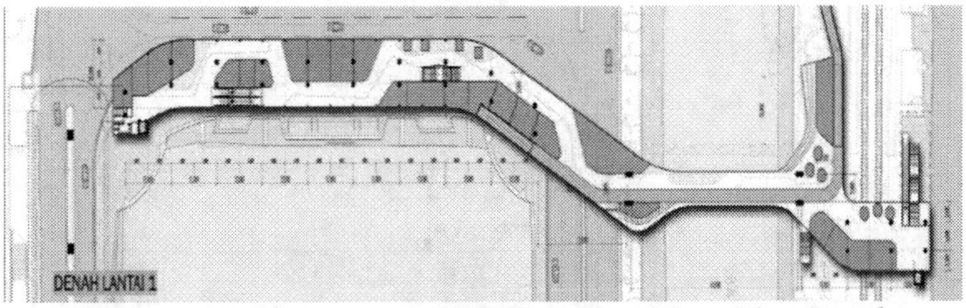

Figure 1. Multipurpose Bridge Crossing Floor Plan Level 1

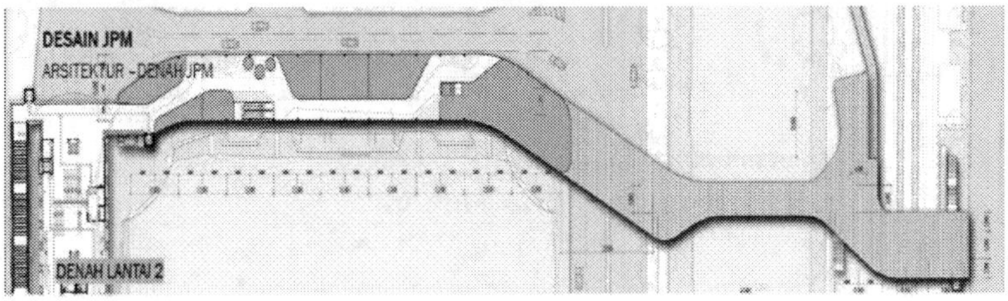

Figure 2. Multipurpose Crossing Bridge Floor Plan Level 2

Figures 1 and 2 are the architectural plans of the Multipurpose Crossing Bridge Dukuh Atas with the floor plan serving as the basis for its integration into the existing model previously developed using the PTV Viswalk. The model proposed using the data obtained showed that the pedestrian access is depicted in white, while the retail area is depicted in orange and the PTV Viswalk considered the retail area an obstacle based on the scenario that the access is expected to be used only for crossing without considering the waiting time due to shopping in retail areas or when the pedestrians enjoy the view. Therefore, the pedestrians were routed statically without waiting time as indicated by the white color on the floor plan.

4.3. Pedestrian Volume

The total number of pedestrians was determined based on the occupancy factor in a series of Jabodebek LRT trains and 5-minute headway through the use of the following scenarios:

Table 6. Pedestrian Volume Scenarios

Scenario	Variable		Total Pedestrian/Occupancy	Total Pedestrian
	Occupancy LRT Train	Headway		
1	25% From LRT		2124	8496
	75% To LRT	5	6372	

IOP Conf. Series: Earth and Environmental Science 1000 (2022) 012022 doi:10.1088/1755-1315/1000/1/012022

2	50% From LRT 50% To LRT	Min	4248 4248	8496

Scenario	From	To	Distribution (%)	Pedestrian Volume
	LRT Dukuh Atas Station	Galunggung Street	5	425
		Sudirman Commuter Line Station	15	1274
		Pedestrian Access Around LRT Dukuh Atas Station	5	425
	Pedestrian Access Around LRT Dukuh Atas Station	LRT Dukuh Atas Station	25	2124
1	Sudirman Commuter Line Station	LRT Dukuh Atas Station	40	3398
	Galunggung Street	LRT Dukuh Atas Station	10	850
	LRT Dukuh Atas Station	Galunggung Street	10	850
		Sudirman Commuter Line Station	30	2549
		Pedestrian Access Around LRT Dukuh Atas Station	10	850
	Pedestrian Access Around LRT Dukuh Atas Station	LRT Dukuh Atas Station	10	850
1	Sudirman Commuter Line Station	LRT Dukuh Atas Station	35	2972
	Galunggung Street	LRT Dukuh Atas Station	5	425

The three access entrances to the Multipurpose Crossing Bridge assumed the distribution of pedestrians affects the determination of the route to be modeled. This was indicated by the observation that those with generation and pull at Sudirman Station were more than the others due to the fact that the Kereta Rel Listrik (KRL) transportation at the station is the mode mostly used in Dukuh Atas TOD Area.

The output from the Multipurpose Crossing Bridge model was observed to be different from the existing condition model due to the fact that the area built in the JPM modeling was not based on the analyzed segments but the area per floor. This means the density of the JPM model is accurate due to its use of feet/area as the unit, while the area built on the floor has some parts which are not pedestrian routes and this means its area accuracy is very non-specific. Therefore, the feature area result used to determine the level of service for floor pedestrians in the bridge modeling analysis can also be used to determine the values based on the parts of an area already constructed. Meanwhile, only the ramps and stairs results were used for the stairs or escalators and were considered accurate because the calculation was based on each vertical pedestrian access.

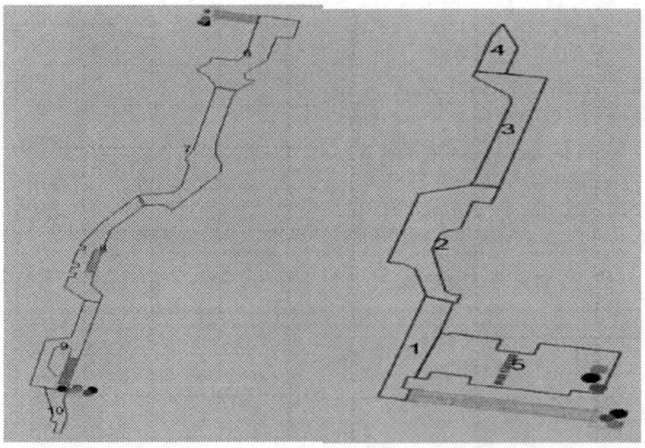

Figure 3. Section Area Measurement for the Multipurpose Crossing Bridge in Dukuh Atas

4.4. Pedestrian Level of Service for the Multipurpose Crossing Bridge in Dukuh Atas

4.4.1. Scenario 1

The simulation conducted for 3600 seconds showed a total of 8496 pedestrians for Scenario 1 and this means the area is categorized as LOS E due to the fact that the entire area of the 1st floor has a density of 1.11 people/m^2 at the final 15-minute interval. Meanwhile, the vertical access was classified as LOS D and F based on Highway Capacity Manual (HCM) adapted from John J Fruin (1971) concerning the stairwell in the area around the Commuter Line Sudirman Station which was modeled as a three-dimensional build-up due to the up and down movement of pedestrians on one side. The results showed that Scenario 1 requires improvement as indicated by the level of service categorized as LOS F for Sections 6 and 7 at the entrance of the Multipurpose Crossing Bridge of Dukuh Atas and around the Commuter Line Sudirman Station.

4.4.2. Scenario 2

The output generated based on the Area as well as the Ramps & Stairs results in Scenario 2 showed several accesses needed to be changed due to the LOS F recorded in the 1st-floor area with the last 15-minute interval. The vertical access for the stairs around Commuter Line Sudirman Station is also observed not to be much different from Scenario 1. Meanwhile, almost all the other results in this scenario are LOS A and LOS B which are considered good and do not require improvement proposals. From the table above which is the modeling output for 1 hour with the number of pedestrians and routes. This means that the areas needed to be improved in this scenario are Section 6 and the entrance stairs around the station to ensure the Multipurpose Crossing Bridge supports the movement of commuters.

5. Improvement Suggestions for the Multipurpose Crossing Bridge in Dukuh Atas

The poor pedestrian service levels observed at different accesses to the Multipurpose Crossing Bridge, led to the simulation of the suggestions for improvement based on the same scenarios used with certain changes such as the redesigning of the walking stairs at the entrance around the Commuter Line Sudirman Station into a conventional staircase with a width of 3 meters. The layout was also proposed to be changed such that the entry and exit placed on one side of the Multipurpose Crossing Bridge was redesigned to be on two different sides for entry and exit as indicated in the following figure where the exit is red and the entrance is blue.

Figure 4. Improvement Illustration

The width of the vertical pedestrian access in the form of a ladder located at the middle of the Multipurpose Crossing Bridge was also changed from 2.4 m to 4 m in order to create a Tawang Pandang area in the JPM as indicated in Figure 5.

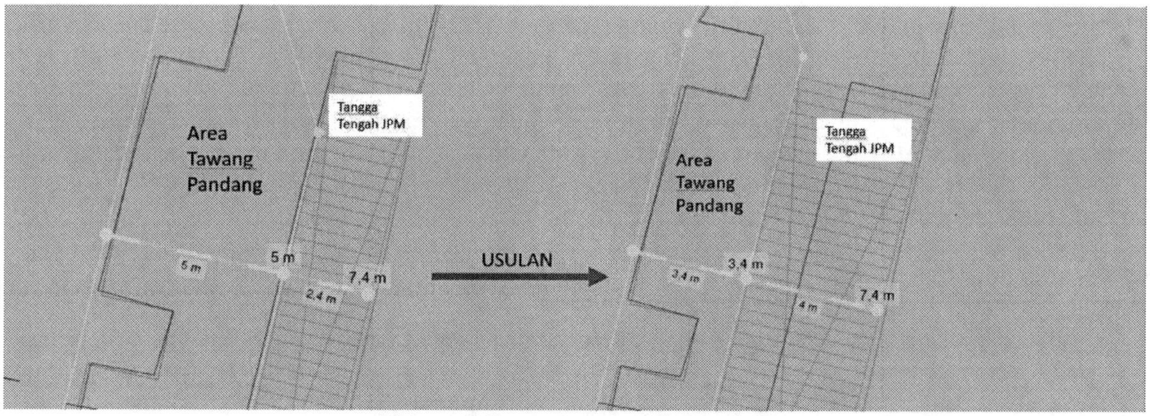

Figure 5. Improvement Illustration

The proposals for improvement were made based on the simulation of Scenarios 1 and 2, and no pedestrian access was observed to be lesser than LOC C after the proposals were simulated.

6. Conclusions

The analysis conducted led to the following conclusions:

1. The level of service for the pedestrians transiting in the Multipurpose Crossing Bridge of Dukuh Atas TOD Area was simulated using PTV Viswalk software based on two scenarios. Scenario 1 represents 25% of passengers leaving and 75 % coming through the LRT while Scenario two indicates 50% and 50% respectively. The results showed that the level of service is very bad in several areas and the LOS was categorized as class F, thereby requiring suggestions for improvement.
2. Some of the proposed suggestions include changing the location of the entry and exit of the Multipurpose Crossing Bridge around KRL Sudirman, converting the elevator to a conventional staircase with a dimension of 3 meters, and changing the width of the middle staircase around the Tawang Pandang area which was originally 2.4 meters to 4 meters.
3. The minimum LOS produced from all accesses to the Multipurpose Crossing Bridge after the implementation of these suggestions through simulation was LOS class C.
4. The walking behavior was validated by comparing the density obtained from the simulation to the default value in the software, results obtained by Wiby from a study conducted in the Cibubur area,

findings from Gari in the Tangerang area, and the density obtained through trial-and-error using the data from observations and surveys conducted by each individual. The results were all validated based on their RMSE values which were lesser than 10%, but the walking behavior from the trial and error in the n-iteration was used in the simulation of the ultimate condition due to its lower RMSE accumulation value when compared to the others.

References

[1] Artawan A Wedagama D & Mataram K 2013 *Analisis karakteristik pejalan kaki dan tingkat pelayanan fasilitas pejalan kaki* (Bali: Universitas Udayana)
[2] Badan Pengelola Transportasi Jabodetabek 2018 *Transit oriented development* (TOD) 9 Desember, 2020 http://bptj.dephub.go.id/transit-oriented-development-tod.
[3] Badan Pusat Statistik 2019 P*royeksi jumlah penduduk DKI Jakarta 2020* 9 Desember, 2020. https://databoks.katadata.co.id/datapublish/2019/12/07/jumlah-penduduk-dki-jakarta-2020#:~:test=Survei%20penduduk%20antar%20sensus%20(SUPAS,yang%20sebanyak%2010.504.100%20jiwa
[4] Calthrope P 1993 The next American metropolis: Ecology, community, and the American dream (New York: Princeton Architectural Press)
[5] CNBC Indonesia 3 Oktober, 2019. *Bank dunia: Macet bikin rugi Indonesia Rp56 T per tahun* 9 Desember, 2020. https://www.cnbcindonesia.com/news/20191003141047-4-104180/bank-dunia-macet-bikin-rugi-indonesia-rp-56-t-per-tahun
[6] Dinas Perhubungan Provinsi Jawa Barat 30 Juni, 2015. *Mengenal bus rapid transit (BRT).* 13 Desember, 2020. http://dishub.jabarprov.go.id/artikel/view/566.html
[7] Institute for Transportation and Development Policy 2017 *TOD standard* 3rd ed. (New York: Author)
[8] NYC Department of City Planning 2006 *Pedestrian level of service study* (New York: Transportation Division of New York City)
[9] Peraturan Gubernur DKI Jakarta 2019 *Peraturan Gubernur no. 67 tahun 2019 tentang pengembangan kawasan TOD*
[10] Prayoga W 2019 *Analisis pergerakan pejalan kaki akibat pengoperasian Stasiun LRT Cibubur* (Depok: Universitas Indonesia)
[11] PT. LRT Jakarta 2021 *LRT Jakarta, pelengkap integrasi moda transportasi Jakarta* 12 Desember, 2020. https://www.lrtjakarta.co.id/lrt_jakarta_pelengkap_integrasi_moda_transportasi_jakarta_berita336.html
[12] PT. MRT Jakarta 2019 *Stasiun Dukuh Atas BNI* 13 Desember, 2020. https://jakartamrt.co.id/id/stasiun/stasiun-dukuh-atas-bni
[13] PT. Railink 2021 *Stasiun kereta api bandara* 13 Desember, 2020. https://www.railink.co.id/train/id
[14] Republika 15 Maret, 2019 Ini rute transjakarta teritegrasi Stasiun MRT Dukuh Atas. 13 Desember, 2020. https://nasional.republika.co.id/berita/nasional/jabodetabek-nasional/poe1zl335/ini-rute-transjakarta-terintegrasi-stasiun-mrt-dukuh-atas
[15] Situmorang L 2019 *Analisis skenario pejalan kaki pada ruang publik (studi kasus: Stasiun LRT Harjamukti, Cibubur)* (Depok: Universitas Indonesia)
[16] Solichin I 2019 *Analisa bangkitan perjalanan dan trip distribution di Surabaya Utara* (Surabaya: Universitas Pembangunan Nasional Veteran Jawa Timur)
[17] Taolin T V 2008 *Kualitas ruang publik kota pada kawasan TOD* (Depok: Universitas Indonesia)

Proposing bus transit fares: buy the service project by ministry of transportation, Indonesia (case study from Palembang, South Sumatera)

[a]Rahayu Sulistyorini, [a]Wiwin Sriniaty Siahaan, [a]Salwa Nabilla Antiqasari, [a]Zenia F Saraswati, [b]Muhammad Alfat Rizki Pratama, [a]Muhammad Zainal Ibad, [b]Reza Asriandi Ekaputra.

[a]Departement of Urban and Regional Planning, Institut Teknologi Sumatra, Jalan Terusan Ryacudu Nomor 1, Kabupaten Lampung Selatan, Provinsi Lampung
[b]Departement of Civil Engineering, Institut Teknologi Sumatera, Jalan Terusan Ryacudu Nomor 1, Kabupaten Lampung Selatan, Provinsi Lampung

sulistyorini.smd@gmail.com

Abstract: Numbers of private vehicle movement in city caused negative externalites. Indonesia's Ministry of Transportation tend to facilitate Palembang city mobility with public transportation called Bus Transit Buy The Service Project. This research aims to identify the equilibrium in passenger willingness to pay and ability to pay as proposing the suitable tariff. Shown in this research, is about 2.400 - 3.500 rupiahs is the range of effective bus transit fares.
Keywords: Fares, Bus Transit, ATP, WTP, Operational Cost.

1. Introduction

The city is a network of life systems characterized by high population density[1]. High population density is influenced by the increase in population. The increase in the population of the city can affect the number of movements and increase the number of road usage in the city[2]. The increasing number of movements leads to displacement caused by certain needs that an area cannot meet. The role of public transportation is to meet human needs for increased movement and mobility in moving from one place to another at close to long distance[3]. The quality of service is an influential aspect in the selection of modes by public transport users. Service users with a good service experience have a high chance of using the service next, while service users with problematic service experience will not use the transportation service next. This explains the importance of improving the quality of service to be able to retain customers and attract new users[4].

Palembang city is the second most populous city of Sumatra Island with various problems of densely populated cities, one of which is the field of transportation services. The need for better and sustainable handling of public transportation services in urban areas as well as the needs of urban communities so that the central government considers taking the decision to provide road-based urban transportation services TEMAN BUS that operates in 2020. TEMAN BUS stands for Transportasi Ekonomis Mudah Andal dan Nyaman as a Bus Rapid Transit (BRT) transportation in support of community mobilization that integrates other mass transit services namely Light Rail Transit (LRT). Bus Rapid Transit Trans Musi Buy The Service is a new program in improving road-based mass transportation from the Ministry of Transportation that adopts the TransJakarta service system to support the creation of an integrated, reliable, and reliable mass transportation system that can support the realization of a sustainable city. Therefore, this research was conducted as identification of satisfaction level for operators and regulators in evaluation materials in maintaining and improving BRT Trans Musi Buy The Service[5].

IOP Conf. Series: Earth and Environmental Science 1000 (2022) 012023 doi:10.1088/1755-1315/1000/1/012023

2. Research Methodology

The type of research that is conducted is deductive-quantitative because researchers verify the data by integrating variables and researching in the field. Research is deductive-qualitative because it regulates the variables of some theories used in research and verifies data in the field. Based on the purpose of the research formulated, the need for a quantitative approach using some statistical analysis that aims to know the results obtained in the field with conformity to the theory used. The analysis in this study used the calculation of Operational Cost (OC) [6]. OC is one of the important components in economic analysis both in the stage of a feasibility study, planning, monitoring, and maintenance consisting of fixed costs, and also non-fixed costs (running costs) that will exist when the vehicle operates[7].

3. Research Result

3.1 Position of BRT Buy The Service Corridor 2 and 4 in Palembang City

In RTRW Palembang City 2012-2032 BRT position in Palembang city will be directed to serve new corridors, especially those leading to new growth centers in support of population movement under the conditions of research sites where existing corridors are new corridors[8]. Then for the position of BRT Buy The Service which is to increase the use of quality, comfortable, safe, and affordable urban public passenger transportation, it is necessary to provide subsidies for urban public passenger transportation on certain routes[9].

A. Push and Pull Strategy

In increasing passenger interest in riding public transportation, the central government implemented a push and pull strategy by:

- Push, The lack of public travel space arrangements in Palembang city and the lack of special parker room facilities at stations or terminals adjacent to bus stops/stops so that parking activities still use the shoulder of the road.
- Pull, The Existence of Standar Pelayanan Minimal (SPM) and vehicle operational systems set by the Ministry of Transportation and supervised by the management of the management so that the quality of service provided is satisfactory with the details of SPM as follows:
    1. Security which includes the availability of CCTV, Driver ID Card, and Hazard Button. In existing conditions, there are facilities in the form of CCTV, DRIVER ID Card, and Hazard Button so that security meets the SPM setting.
    2. Safety which includes the availability of vehicle operating SOP, emergency SOP, etc. Based on interviews with operators and bus drivers, in existing conditions, there is an SOP that is understood and adhered to by each driver so that security meets the SPM setting.
    3. Conveniences include bus temperature, cleanliness, and lighting. In existing conditions, there are facilities in the form of air conditioning that works well and has a low temperature, the availability of trash can facilities and the responsibility of bus cleanliness held by each bus driver, and lighting lights in the bus that function well at night and when the lack of lighting so that comfort meets the SPM setting.
    4. Affordability that includes accessibility and fares Based on existing conditions, access to use the bus there are few obstacles complained by service users in Corridor 4, namely the location of bus stops on the right and left roads that are not in the opposite location but have a difference in the distance so confusing for service users who are the first to use the bus service. In the current condition of affordability of tariffs can be said to be affordable because there is still a subsidy policy for the Buy The Service program that is Rp. 0,- so that for service users tariffs meet the SPM setting.
    5. Equality which includes the availability of priority seats. In existing conditions, there are priority seats reserved for the elderly, pregnant women, and people with disabilities as well as the availability of a special place for wheelchair users in the bus so that it meets the existing SPM.

6. Regularity which includes waiting time, travel speed and stop time at the stop. waiting times, travel speeds and stop times at stops already have rules set and met by each driver but in the existing conditions, these three things are affected by the level of congestion that exists.

Then with the 100% subsidy provided by the central government that is charged to the state budget in the budget of the Ministry of Transportation and/or the regional budget so that BRT Buy The Service tariff can be carried out Rp, 0 under existing conditions and service users only need to prepare electronic cards in the meantime since the inauguration of bus operations in 2020 until the time of this research. From the analysis, it can be concluded that corridors 2 and 4 support in BRT position in Palembang city which is directed to serve new corridors in support of the movement. Then for the position of BRT Buy The Service also supports to increase the use of quality, comfortable, safe, and affordable urban public passenger transportation that can be seen from almost the fulfillment of all existing SPM namely security, safety, comfort, affordability, equality, and regularity with the procurement of subsidies for urban public passenger transportation on certain routes.

3.2 Operational Cost Analysis

Vehicle Operational Costs in Corridors 2 and 4 have no difference because km traveled per day both corridors are the same 190 km. Detailed OC can be seen in the table below:

Tabel 1. Direct Cost Component
BRT Coridor 2 And 4 Buy The Service Palembang City

No	Direct Cost Components	Cost	OC /years	OC /day	OC /rit (PP)	OC /trip (PP)	OC /km	OC /hour	0C /seat
1	Bus Depreciation Fee	140,217,000	14,021,700	384,156	48,020	24,010	2,022	24,010	600
2	Capital Interest Cost	6,070,000	6,070,000	16,630	2,079	1,039	88	1,039	26
3	Bus Crew Salaries and Benefits	49,051,407	49,051,407	134,387	16,798	8,399	707	8,399	210
4	Cost of Fuel (BBM)	76,285,000	76,285,000	209,000	26,125	13,063	1,100	13,063	327
5	Tire Fee	43,200,000	43,200,000	118,356	14,795	7,397	623	7,397	185
6	Small Service Fee	7,896,000	7,896,000	21,633	2,704	1,352	114	1,352	34
7	Big Service Fee	13,192,000	13,192,000	36,142	4,518	2,259	190	2,259	56
8	General Overhaul Fee	6,488,825	6,488,825	17,778	2,222	1,111	94	1,111	28
9	Engine Oil Addition Fee	2,920,000	2,920,000	8,000	1,000	500	42	500	13
10	Bus Wash Fee	18,250,000	18,250,000	50,000	6,250	3,125	263	3,125	78
11	Vehicle Registration/Tax Fee	2,124,500	2,124,500	5,821	728	364	31	364	9
12	Vehicle Feasibility Test Fee	150,000	150,000	411	51	26	2	26	1
13	Cost of Parts and Body Repair	5,311,250	5,311,250	14,551	1,819	909	77	909	23
14	Additional Facility Fee	83,345,000	83,345,000	228,342	28,543	14,271	1,202	14,271	357
	Amount	454,500,982	328,305,682	1,245,207	155,651	77,825	6,555	77,825	1,947

Source: Research Result, 2021

Tabel 2. In-Direct Cost Component
BRT Coridor 2 And 4 Buy The Service Palembang City

No	In-direct Cost Components	Cost	OC /years	OC /day	OC /rit (PP)	OC /trip (PP)	OC /km	OC /hour	OC /seat
1	Bus Crew Salaries and Allowances	25,235,223	25,235,223	69,138	8,642	4,321	364	4,321	108
2	Cost Management	1,741,515	1,741,515	4,771	596	298	25	298	7
	Amount	26,976,738	26,976,738	73,909	9,239	4,619	389	4,619	115

Source: Research Result, 2021

Tabel 3. The Total Amount of Direct and In-Direct
BRT Coridor 2 And 4 Buy The Service Palembang City

No	In-direct Cost Components	Cost	OC /years	OC /day	OC /rit (PP)	OC /trip (PP)	OC /km	OC /hour	OC /seat
1	Direct Cost Component	454,500,982	328,305,682	1,245,207	155,651	77,825	6,555	77,825	1,947
2	In-direct Cost Components	26,976,738	26,976,738	73,909	9,239	4,619	389	4,619	115
	Amount	481,477,720	355,282,420	1,319,116	164,890	82,445	6,944	82,444	2,062

Source: Research Result, 2021

Based on the calculation results in the table, the total per-seat fare for bus operation is Rp. 2,061 in one trip. This calculation is based only on operational costs in the form of direct costs and indirect costs of transit bus services corridors 2 and 4. To identify the value of OC to fares, it is necessary to prepare fares in field conditions with the average number of passengers, as follows;

Cost/*seat* = Rp. 0
Average Passenger = LF x C
Average Passenger = 40% x 40= 16 Penumpang

Based on the results of the calculation taking into account these things, the difference between the income and Operational Cost value of Corridors 2 and 4 is as follows;

Table 2. OC Difference by BRT Cost In Corridor 2 And 4
Buy The Service Palembang City

Income/ years	Income / day	Income / trip	Income / km	Income / hour	Income / seat
0	0	0	0	0	0
Difference/ years	**Difference/ day**	**Difference/ Trip**	**Difference/ km**	**Difference/ hour**	**Difference/ Seat**
-481,477,720	-1,319,117	-82,444.82	-6,943	-82,445	-2,061

Source: Research Result, 2021

Operational Cost analysis in the table above with BRT buy the service tariff corridor 2 and corridor 4 is Rp. 0.00 / passenger. From the data processing obtained that the Operational Cost of BRT Buy The Service Vehicle per year amounted to Rp. 481,477,720.00 and Vehicle Operating Costs per km amounted to Rp. 6,943.00. The amount of Operational Cost (OC) analysis of Corridor 2 and Corridor 4 has the same result because the data obtained from interviews with the operators have the same data on both kilometer travel per day and bus maintenance/maintenance data for both Mercedes Benz and Isuzu buses. But in determining tariffs in the future it is necessary to consider the perception of tariffs from BRT Buy The Service users. To see the suitability between demand and supply from regulators, operators, and users in making tariff policies.

3.3 Cost Based on User ATP and WTP Analysis

The perception of the user's finances is identified based on the type of work based on the results of the questionnaire that has been conducted[10]. The identification was continued by analyzing using The Ability To Pay (ATP) and Willingness To Pay (WTP) analysis on bus users based on routes in each corridor of the study location obtained as follows[11]:

i. Corridor 2 in route Sako – Asrama Haji

Table 3. Perception of Financial In Corridor 2

Category	ATP	WTP	Future WTP
Civil Servant	Rp 20,774	Rp 3,444	Rp 4,611
Students	Rp 5,729	Rp 4,500	Rp 4,606
Entrepreneur	Rp 6,779	Rp 3,527	Rp 4,147

Source: Research Result, 2021

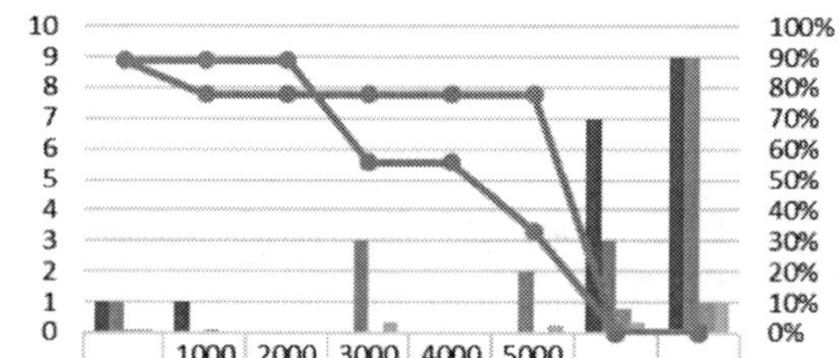

	< 999	1000 - 1999	2000 - 2999	3000 - 3999	4000 - 4999	5000 - 5999	6000 <	Total
WTP Frequency	1	1	0	0	0	0	7	9
ATP Frequency	1	0	0	3	0	2	3	9
WTP % Frequency	11%	11%	0%	0%	0%	0%	78%	100%
ATP % Frequency	11%	0%	0%	33%	0%	22%	33%	100%
WTP Frequency Commulative	89%	78%	78%	78%	78%	78%	0%	0%
ATP Frequency Commulative	89%	89%	89%	56%	56%	33%	0%	0%

Chart 1. ATP WTP ASN in Corridor 2

Source: Research Result, 2021

Based on the graph, you can see the meeting point between ATP and WTP values for the ASN category in corridor 2. Based on these results, it can be identified that the ability of respondents to pay for the bus service is 78% in the price range of Rp. 2,000 - 2,999. 89% of users are willing to pay that price. This means that the value of ATP owned by users with the ASN category is under the value of its WTP if it is in the tariff range of Rp. 2,000 - 2,999. Based on the results of the analysis, in the theory of ATP and WTP relationship the state of the ASN category corridor 2 entered into the ATP relationship is greater than WTP because of the condition that shows the ability to pay transportation services is greater than the willingness to pay for transportation services this is characterized by relatively high ASN income.

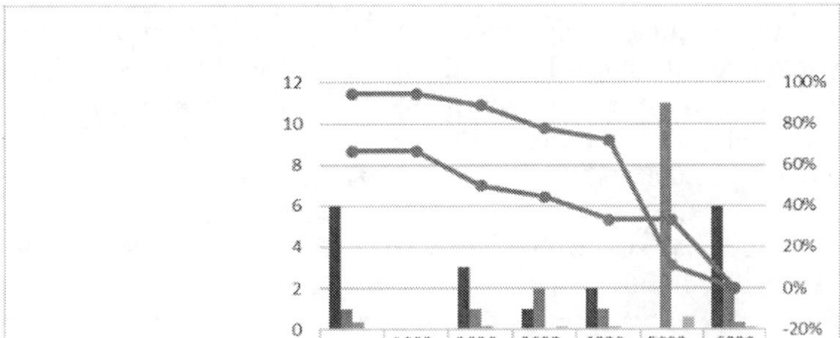

	< 999	1000 - 1999	2000 - 2999	3000 - 3999	4000 - 4999	5000 - 5999	6000 <
WTP Frequency	6	0	3	1	2	0	6
ATP Frequency	1	0	1	2	1	11	2
WTP % Frequency	33%	0%	17%	6%	11%	0%	33%
ATP % Frequency	6%	0%	6%	11%	6%	61%	11%
WTP Frequency Commulative	67%	67%	50%	44%	33%	33%	0%
ATP Frequency Commulative	94%	94%	89%	78%	72%	11%	0%

Chart 2. Chart of ATP WTP Student in Corridor 2

Source: Research Result, 2021

Based on the graph, a meeting point between ATP and WTP values for the Student category in corridor 2. Based on these results, it can be identified that the ability of respondents to pay for the bus service is 33% in the price range of Rp. 4,000 - 4,999. 72% of users will pay that price. This means that the value of ATP owned by users with the category of Students / Students is under the value of its WTP if it is in the tariff range of Rp. 4,000 - 4,999.

Based on the analysis, the theory of ATP and WTP state of Student category corridor 2 entered into two relationships, namely ATP is greater than WTP because of the condition that shows the ability to pay transportation services greater than the willingness to pay transportation services this is characterized by relatively high income Students while the condition of ATP is lower than WTP because of conditions that indicate the ability to pay transportation services lower than the willingness to pay transportation services this is characterized by the income of Students who are relatively low.

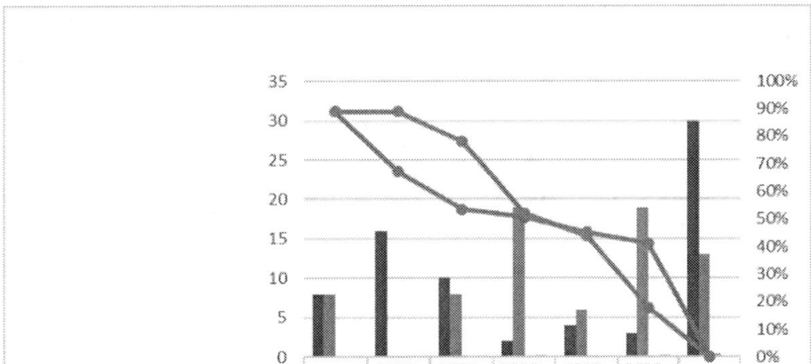

	< 999	1000 - 1999	2000 - 2999	3000 - 3999	4000 - 4999	5000 - 5999	6000 <
WTP Frequency	8	16	10	2	4	3	30
ATP Frequency	8	0	8	19	6	19	13
WTP % Frequency	11%	22%	14%	3%	5%	4%	41%
ATP % Frequency	11%	0%	11%	26%	8%	26%	18%
WTP Frequency Commulative	89%	67%	53%	51%	45%	41%	0%
ATP Frequency Commulative	89%	89%	78%	52%	44%	18%	0%

Chart 3. Chart of ATP WTP Enterpreneur in Corridor 2

Source: Research Result, 2021

Based on the graph, the meeting point between ATP and WTP values for non-ASN category in corridor 2. Based on these results, it can be identified that the ability of respondents to pay for the bus service is 51% in the price range of Rp. 3,000 - 3,999. 52% of users are willing to pay that price. This means that the value of ATP owned by users with a non-ASN category is under the value of its WTP if it is in the tariff range of Rp. 3,000 - 3,999.

Based on the results of the analysis, in the theory of ATP and WTP relation, the state of non-ASN category corridor 2 is included in the ATP relationship is greater than WTP because of the condition that shows the ability to pay transportation services is greater than the willingness to pay for transportation services this is characterized by relatively high non-ASN income.

B. Corridor 4 inroute Terminal Alang – Alang Lebar – Talang Jambe

Table 4. Perception of Financial in Corridor 2

Kategori	ATP	WTP Existing	WTP Expectations
Civil Servant	Rp 10,496	Rp 4,666	Rp 5,533
Students	Rp 6,476	Rp 3,583	Rp 4,116
Entrepreneur	Rp 5,513	Rp 3,507	Rp 4,154

Source: Research Result, 2021

From the table above known job identification is classified into three (3) namely Civil Servant, Student, and Entrepreneur were included in the Non-ASN is a worker and non-worker. The dominant type of work in this corridor is the type of Non-ASN work based on the results of the analysis above, for ATP Non-ASN of Rp. 5,513 per seat. The amount in the ATP means the ability of users of non-ASN classification services to be able to pay for services up to the value of the rupiah even though the existing tariff price is still Rp 0 per seat. As for the amount of existing WTP where the intended is the service user only willing to pay for services in the existing condition when conducted this study amounted to Rp 3,507. If the quality of service is improved then service users with non-ASN classification will pay higher services with WTP expectations of Rp. 4,154.

In addition to the type of Non-ASN work that became dominant in the classification of corridor 4 recruitment types, in the type of work Students / Students obtained ATP amounting to Rp. 6,476 with existing WTP of Rp. 3,583 and WTP Harapan of Rp. 4,116. As for the type of work, ASN can pay ATP of Rp. 10,496 with existing WTP of Rp. 4,666 and WTP expectation of Rp. 5,533. Existing WTP for corridor 2 amounted to Rp. 5,513 – Rp. 10,496 and WTP expectations for corridor 4 amounted to 4,154– Rp. 5,533. The amount of the price of WTP, can be a reference in the determination of tariffs per seat in the future. ATP and WTP graphs for ASN, Student/Student, and Non-ASN job types to see the differences between the categories that can be seen in the chart below.

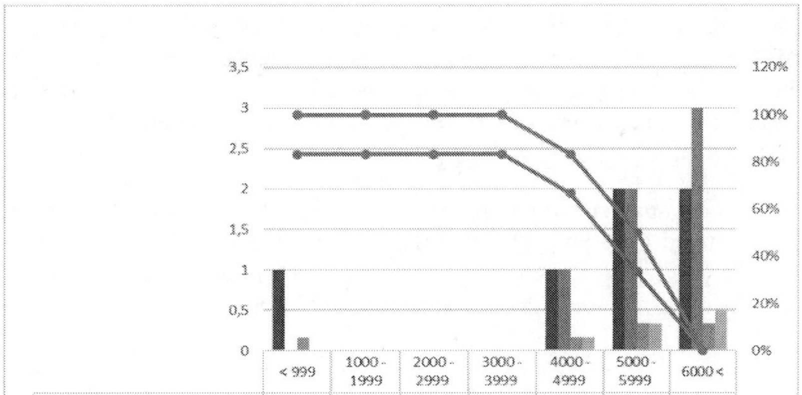

	< 999	1000 - 1999	2000 - 2999	3000 - 3999	4000 - 4999	5000 - 5999	6000 <
WTP Frequency	1	0	0	0	1	2	2
ATP Frequency	0	0	0	0	1	2	3
WTP % Frequency	17%	0%	0%	0%	17%	33%	33%
ATP % Frequency	0%	0%	0%	0%	17%	33%	50%
WTP Frequency Commulative	83%	83%	83%	83%	67%	33%	0%
ATP Frequency Commulative	100%	100%	100%	100%	83%	50%	0%

Chart 4. ATP WTP ASN in Corridor 4

Source: Research Result, 2021

Based on the graph, the meeting point between ATP and WTP values for the ASN category in corridor 4. Based on these results, it can be identified that the respondent's ability to pay for the bus service is Rp. 6000< so that the ASN category in corridor 4 does not mind if paying at a rate of Rp. 6,000< for one way.

Based on the results of the analysis, in the theory of ATP and WTP relationship the state of ASN category corridor 4 is included in two relationships, namely ATP is greater than WTP because of conditions that show the ability to pay transportation services greater than the willingness to pay for transportation services this is characterized by relatively high ASN income and ATP conditions are the same as WTP because of conditions that show balance to the costs incurred to pay for transportation services[12].

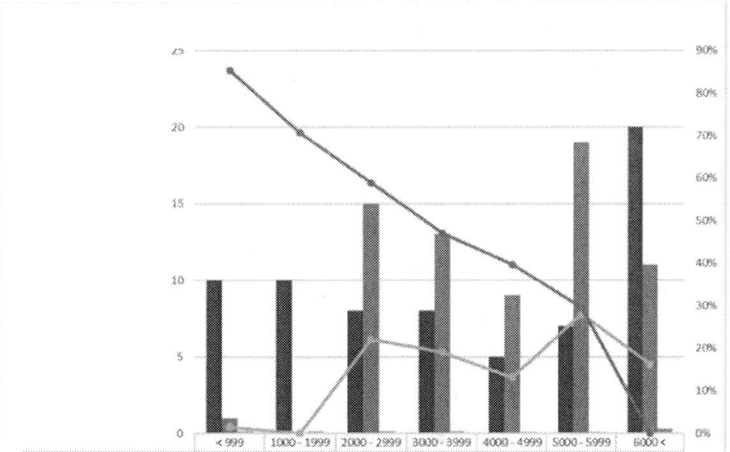

	< 999	1000 - 1999	2000 - 2999	3000 - 3999	4000 - 4999	5000 - 5999	6000 <
WTP Frequency	10	10	8	8	5	7	20
ATP Frequency	1	0	15	13	9	19	11
WTP % Frequency	15%	15%	12%	12%	7%	10%	29%
ATP % Frequency	1%	0%	22%	19%	13%	28%	16%
Frequency Commulative	85%	71%	59%	47%	40%	29%	0%

Chart 5. Chart ATP WTP Enterpreneur in Corridor 4

Source: Research Result, 2021

Based on the graph, the meeting point between ATP and WTP values for a non-ASN category in corridor 4. Based on these results, it can be identified that the ability of respondents to pay for the bus service is 28% in the price range of Rp. 5,000 - 5,999. 29% of users will pay that price. This means that the value of ATP owned by users with a non-ASN category is under the value of its WTP if it is in the tariff range of Rp. 3,000 - 3,999.

Based on the results of the analysis, in the theory of ATP and WTP relationship, the state of non-ASN category corridor 4 entered into the ATP relationship is greater than WTP because of the condition that shows the ability to pay transportation services is greater than the willingness to pay transportation services this is characterized by a relatively high non-ASN income[13].

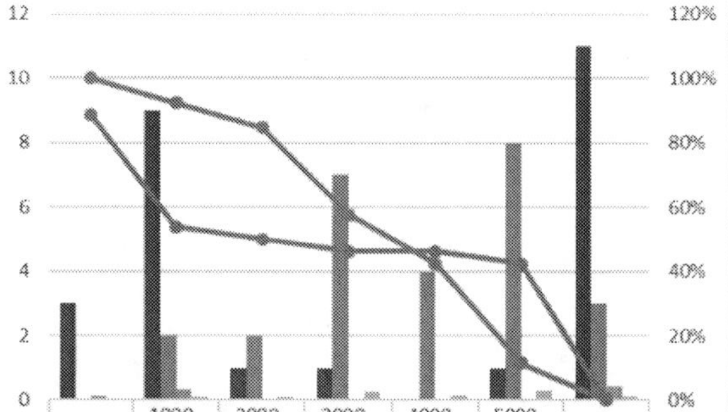

	< 999	1000 - 1999	2000 - 2999	3000 - 3999	4000 - 4999	5000 - 5999	6000 <
WTP Frequency	3	9	1	1	0	1	11
ATP Frequency	0	2	2	7	4	8	3
WTP % Frequency	12%	35%	4%	4%	0%	4%	42%
ATP % Frequency	0%	8%	8%	27%	15%	31%	12%
WTP Frequency Commulative	88%	54%	50%	46%	46%	42%	0%
ATP Frequency Commulative	100%	92%	85%	58%	42%	12%	0%

CHART 6. ATP WTP STUDENT IN CORRIDOR 4

Source: Research Result, 2021

Based on the graph, you can see the meeting point between ATP and WTP values for the Student category in corridor 4. Based on these results, it can be identified that the ability of respondents to pay for the bus service is 46% in the price range of Rp. 4,000 - 4,999. 42% of users will pay that price. This means that the value of ATP owned by users with the category of Students / Students is under the value of its WTP if it is in the tariff range of Rp. 4,000 - 4,999.

Based on the results of the analysis, the theory of ATP and WTP relationship of the category of Student corridor 4 entered into the ATP relationship is greater than WTP because of the condition that shows the ability to pay transportation services is greater than the willingness to pay for transportation services this is characterized by relatively high income students.

4. Conclussion

BRT's position in Palembang city in Planning Document of Palembang city in 2012-2032 aims to facilitate users to switch modes in achieving their travel destination to support Palembang intermoda. However, there is still a gap between existing policies such as planning documents and existing conditions in the field that have not met the needs of intermodal facilities. Due to the policy related to tariff exemption by the central government in the management of using the subsidy system, it can not be known the benefits and losses of the operator but after the analysis conducted obtained a range for the value of Operational Cost issued annually to per-seat. Therefore, in helping the government later determine the continued determination of tariffs can consider the perspective of the user. that is, in terms of fares, passengers can afford and want to pay for BRT BTS service is worth Rp. 3,000 in one trip Travel bus service users are satisfied with the performance and quality of services provided[14].

5. Reference

[1] Nelson, T. D. (2010). The Impact of Bus Rapid Transit on Land Development: A Case Study of Beijing, China . International Journal of Social.

[2] Warpani, S. P. (2002). Pengelolaan Lalu Lintas dan Angkutan Jalan. Bandung: ITB.

[3] Siahaan, E. N. (2018). Analisis Rute Operasional Trayek Langsung Transjakarta (Studi Kasus: Transjakarta Rute 6H). Depok: Universitas Indonesia.

[4] Bertini, R. L. (2014). Bus Rapid Transit: An Alternative for Developing Countries. 1-2.

[5] Das, S. (2013). Importance of user perception in evaluating level of service for bus transit for a developing country like India: a review. Transport Reviews.

[6] Indrawati, S. (2015). Analisis Dampak Integrasi Bus Sedang Reguler Ke Sistem Transjakarta Terhadap Aspek Operasional Dan Finansial (Studi Kasus: Metromini S.640 Rute Pasar Minggutanah Abang). Depok: Universitas Indonesia.

[7] Jhon W, B. (1986). Definition of Practice for Bus Transit One Time Performance: Pleminary Study. Transportation Reserch Board, 1.

[8] Badan Perencanaan Pembangunan Daerah. (n.d.). Rencana Tata Ruang Wilayah (RTRW) Kota Palembang Tahun 2012 - 2032.

[9] Departemen Perhubungan RI. (2002). Pedoman Teknis Penyelenggaraan Angkutan Penumpang Umum Di Wilayah Perkotaan Dalam Trayek Tetap Dan Teratur.

[10] Tamin, O. Z. (1999). Evaluasi Tarif Angkutan Umum dan Analisis "Ability To Pay" (ATP) dan "Willingness To Pay" (WTP). Jurnal Transportasi Forum Studi Transportasi Antar Perguruan Tinggi (FSTPT), 141-242.

[11] Fatmawati, Z., & Susanty, A. (n.d.). Analisis Tingkat Kepuasan Pengguna Bus Rapid Transit (BRT) Trans Semarang Dengan Metode Heterogeneous Customer Satisfaction Index Dan Importance Performance Analysis.

[12] Saraswati, Z. F. (2020). Analisis Biaya Operasional Kendaraan (OPERATIONAL COST) Bus Rapid Transit (Studi Kasus: Trayek Rajabasa - Panjang). Journal of Civil Enginering and Vocational Education, 73-79.

[13] Ramadhan, Z. J. (2014). Analisis Perhitungan dan Perbandingan Biaya Operasional Kendaraan (OPERATIONAL COST) Bus Rapid Transit (BRT) Transmusi jenis Mercedes Benz OH1521 dan Hino RK8-235. Palembang: Universitas Sriwijaya.

[14] Sulistyorini, R. (2012). Peluang Pengembangan Transportasi Intermoda Di Propinsi Lampung.

IOP Conf. Series: Earth and Environmental Science 1000 (2022) 012024 doi:10.1088/1755-1315/1000/1/012024

Study of Refinancing Scheme On Toll Road Infrastructure (Case Study: Gempol-Pandaan Toll Road)

Nesa Nurhadi Sunarya[a], Rudy Hermawan Karsaman[a], Idwan Santoso[a]

Highway Engineering and Development Department, Faculty of Civil and Environmental Engineering, Bandung Institute of Technology – Indonesia

[a]*E-mail: nesanurhadi17@gmail.com*

Abstract: PT. Jasamarga Pandaan Tol (JPT) is a toll road operator that officially operates the Gempol-Pandaan section located in East Java. JPT made adjustments to the concession scheme through a business plan addendum in March 2015, wherein in this model the financing process involves the use of shareholder loan funds. The profit generated by this business plan model is considered to have a high level of sensitivity during the loan tenor and has the potential for default to creditors. To avoid this, it is necessary to compare other alternative financing methods such as Refinancing and Infrastructure Investment Fund (IIF). The method used is financial feasibility analysis by taking into account the value of NPV, B / C, PP, IRR, WACC, and ROI as parameters. Based on the results of the financial feasibility analysis, the refinancing model provides better PP and ROI parameter values than the business plan model.

1. Introduction

The operation of toll roads is intended to realize equitable development and results as well as balance in regional development with due regard to justice, which can be achieved by fostering a road network whose funds come from road users Indonesia conducted toll road operations for the first time in 1978, namely the 59 km Jagorawi toll road. The government continues to increase toll road project investment in Indonesia to realize the 1000 km toll road program as stated in the 2015-2019 RPJMN (National Medium Term Development Plan) [9]. Data from the Ministry of PUPR (2019) [8], and the Toll Road Regulatory Agency (2020) show that toll road construction in the 2015 - 2019 period did not reach the expected target. LAKIP BPJT (2017) states that the factors affecting toll road concessions are as follows: 1) Land is not fully available, 2) Land allocation is insufficient, 3) There is no Toll Road Business Entity (TRBE), 4) Low feasibility - marginal, 5) Government support is not yet available, 6) There is no government guarantee, 7) Full access arterial road, 8) Low delivery of 20 km per year, most of these factors are related to finance [7].

PT. Jasamarga Pandaan Tol (JPT) is a TRBE that officially operates the Gempol - Pandaan section along 13.61 km. In 2015, JPT made adjustments to the business plan that took into account several factors, including the occurrence of the monetary crisis starting in 1996, the disconnection of the Surabaya-Gempol toll road, the Porong-Gempol section due to being buried by Lapindo mud, as well as land acquisition process efforts that are still ongoing during construction started in 2011 [12]; [13]. This business plan revises

IOP Conf. Series: Earth and Environmental Science 1000 (2022) 012024 doi:10.1088/1755-1315/1000/1/012024

the projected value of traffic flow growth during the operational period and involves additional capital through Shareholder Loans in the 2015-2017 period as an effort to maintain the sustainability of toll road concessions [1]; [2]; [3]; [4]. However, this method is considered to have high default potential due to the low rate of return during the loan tenor

In this regard, the government has a special policy related to credit implementation through Bank Indonesia Regulation (PBI) no. 14/15 / PBI / 2012 Chapter VI concerning Credit Restructuring, and infrastructure financing policies through the capital market, based on Financial Services Authority Regulation (POJK) no. 52 / POJK.04 / 2017 concerning Infrastructure Investment Fund (IIF). This study will try to examine the data on the 2015 JPT business plan based on the corporate financing scheme, credit restructuring (refinancing), IIF equity, and IIF bonds.

2. Literature review

2.1. Refinancing

Credit restructuring is an effort made by the Bank in lending activities for debtors who are experiencing difficulties in fulfilling their obligations. Based on PBI 14/15 / PBI / 2012 Chapter VI Article 52 explains that Banks can only perform Credit Restructuring for debtors who meet the following criteria:

- debtors experiencing difficulties in paying Credit principal and/or interest; and
- the debtor still has good business prospects and is considered capable of meeting obligations after the credit restructuring.

Figure 1. provides information regarding the determination of credit restructuring and the components for determining credit quality.

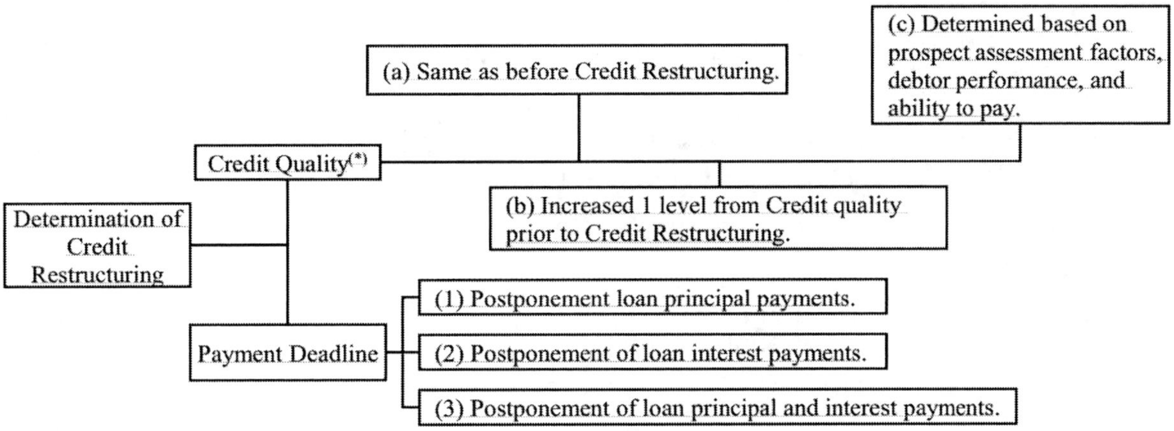

Credit Quality Assignment Components (*)	Business prospect	Potential for Business Growth
		Market Conditions and Debtor's Position in Competition
		Management Quality and Labor Competition
		Debtor's Efforts to Preserve the Environment
	Debtor Performance	Earned Profit
		Capital Structure
		Cash Flow
		Sensitivity to Market Risk
	Ability to Pay	Principal and Interest Payment Terms

	Availability and Accuracy of Debtor Financial Information
	Completeness of Credit Documentation
	Compliance with Credit Agreements
	Appropriate Use of Funds
	Fairness of Sources of Payment of Obligations

Figure 1. Determination of credit restructuring and credit quality components

2.2. Infrastructure Investment Fund

Financial Services Authority Regulation (POJK) no. 52 / POJK.04 / 2017 (2017) explains that IIF is a container in the form of a Collective Investment Contract (CIC) which is used to raise funds from the investor community which is then mostly invested by investment managers in infrastructure assets (including toll roads) directly either with or without using a Special Purpose Company, in this case, IIF's Collective Investment Contract (CIC) is a type of mutual fund product [14]; [16]; [17]. Figure 2. provides information about the flow of mutual fund transactions.

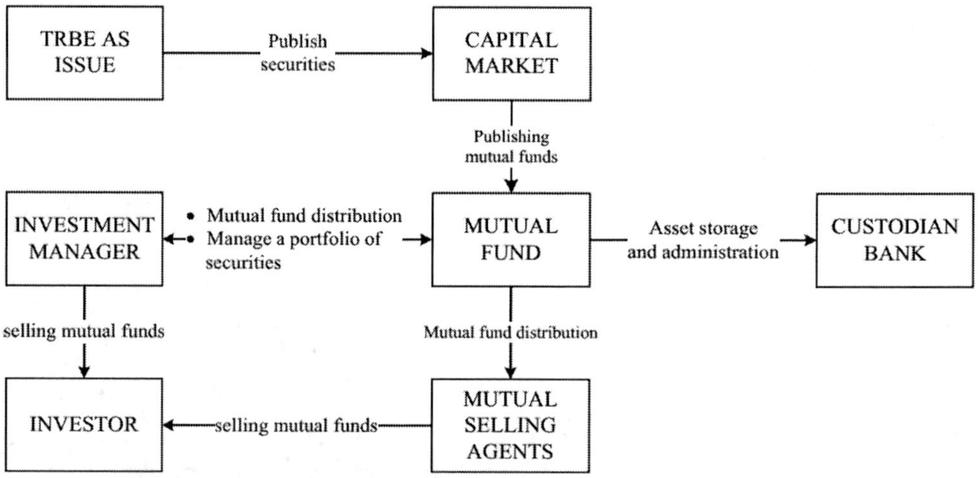

Figure 2. Mutual fund transaction flow (IIF)

2.3. Financial feasibility analysis

Soeharto (1995) states that the parameters that can be used to assess the financial feasibility of a project are as follows: Net Present Value (NPV), Benefit-Cost Ratio (B / C), Internal Rate of Return (IRR), Payback Period (PP), Weight Average Cost of Capital (WACC), and Return of Investment (ROI) [15].

$$NPV = \sum_{t-1}^{T} \frac{C_t}{(1+r)^t} - C_o \tag{1}$$

$$BCR = \sum_{t=1}^{t=n} \frac{B_t}{(1+i)^t} : \sum_{t=1}^{t=n} \frac{C_t}{(1+i)^t} \tag{2}$$

$$IRR = i_1 + \frac{NPV_1}{(NPV_1 - NPV_2)} x(i_2 - i_1) \tag{3}$$

$$PP = n + \frac{(a-b)}{(c-b)} x\, 1\, year \quad (4)$$

$$WACC = r_e\, x \left[\frac{E}{(D+E)}\right] + (1-\mathrm{T})\, x\, r_d\, x \left[\frac{D}{(D+E)}\right] \quad (5)$$

$$ROI = \frac{Annual\ average\ profit}{Initial\ Investment\ Value} x100\% \quad (6)$$

3. Research Methodology

This research was conducted by analyzing the calculation of cash flow and financial feasibility in several models, namely the initial model, the credit restructuring model, and the IIF model, then comparisons were made between these models. The primary data component was obtained from the business plan data of PT. Jasamarga Pandaan Tol (JPT) in 2015, while the secondary data component was obtained from reports from similar entities and other agencies related to toll road concessions.

Primary data consists of toll road investment value, the authorized capital of the entity, debt capital, credit period, loan interest rate, internal financing, the entity's cash flow. Secondary data consists of financial statements of similar TRBE, Bank Indonesia inflation rate data, data on the financial services authority's Basic Credit Interest Rate, financial services authority regulations specifically regarding IIF, Bank Indonesia regulations specifically regarding credit restructuring, Toll Road Management Agency (TRBA) data. Primary and secondary data were analyzed through some credit restructuring models based on components of loan principal installments, loan interest installments, credit interest rates, credit terms, and grace period. The analysis is continued by calculating the financial feasibility of each credit restructuring model and classifying the indicator values of the results of the financial feasibility analysis. Then proceed with a comparison of exploitation models that utilize shareholder loans, and IIF.

4. Data analysis and discussion

4.1. Data

The total investment value for the Gempol-Pandaan toll road is IDR 1.472.370.000.000 (one trillion four hundred seventy-two billion three hundred and seventy million rupiahs). The construction is carried out in two stages, and there is a road-widening investment plan during the concession period. JPT utilizes a combination of capital between equity and debt in implementing the Gempol-Pandaan toll road concession with a composition of 30:70. The term of the toll road concession is 35 years. Referring to PBI number 14/15 / PBI / 2012 concerning asset quality assessment for commercial banks, credit restructuring modeling is carried out with the following assumptions:

a. credit restructuring is only valid for Phase 1 (one) investment credit installments and Phase 1 (one) IDC credit installments because the Phase 2 (two) investment credit installments and Phase 2 (two) IDC credit installments will only begin in 2019 when the company is in condition. finance is considered good;
b. the testing of the credit restructuring model is carried out by changing the combination of principal and loan interest installments and increasing the duration of the grace period;
c. changes in the combined installments of principal and loan interest are made by adjusting the growth in toll road revenue at the operating stage;

d. the period for adding to the grace period is a maximum of four years after the credit restructuring agreement is agreed;
e. the grace period restructuring modeling will be divided into three forms, namely additional grace period for loan principal installments, the additional grace period for loan interest installments, and the additional grace period for principal and loan interest installments.

Figure 3. provides information regarding JPT's cash flow projection from the construction period to the end of the concession period.

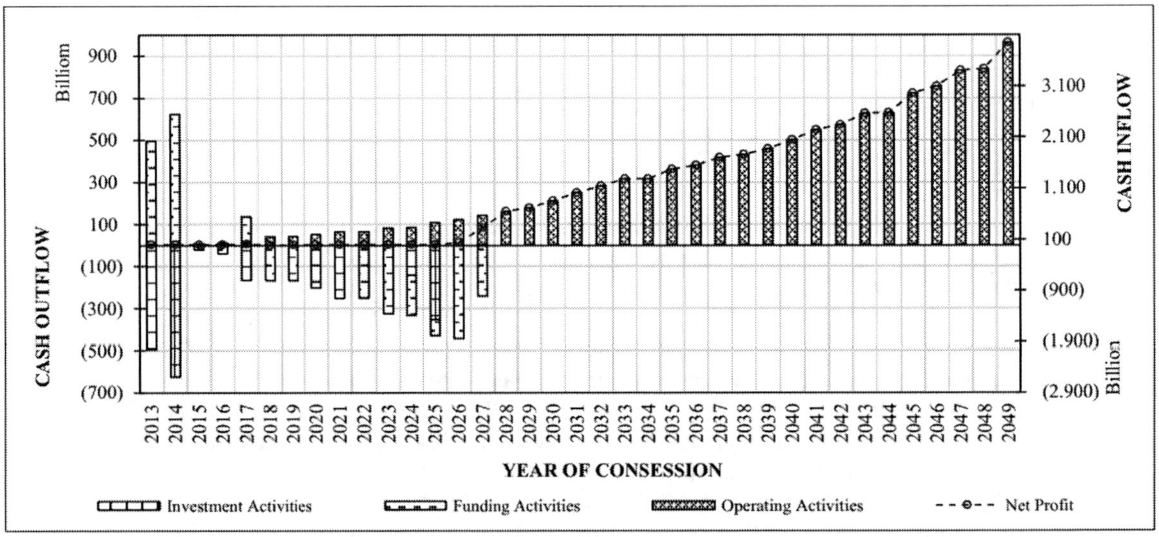

Figure 3. Cash flow projection of PT. Jasamarga Pandaan Tol

Tables 1., and 2. provide information on requirements for business plan modeling, credit restructuring, and IIF.

Table 1. Credit restructuring modeling

JPT BUSINESS PLAN ADDENDUM FOR MARCH 2015				
Installment of principal + interest (baseline)	The installment value per year is calculated based on the type of annuity interest in full (100%).			
Grace period (baseline)	4 (four) years from 2012 (two thousand and twelve).			
CREDIT RESTRUCTURING BEGINS IN 2015				
Installment of principal + interest	The installment value per year is calculated based on the type of annuity interest, but by following the toll road revenue growth rate until a stable financial condition is achieved, namely being able to pay full installments (100%).			
Grace period	The period is increased to a maximum of 4 (four) years starting in 2015.			
Varian	01	02	03	04

	4+ (1 year)	4+ (2 years)	4+ (3 years)	4+ (4 years)

CREDIT RESTRUCTURING MODEL			
Model 05	*Grace Period* 01	*Grace Period* 02	*Grace Period* 03
Installment of principal + interest	Installment of principal	Installment of interest	Installment of principal + interest

Table 2. Provision of business plan and IIF

NO.	SOURCE OF FUNDS	FORM OF RETURN	INTEREST RATE	RETURN OF BENEFIT	TENOR
1.	Business plan.	The loan principal and interest.	11% per year.	-	10 years.
2.	IIF bonds (released in 2017).	Loan principal and coupon (voucher).	9%-10% per year.	-	10 years
3.	IIF equity (released in 2017).	Dividend.	-.	9% per year of net income.	As long as the entity operates.

4.2. *Cash Flow Analysis*

Table 3. provides information that all models produce positive final cash flow conditions during the loan tenor except for the restructuring of the 5-year and 6-year Grace Period 03 models which experienced an imbalance between income and expenditure in the 2016-2021 period.

Table 3. Table of cash flow calculation results for each model[a]

YEARS	BUSINESS PLAN	CR M 05[b]	CR M GP[c] 03 (5 YRS)	CR M GP 03 (6 YRS)	CR M GP 03 (7 YRS)	CR M GP 03 (8 YRS)	IIF EQUITY	IIF BONDS COUP 9%	IIF BONDS COUP 10%
2015	353	353	21,099	21,099	21,099	21,099	353	353	353
2016	353	353	- 86,059	59,972	59,972	59,972	353	353	353
2017	353	353	- 187,752	- 41,721	104,310	104,310	147,528	147,528	147,528
2018	353	605	- 197,248	- 51,217	94,814	240,845	138,031	92,412	87,343
2019	353	1,197	- 201,926	- 55,895	90,135	236,166	133,353	42,115	31,977
2020	353	4,908	- 166,347	- 20,317	125,714	271,745	168,932	32,074	16,868
2021	353	11,607	- 80,924	65,107	211,138	357,169	254,355	71,879	51,604
2022	353	12,333	3,603	149,634	295,665	441,695	338,882	110,787	85,443
2023	353	15,787	161,818	307,849	453,879	599,910	497,097	223,382	192,970
2024	353	38,717	194,473	340,504	486,535	632,566	520,027	200,693	165,212
2025	353	7,938	244,208	390,239	536,270	682,301	429,228	64,276	23,725
2026	44,852	286,636	479,003	625,034	771,065	917,095	749,746	339,174	293,555
2027	378,233	680,539	800,294	946,324	1,092,355	1,238,386	1,156,760	193,690	143,003
2028	1,033,409	1,335,715	1,309,371	1,455,402	1,601,433	1,747,463	1,811,936	848,866	798,179

2029	1,751,498	2,053,804	2,027,460	2,027,460	2,173,491	2,319,522	2,530,025	1,566,955	1,516,268
2030	2,603,472	2,905,778	2,879,434	2,879,434	2,879,434	3,025,465	3,381,999	2,418,929	2,368,242
2031	3,618,304	3,920,610	3,894,266	3,894,266	3,894,266	3,894,266	4,396,831	3,433,761	3,383,074
2032	4,764,967	5,067,273	5,040,929	5,040,929	5,040,929	5,040,929	5,543,494	4,580,424	4,529,737
2033	6,050,778	6,353,084	6,326,740	6,326,740	6,326,740	6,326,740	6,829,305	5,866,235	5,815,548
2034	7,334,539	7,636,845	7,610,501	7,610,501	7,610,501	7,610,501	8,113,066	7,149,996	7,099,309
2035	8,808,472	9,110,778	9,084,434	9,084,434	9,084,434	9,084,434	9,586,999	8,623,929	8,573,242
2036	10,356,165	10,658,471	10,632,127	10,632,127	10,632,127	10,632,127	11,134,692	10,171,622	10,120,935
2037	12,056,087	12,358,393	12,332,049	12,332,049	12,332,049	12,332,049	12,834,614	11,871,544	11,820,857
2038	13,812,251	14,114,557	14,088,213	14,088,213	14,088,213	14,088,213	14,590,778	13,627,708	13,577,021
2039	15,682,284	15,984,590	15,958,246	15,958,246	15,958,246	15,958,246	16,460,811	15,497,741	15,447,054
2040	17,724,635	18,026,941	18,000,597	18,000,597	18,000,597	18,000,597	18,503,162	17,540,092	17,489,405
2041	19,962,996	20,265,302	20,238,958	20,238,958	20,238,958	20,238,958	20,741,523	19,778,453	19,727,766
2042	22,306,397	22,608,703	22,582,359	22,582,359	22,582,359	22,582,359	23,084,924	22,121,854	22,071,167
2043	24,876,802	25,179,108	25,152,764	25,152,764	25,152,764	25,152,764	25,655,329	24,692,259	24,641,572
2044	27,457,881	27,760,187	27,733,843	27,733,843	27,733,843	27,733,843	28,236,408	27,273,338	27,222,651
2045	30,416,799	30,719,105	30,692,761	30,692,761	30,692,761	30,692,761	31,195,326	30,232,256	30,181,569
2046	33,514,469	33,816,775	33,790,431	33,790,431	33,790,431	33,790,431	34,292,996	33,329,926	33,279,239
2047	36,920,722	37,223,028	37,196,684	37,196,684	37,196,684	37,196,684	37,699,249	36,736,179	36,685,492
2048	40,354,105	40,656,411	40,630,067	40,630,067	40,630,067	40,630,067	41,132,632	40,169,562	40,118,875
2049	44,304,468	44,606,774	44,580,430	44,580,430	44,580,430	44,580,430	45,082,995	44,119,925	44,069,238

[a]In million rupiah [b]Credit Restructuring Model 05 [c] Credit Restructuring Model Grace Period

4.3. Financial Feasibility Analysis

Table 4. provides information regarding the recapitulation of parameter data from the financial feasibility analysis of all analyzed models.

The business plan model has a good financial feasibility analysis indicator value, however, this model will burden JSMR's expenses as the parent entity because it seeks internal financing through shareholder loans. If internal financing fails, JPT will certainly experience a default.

The IIF bond model can provide the highest NPV and B/C values, but one of the bond issuance requirements states that the issuer (JPT) must have been operating for at least 3 (three) consecutive years in the same core business, So the IIF option is a bond that does not can be implemented in 2015 (two thousand and fifteen) which is the limitation of this research analysis.

The equity IIF model can help JPT to avoid internal financing, and also prevent the addition of new debt after the construction period. Based on JSMR's public exposure information (2019), it is explained that currently, JSMR is pushing an equity-based funding scheme to balance profitability and capital structure, so that JSMR is still able to maintain the cost of debt for additional loans to finance the construction of new toll roads. However, the issuance of new shares and the sale of JSMR's old shares to TOL caused the entity to become more capital intensive, so that the WACC value became larger, then had an impact on the decrease in the NPV and B/C values. This will also reduce the dividend projection that JSMR will receive because it has carried out the divestment of shares before the concession period ends.

The grace period 03 model is considered to be able to provide the best IRR and PP benefits, but the possibility to implement this model in real companies is considered very small. This is due to the large number of additional grace periods that are too long, reaching eight years, which is difficult for creditors (banks) to provide.

Model 05 has a good financial feasibility analysis indicator value and provides the highest ROI value compared to other models. Another advantage that this model offers is that TRBE does not need to divest shares or seek new sources of debt. In proposing debt rescheduling, TRBE can try to convince creditors by considering the projected toll road revenue growth rate until the end of the concession period.

Table 4. Recapitulation of financial feasibility analysis parameters

MODEL	NPV	B/C	IRR	PP	WACC	ROI
Business plan	3,913,793	1.989	13.614%	230.3 months	11.62%	66.22%
Model 05	3,365,204	1.710	14.664%	218.3 months	12.37%	86.56%
GP 03 5 years	3,636,490	1.848	14.418%	221.2 months	12.07%	78.50%
GP 03 6 years	3,694,460	1.877	14.714%	219.5 months	12.07%	78.50%
GP 03 7 years	3,748,253	1.904	14.987%	216.4 months	12.07%	78.50%
GP 03 8 years	3,798,168	1.930	15.237%	213.1 months	12.07%	78.50%
IIF equity	1,715,421	0.872	13.710%	230.7 months	13.63%	58.24%
IIF bonds coupon 9%	5,411,807	2.750	13.029%	237.1 months	10.97%	57.00%
IIF bonds coupon 10%	5,107,627	2.595	12.982%	237.8 months	10.65%	56.93%

[a] *In million rupiah*

5. Conclusions and recommendations

5.1. Conclusions

- The 2015 JPT business plan model can burden the financial condition of the parent entity which experiences large capital expenditures due to the simultaneous implementation of new toll road investments;
- Model 05 provides a better IRR, PP, ROI, and projected total dividend at the end of the concession than the business plan model which are 14.664% for IRR, 218.3 months for PP, 86.56% for ROI, a total dividend of IDR 20,218,257,000,000 for PT. Jasa Marga (Persero) Tbk., and IDR 1,958,063,000,000 for PT. Jalan Tol Kab. Pasuruan.
- JPT cannot use IIF Bonds in the 2015 analysis because stock exchange regulations require the issuer to operate for a minimum of three consecutive years before the securities are issued.
- IIF's equity issuance causes the entity to become capital intensive. This has an impact on the decline in the value of the financial feasibility analysis indicator compared to other models. In addition, with the reduction in JSMR's ownership of JPT, the dividend value will also be smaller.

5.2. Recommendations

- Analysis may include the imposition of fines on debtors to compensate creditors for changes in loan repayment schedules;
- Analysis may include the implementation of the buyback option by JSMR consecutively in the first five years after the issuance of IIF equity;
- Conducted analysis in 2018 or thereafter, to accommodate bond issuance requirements;
- Perform analysis by replacing loans from banks with sources of funds from the capital market in full (take over).

6. References

[1] Jasa Marga (Persero). 2015. Consolidated Financial Statements of PT. Jasa Marga (Persero) and its Subsidiaries.
[2] Jasa Marga (Persero). 2016. Prospectus Book: Limited Public Offering to Increase Capital by Providing Pre-emptive Rights ("PMHMETD I").
[3] Jasa Marga (Persero). 2016. Consolidated Financial Statements of PT. Jasa Marga (Persero) and its Subsidiaries.
[4] Jasa Marga (Persero). 2017. Consolidated Financial Statements of PT. Jasa Marga (Persero) and its Subsidiaries.
[5] Jasa Marga (Persero). 2019. Public Expose PT. Jasa Marga (Persero) Tbk.
[6] Jasa Marga (Persero). 2019. Report on the Implementation of the Mandatory Public Expose of PT. Jasa Marga (Persero) Tbk.
[7] Ministry of Public Works of the Republic of Indonesia. 2017. Government Agency Performance Reports
[8] Ministry of Public Works of the Republic of Indonesia. 2019. Toll Road Development Policy in Indonesia.
[9] State Minister for The Chairperson of the National Development Planning Agency. 2017. Midterm Evaluation of the 2015-2019 RPJMN.
[10] Presidential Regulation of the Republic of Indonesia Number 38 of 2015 Cooperation between the Government and Business Entities in the Provision of Infrastructure. March 20th 2015.
[11] PT. Margabumi Adhikarya. 1998. Environmental Impact Analysis Study (ANDAL) for the Gempol - Pandaan Toll Road Development Project.
[12] PT. Margabumi Adhikarya. 2011. Environmental Management Plan (RPL) and Environmental Monitoring Plan (RPL) Additional Gempol - Pandaan Toll Road Development Projects.
[13] Copy of Financial Services Authority Regulation Number 52 / POJK.04 / 2017 of 2017 Infrastructure Investment Funds in the Form of Collective Investment Contracts. July 27th 2017.
[14] Soeharto, I. (1995): Project Management: From Conceptual To Operational.
[15] Sihombing, L. 2011. The Risk of Toll Road in Indonesia. DOI: 10.2139/ssrn.1984556. https://www.researchgate.net/publication/228304230.
[16] Tandelilin, E. (2017): Capital Markets: Portfolio & Investment Management.
[17] Law of the Republic of Indonesia Number 8 of 1995 Capital Market. November 10th 1995.

IOP Conf. Series: Earth and Environmental Science 1000 (2022) 012025 doi:10.1088/1755-1315/1000/1/012025

Drivers Behavior at Signalized Intersections with Countdown Timer Reduces Air Pollution by Gender

Supiyono[1], Ludfi Djakfar[1], Achmad Wicaksono[1]

[1]Department of Civil Engineering, Faculty of Engineering, University of Brawijaya, Mas Tirtodarmo Haryono Street 167, Malang 65145, East Java, Indonesia

Correspondence: supiyono10@gmail.com

Abstract. Air pollution is transported via human conduct [22]. The goal of this study is to determine how drivers behave differently based on their gender at a signalized intersection with a Countdown Timer. The study enrolled 50 individuals who completed a questionnaire and delivered it to Bappeda, the transportation agency, drivers who were extending the KIR (motor vehicle test) at the transportation service, and the general public via Google Form via Whatsapp (Wa). The data were collected using a questionnaire and a Likert scale and analyzed using SPSS 20 and logistic binary regression analysis. The Binary Logistic R2 Nagelkerke model is used to determine the contribution of all independent variables to the dependent variable. The R2 coefficient discovered is 0.157. (15.7 percent). With an R2 score of 15.7%, 84.3 percent of the independent variables remain unexplained. And with an exp (X1) value of 0.463, increasing X1 results in a 0.463 change in Y. As a result, when individuals agree to the yellow light, their likelihood of agreeing to gender influence increases by 0.463 times. This conclusion can be used to help stakeholders in developing regulations that need a more thorough evaluation of the use of yellow flame before and after red.

Keywords: Air pollution, Driver Behavior, Signalized Intersection, Countdown Timer, and Gender

1. Introduction

1.1. Background
Transportation is integrally tied to environmental concerns, most notably air pollution [20], [21], and [9]. Due to traffic congestion or violations at intersections, energy is wasted, increasing air pollution.

Congestion at the intersection as a result of the driver's violations. Examples include research [14], [15], [19], [16], [3], [7], [22]. Both men and women have violated the law.

Numerous studies [10], [12], [9] have examined the disparities in gender-based infractions perpetrated by men and women. There are currently few studies on gender in transportation that do not include a discussion of signal infractions; hence, the conduct of vehicles at signalized intersections varies by gender.

1.2. Literature Review
Transportation is inextricably linked to environmental concerns, particularly air pollution. Automobiles are the most often used mode of transportation. The logit model for green transportation

can maximize gen [20], and green transportation programs can help reduce urban air pollution concerns and promote energy saving and emission reductions in trash transportation [21]. Green transportation strategies can help communities combat air pollution by encouraging energy efficiency and emission reductions in trash transportation [21]. The majority of transportation-related pollution occurs near intersections as a result of traffic congestion [9]. Congestion or confrontations at crossings contribute to an increase in air pollution.

Driver infractions contribute to traffic congestion. Numerous factors influence traffic light violations, including the absence of an adaptive signal to yellow [14], while waiting for a green light [15], while waiting for a red-light [19], reducing traffic light violations [16], at intersection 3, red-light violations occurring in less than 1 second from the start of the red-light to the time of the violation [3], and at intersection 4, red-light violations occurring in less than 1 second from the start of the red-light to the time of the violation [4]. Four out of ten (4/10) drivers run red-lights [2,], which increases traffic infractions and aggression by making drivers upset while waiting for the green-light [15], and the transportation path of air pollution is linked to human behavior [22].

When drivers are waiting for the green light, more precisely during the yellow phase (green waiting period) and the red phase following the green light, they are more aggressive and commit violations. The red component contributes significantly to the reduction of wasted start-up time and also affects red light violations at junctions, raising infractions in the final ten seconds of the red light and decreasing them in the first ten seconds of the red-light. According to [4], red-light offenses are associated with four factors: The number of approaches, their speed, the width of the road, and the speed at intersections [1], traffic light offenses are related to five factors: the time of day (weekdays or weekends), the location of the camera, the vehicle type (two-wheeled or four-wheel drive), the cycle time (long or short), and the type of traffic signal (with Countdown Timer or normal) [13], the presence of cameras significantly reduced walking red-light violations [16], traffic violations are affected by one's sense of priority, speed, and understanding of the rules [18], private automobiles are responsible for the majority of violations at signalized intersections [5], red-light cameras are effective at reducing red-light violations and tend to be effective at reducing certain types of traffic violations [5], red light cameras are effective at reducing red-light violations and tend to be effective at reducing certain types of traffic violations

2. Methodology

2.1. Research Stages

This research was carried out in four parts. The first stage entails conducting a survey and amassing data on drivers' perceptions via the Likert scale. The second stage is data analysis, which entails descriptive analysis and an examination of the driver's behavior model at a signalized intersection equipped with a Countdown Timer when all of the lights are red. The third stage involves analyzing the driver's behavior using Binary Logistics Regression Analysis. The fourth stage utilizes a Countdown Timer to analyze the driver's behavior model and generate recommendations for all red-lights at signalized intersections.

Table 1. Determining the value of the Linkert scale

Statement	Positive Score
Strongly Agree/Always	5
Agree/Often	4
Hesitant/Sometimes/Normal	3
Disagree	2
Strongly Disagree	1

Source: Sugiyono (2012)

Table 2. List of Survey Question

No	Pertanyaan	No	Pertanyaan
X_1	Every driver, (2 wheel / 4 wheel) must have a SIM	X_6	I will drive even though the signal is red
X_2	I prefer an intersection with a yellow light before a red-light	X_7	I prefer wide roads
X_3	I prefer the old green flame	X_8	I prefer to pass through the intersection of four rather than through the intersection of three
X_4	I will drive even though the signal is not green yet	Y	It is recommended that the signalized intersection be installed with a countdown timer.
X_5	I will drive even though the signal is yellow		

In this script X1 is Yellow flame, X2 is Red flame and Y is Gender.

2.2. Information

On the one hand, we sampled internet drivers; on the other hand, we sampled respondents personally. Respondents were carried out directly at the Transportation Office. Transportation Department employees and KIR drivers are among those who responded to the Transportation Office's survey (extension of vehicle license). As a result, 50 individuals have been contacted. With the following information, as detailed in Table 3:

Table 3. Questionnaire respondents

No	Origin	Quantity
1	Department of Transportation	24
2	Drivers who are KIR	16
3	Online	10
	Total	50

2.3. Analysis of Regression

The processes that follow data collecting are data tabulation and data analysis. Among the variables analyzed are the independent variables and independent variables. The dependent variables are X1 (Yellow) and X2 (Red). The dependent variable is gender (Y). Data analysis includes a partial test and a hypothesis test.

2.3.1 Incomplete Examination

The hypothesis is as follows: Using the t test to determine the effect of each independent variable on the dependent variable, the hypothesis is as follows: The hypothesis is as follows: Using t-test to determine the influence of each independent variable on the dependent variable: The hypothesis is as follows: Using t-test to determine the influence of each independent variable on the dependent variable:

Ho: $\rho \leq 0$: Gender has no positive effect on lamp violations.
Ha: $\rho > 0$: Gender has no positive effect on lamp violations.
The recognition criteria are as follows:
Ho is rejected if t-count < T-table ($\alpha = 0.05$)
If using the error rate ($\alpha = 0.01$) to be tested by two parties, then the criteria for accepting or rejecting the hypothesis are as follows:

1) If t-count $\geq$ t-table then Ho is in the rejection area, meaning that Ha is accepted, meaning that there is a relationship between variable X and variable Y.

IOP Conf. Series: Earth and Environmental Science 1000 (2022) 012025 doi:10.1088/1755-1315/1000/1/012025

2) If t-count ≤ t-table then Ho is in the acceptance area, meaning Ha is rejected, meaning that there is no relationship between the X variable and Y variable.

2.3.2. Hypothesis

Ho: β_1, β_2 = 0 (indicating that the independent variables (X1, X2) have no meaningful effect on the dependent variable at the same time)

At least one of the $\beta i \neq 0$ (i=1-2) indicates that the independent variables (X1, X2) have a significant effect on the audit quality variable at the same time

3. Result

The following results were obtained after using Binary Logistics Regression to analyze the data:

Table 4. Iteration History

Iteration		-2 Log-likelihood	Coefficients		
			Constant	X1	X2
Step 1	1	48.340	2.858	-.504	-.093
	2	47.331	3.845	-.725	-.122
	3	47.303	4.031	-.769	-.125
	4	47.303	4.038	-.771	-.126
	5	47.303	4.038	-.771	-.126

[a] Method: Enter
[b] The model is included a constant.
[c] 52.691 Initial -2 Log-Likelihood
[d] The estimation was stopped at iteration 5 since the parameter estimations had changed by less than .001

The Value -2 Log-Likelihood (52.691) < tabel (66,33) accepts Ho, indicating that the model is FIT with the data when the independent variable is included.
Value -2 Log-Likelihood : 52.691
Table value
Db= 50-1 = 49
$\chi^2_{0,05(49)} = 66{,}33$

Table 5. Omnibus Tests of Model Coefficients

		Chi-square	df	Sig.
Step 1	Step	5.388	2	.068
	Block	5.388	2	.068
	Model	5.388	2	.068

The hypothesis for this test is as follows: (It should be noted that this is not a statistical notation)
Ho: no significant variables affect the Y variable.
H1: if there is a single variable with a sufficiently significant effect
The significant value / P-value = 0.068 is obtained from the omnibus output, in comparison to = 0.05. Accept Ho if the P-value is greater than 0.005. This shows that no significant variable has an effect on Y, or that the independent variable has no effect on the dependent variable.

Table 6. Model Summary

Step	-2 Log likelihood	Cox & Snell R Square	Nagelkerke R Square
1	47.303[a]	.102	.157

[a] Estimation terminated at iteration number 5 because parameter estimates changed by less than .001

Summary of the Model (Table 6): The Cox & Snell and Nagelkerke R Square values are used to determine the degree to which the independent variable can adequately explain the dependent variable. These values are also referred to as Pseudo R-Squares or R-Squares in the context of linear regression (OLS). The Nagelkerke R Square value of 0.157 indicates that the independent variable may explain 15.7 percent of the variance in the dependent variable, with the other variables impacting the outcome.

Table 7. Hosmer and Lemeshow Test

Step	Chi-square	df	Sig.
1	3.277	4	.513

This test is used to determine the viability of the logistics model.
Ho: The model is capable of making a meaningful interpretation of the data.
H1: The model is insufficiently capable of explaining the data.
If the significance is more than 0.05, Ho is rejected.
The table's sig value is 0.513.
Ho's acceptance decision
Conclusion: At the 5% level of significance, the logistic regression model used was capable of describing the data/according to.

Table 8. Table of Classification

Observed			Predicted		
			Y (Gender)		Percentage
			Female	Male	Correct
Step 1	Y (Gender)	Perempuan	0	11	.0
		Laki-laki	0	39	100.0
		Overall Percentage			78.0

According to Table 8, the sample size will be 50 individuals. The group has 11 female members and 39 male members. Women make up 22% of the population, while men make up 78%.

Table 9. Shows the equation's variables

		B	S.E.	Wald	df	Sig.	Exp(B)	95% C. I. for EXP(B)	
								Lower	Upper
Step 1	X1	-.771	.352	4.792	1	.029	.463	.232	.922
	X2	-.126	.407	.095	1	.758	.882	.397	1.960
	Constant	4.038	2.243	3.242	1	.072	56.719		

Table 9 summarizes the coefficients for each independent variable and evaluates their impact on the dependent variable (equivalent to t-test in regression analysis)
The case of X1 (Yellow Flame)
The significance level is 0.029.
If the significant value is less than 0.05, Ho is accepted.
At the 5% level of significance, it can be determined that the X1 variable has a significant effect on Y.
Regarding the X2 (Red Flame)
The significance level is 0.758.
Because since sig > 0.05, the decision is made to reject Ho.
At the 5% level of significance, the X2 variable has no discernible effect on Y.
Column Exp indicates the nature of the influence on the variables that have a significant effect (B). If there are multiple "1s," the likelihood of Y increases. The value of exp (X1) is 0.463, implying that raising X1 results in a 0.463 increase in Y. As a result, increasing the number of individuals who agree with the yellow light increases the likelihood of someone agreeing by 0.463.
This does not apply, however, if the Wald test indicates that the independent variable does not affect the dependent.

4. Conclusion

The following model was developed as a result of the analysis model of binary logistic regression:

$$Ln\left(\frac{p}{1-p}\right) = 4.038 - 0.771\,X1 - 0.126\,X2$$

With a Wald test significance value of 0.029, which is less than 0.050, the X1 (Yellow Flame) variable has a partially negative and significant effect on the Y variable. With a significance value of 0.758 Wald's test, which is greater than 0.050, it has a negative influence on the X2 (Red Flame) variable but no effect on the Y variable. The negative coefficient indicates that the scores of variables X1 and X2 are trending in the direction of Y category 0 (no), but not with certainty. The value of exp (X1) is 0.463, which suggests that increasing the value of X1 will result in a 0.463 change in Y. As a result, if people agree to the yellow light, their chances of agreeing to the influence of gender increase by 0.463 times.

To calculate the contribution of all independent factors to the dependent variable, R2 Nagelkerke is utilized. The R2 value found is 0.157. (15.7 percent). With an R2 score of 15.7 percent, 84.3 percent of the independent variables is still unaccounted for. As a result of this conclusion, there are still numerous potential for further research to improve this study. This finding can be used as a guide for stakeholders in formulating policies to ensure that the usage of yellow flame before and after red is more carefully evaluated

References

[1] Al-Attawi A M 2014 Characteristics of red-light running violations in urban areas in Tabuk, Kingdom of Saudi Arabia. *IATSS Research*, 37(2), 119-123.
[2] Alexandros K, Panagiotis P, Sokratis B & Ioannis P 2017 An intertemporal evaluation of highway intersections red-light running. *International journal of transportation*, 5(1), 47-58.
[3] Alghafli A, Mohamad E & Zaidy A A 2021 The Relationship between the Elapsed Time from the Onset of Red Signal until Its Violation and Traffic Accident Occurrence in Abu Dhabi, UAE. *Safety*, 7(3), 53.
[4] Biswas S, Ghosh I, & Chandra S 2016 Effect of Countdown Timers on Traffic Characteristics and Driver Behavior at Signalized Intersections. In *95th Annual Meeting of the Transportation Research Board, Washington, DC.*
[5] Campisi T, Tesoriere G, Canale A, Basbas S, Vaitsis P, Nikiforiadis A & Nikolaidis M 2020 Comparison of Red-Light Running (RLR) and Yellow-Light Running (YLR) traffic

violations in the cities of Enna and Thessaloniki. *Transportation Research Procedia*, 45, 947-954.

[6] Cohn EG, Kakar S, Perkins C, Steinbach R & Edwards P 2020 Red-light camera interventions for reducing traffic violations and traffic crashes:/ A systematic review. *Campbell Systematic Reviews*, 16(2), e1091.

[7] Devalle J, Biswas S & Ghosh I 2015 The effect of countdown timer on the approach speed at signalized intersections. *Procedia Computer Science*, 52, 920-925.

[8] Elfar A, Mahmassani HS, Mittal A, Ostojic M, Verbas Ö & Schofer J 2017 Determinants of Red-light Camera Violation Behavior: Evidence from Chicago, Illinois. In *TRB 2017 Annual Meeting*.

[9] Wang Q & Sun H 2019 Traffic structure optimization in historic districts based on green transportation and sustainable development concept. *Advances in Civil Engineering*.

[10] Hezaveh A M, Zavareh M F, Cherry C R & Nordfiaern T 2018 Errors and violations in relation to bicyclists' crash risks: Development of the Bicycle Rider Behavior Questionnaire (BRBQ). *Journal of Transport & Health*, 8, 289-298.

[11] Jantosut P, Satiennam W, Satiennam T & Jaensirisak S 2021 Factors associated with the red-light running behavior characteristics of motorcyclists. *IATSS Research*, 45(2), 251-257.

[12] Karacasu M & Er A 2011 An analysis on the distribution of traffic faults in accidents, based on driver's age and gender: Eskisehir case. *Procedia-Social and Behavioral Sciences*, 20, 776-785.

[13] Kulanthayan S, Phang W K & Hayati K S 2007 Traffic light violation among motorists in Malaysia. *IATSS Research*, 31(2), 67-73.

[14] Lin X & Cheng L 2013 Engineering countermeasures to reducing unintentional yellow-light running owing to dilemma zone. *Procedia-Social and Behavioral Sciences*, 96, 900-904.

[15] Papaioannou P & Politis I 2014 Preliminary impact analysis of countdown signal timer installations at two intersections in Greece. *Procedia Engineering*, 84, 634-647.

[16] Shaaban K & Pande A 2018 Evaluation of red-light camera enforcement using traffic violations. *Journal of traffic and transportation engineering (English edition)*, 5(1), 66-72.

[17] Sugiyono 2012 *Metode Penelitian Pendidikan*, Bandung: ALfabeta, 2012, hal. 93.

[18] Yoh K, Okamoto T, Inoi H & Doi K 2017 Comparative study on foreign drivers' characteristics using traffic violation and accident statistics in Japan. *IATSS Research*, 41(2), 94-105.

[19] Yu K & Lu H 2014 Effects of countdown signals in red phase on drivers: a comparative study between Japan and Turkey. *Mathematical Problems in Engineering*.

[20] Wang W, Wets G, Bubb H & Niu H 2014 Green intelligent transport system.

[21] Xin C, Wang L, Liu B, Yuan Y H & Tsai S B 2021 An Empirical Study for Green Transportation Scheme of Municipal Solid Waste Based on Complex Data Model Analysis. *Mathematical Problems in Engineering*.

[22] Fan X, Chen B, & Zhang X 2015 Field Survey on Indoor Air Pollution Transport Path in Rural House in Northeast China. *Procedia Engineering*, *121*, 430-437.

Development Strategy of Malang Kota Baru Station Area Using Transit-Oriented Development (TOD) Principle Approach

C K Harmadi [1], S Sulistyono[2], R N Listyawati[3], N N Hayati[3], R Alfiah[3]

[1] Regional and Urban Planning Undergraduate Study Program, Universitas Jember, Jember-68121, East Java, Indonesia
[2] Civil Engineering Study Program, Universitas Jember, Jember-68121, East Java, Indonesia
[3] Regional and Urban Planning Study Program, Universitas Jember, Jember-68121, East Java, Indonesia

Corresponding author: sonya.sulistyono@unej.ac.id

Abstract. Malang Kota Baru Station is located in the center of Malang City with a variety of land uses occurring around the area. The concept of an area supports aspects of building density, diversity of land use, and the proximity of the area to transit points, one of which is Transit-Oriented Development (TOD). The purpose of this research is to obtain a development strategy that can be carried out in the area. The TOD principle approach is used in the Area of suitability analysis. The AHP method and SWOT analysis are used to obtain a regional development strategy. The results of the suitability analysis show that almost all of the existing condition variables are not under the TOD principle parameters. Furthermore, all parameters are used in the AHP analysis, and the order of priority for regional development is obtained, namely: diversity, design, and density. Determination of the grand strategy for regional development based on IFAS and EFAS obtained recommendations for aggressive maintenance strategy. This strategy needs to be carried out in regional development by maximizing various opportunities, to resolve or minimize internal weaknesses that occur.
Keywords. Transit-Oriented Development, Analytical Hierarchy Process, SWOT, IFAS, EFAS

1. Introduction

According to [1] transportation has two main roles, namely as a tool to direct development in urban areas, and as a means for the movement of people and goods arising from activities in urban areas. Urban areas are areas that have a significant movement of goods and services. A common problem related to transportation that is often encountered in urban areas is congestion due to the high use of private vehicles as the main mode of transportation.

One of the efforts that can be done to overcome the problems that arise due to the high mobility of people using private vehicles, is necessary to have an integrated public transportation mode that can accommodate the needs of the community [2]. One of the urban planning concepts that prioritize the function of public transportation is Transit-Oriented Development (TOD). The concept of regional development using the TOD principle has been carried out in several big cities in developed countries.

Malang City is the second-largest city in East Java Province and is known as an education city with many universities. Malang City Government data recorded that there were 59 universities [3]. So that the increase in population that occurs can be caused by the addition of students who come from outside the city. One of the congestion problems caused by the high use of private vehicles can be overcome by using public transportation. Until now, Malang City has several modes of public transportation that can be used by the community, including trains, planes, city transportation, and inter-city buses. One of the transit stations located in East Java is Malang Kota Baru Station, which is located in the center of Malang City.

The location of the station in the city center causes the surrounding area to be filled with various activities, ranging from trade and services, settlements, educational facilities, public facilities, defense and security, health facilities, offices, to tourism activities. The diversity of land uses makes the area around the station the center of community activities.

The characteristics of the area around Malang Kota Baru Station are related to the characteristics of the transit area, with the potential to be developed using a transit-based approach. The purpose of this research is to find out what the suitability of the characteristics of the area is to the concept or principle of TOD, then the priority of regional development is arranged based on the principle of TOD. The ultimate goal of the research is to obtain a viable regional development strategy.

2. Method

2.1. Research sites

One area concept that supports aspects of building density, diversity of land use, and proximity of the area to transit points is TOD [3]. In Indonesia, the TOD concept is better known as the Transit Oriented Area which is regulated in the Regulation of the Minister of Agrarian Affairs and Spatial Planning Number 16 of 2017 concerning Guidelines for the Development of Transit-Oriented Areas [4]. In the Ministerial Regulation, it is stated that transit-oriented areas are areas within a radius of 400 to 800 meters from the transit point. In the guidelines published by the Florida TOD Guidebook [5], it is stated that the TOD principle is divided into three parts: density, diversity, and design.

This research was conducted in the Malang Kota Baru Station Area, which is located in Klojen District, Malang City, East Java. In general, the area around Malang Kota Baru Station complies with the above criteria, namely the high density of buildings, the diversity of land uses, and the availability of pedestrian facilities, as well as public spaces. The area as the study area in the research is an area with a radius of 800 meters from Malang Kota Baru Station.

2.2. Data collecting

Data collection is an activity carried out to compile a systematic analysis based on the required input. Data collection methods in this study are divided into two, namely primary data and secondary data. The primary data in this study were obtained through observation, interviews, and questionnaires. While for secondary data, it is done by collecting data from related parties, including Spatial Plans (RTRW) of Malang City, Medium Term Development Plan (RPJM) and Long Term Development Plan (RPJP) of Malang City, Detailed Spattials Plans (RDTR) of Malang Tengah, Malang City public transportation documents, and theories related to the development of TOD-based areas.

2.3. Research variable

The indicators and variables used in this study were compiled based on the results of research related to TOD and transit area development. The indicators, variables, and parameters used in the study are shown in table 1.

Table 1. Research variable

Indicator	Variable	Parameter
Density	Building density	100-1000 building/Ha, with residential functions > 20 unit/ Ha.
	Building Base Coefficient (KDB)	Minimum 70%.
	Building Floor Coefficient (KLB)	Minimum 2.0.
Diversity	Residential	The calculation of the percentage of land use is as follows: 5% - 15% Public Space. 30% - 70% Commercial and Office Area. 20% - 60% Residential Area.
	Non-residential	
Design	Availability of pedestrians	100% available in the area. Pedestrian width 2-3 meters. 100% disabled facilities, with bollards or tactile paving.
	Availability of crossing facilities	The crossing facilities can be in the form of: Zebra Cross. Pelican Crossing.
	Availability of bike paths	Minimum width 1.5 meters.
	Node of transit	Active transit node between public transport with high accessibility. Travel time 5-10 minutes on foot from the activity center or vice versa.

2.4. Approach method

The approach used in this research is mixed methods research. Researchers combine two forms of approach in qualitative and quantitative research. Conformity analysis is carried out to obtain a portrait of the suitability of the existing condition of the area to the indicators and components in the TOD principle. The results of the analysis are then used as the basis for obtaining the priority order which is analyzed using the Analytical Hierarchy Process (AHP) method [6]. The respondents that are involved in this method are from various agencies related to the urban planning field. The results of the priority order of indicators and components in the TOD principle are then used as one of the inputs for analysis to obtain an Area development strategy. SWOT analysis by conducting an assessment using IFAS and EFAS matrices is carried out to obtain a recommended strategy according to existing conditions.

3. Results and Discussion

3.1. Suitability analysis of TOD components.

The components that will be used at the study site consist of three TOD criteria, namely Density, Diversity, and Design. To be able to know the components of Transit-Oriented Development at the research location, it is necessary to collect data according to the variables and indicators of the research. The data collection technique used to determine the TOD component in the existing condition of the study area is observation. Observation activities are carried out to observe directly the conditions in the field. The research instrument used in the observation technique is a block map, where the study area is divided into 8 blocks.

3.1.1. Density. Calculation of building density is carried out based on predetermined blocks with the results as shown in table 2.

IOP Conf. Series: Earth and Environmental Science 1000 (2022) 012026 doi:10.1088/1755-1315/1000/1/012026

Table 2. The density of buildings and residential buildings per-block

Block	Building Density per-Block (building/Ha)	Residential Buildings per-block (unit/Ha)
1	48	7
2	34	3
3	27	2
4	30	11
5	67	57
6	26	26
7	10	1
8	31	29

The average building density is 35 buildings/ha where the largest density is seen in block 5 of 67 buildings/ha. The parameter states that the building density is at a value of 100-1000 buildings/ha. Meanwhile, the density of residential buildings obtained an average of only 17 units/ha, where the parameters for residential functions are > 20 units/ha. However, in block 5, block 6, and block 8 the density of residential buildings has reached > 20 units/ha. The building density at the research site as a whole does not meet the parameter requirements.

The Basic Building Coefficient Interpretation (KDB) is calculated based on the block division that has been done. Based on Figure 1, the KDB condition can be interpreted. KDB at research sites has various ranges, namely 60% to 100%, while the parameters require a minimum of 70%. So that in the review of the KDB variables, it can be said that only some of them meet the parameter criteria.

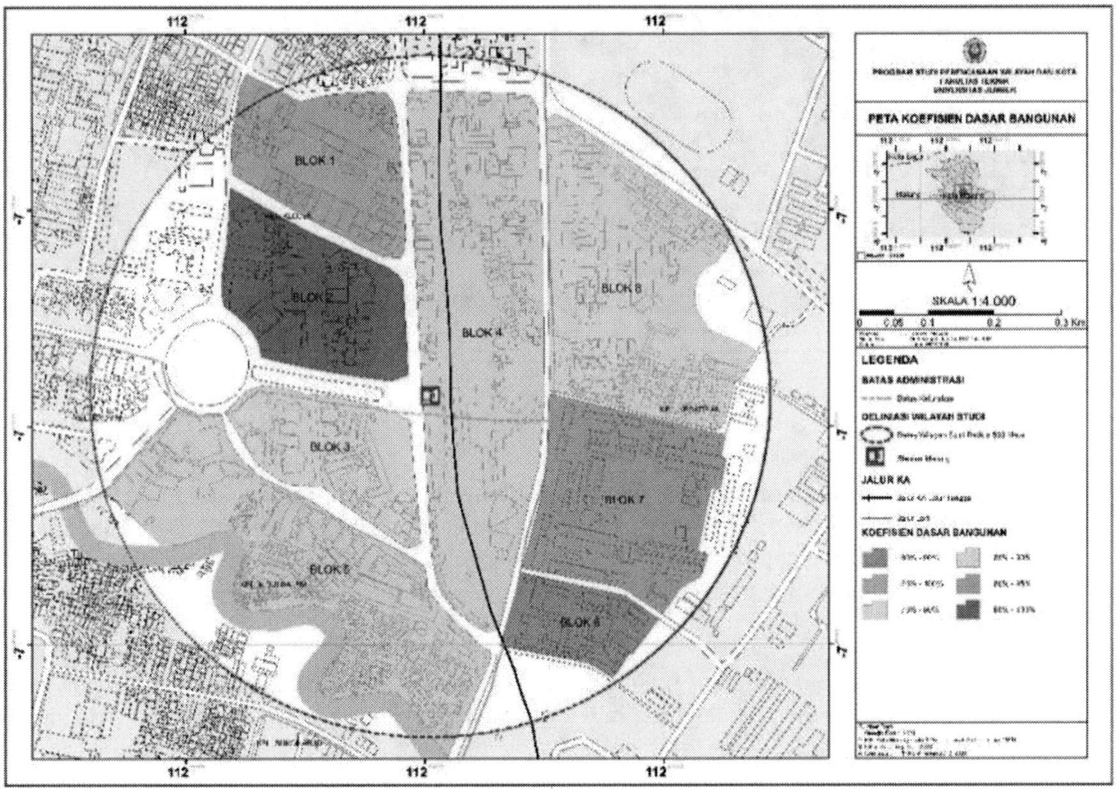

Figure 1. Interpretation of Building Basic Coefficients (KDB) map

The results of the calculation of the Building Floor Coefficient (KLB) show the lowest value of 1 and the highest of 5. The area with the highest KLB average value is in block 1, which is dominated by trade and service land uses and settlements. The lowest KLB average values are in blocks 4, 6, 7, and 8 which are dominated by land use functions for transportation, defense and security, trade and services, and settlement infrastructure.

3.1.2. Diversity. There are several types of land use with a total of 1,920 buildings. The land use in question consists of residential land use, health facilities, defense and security, and other land use. The interpretation of diversity at the research site is shown in Figure 2.

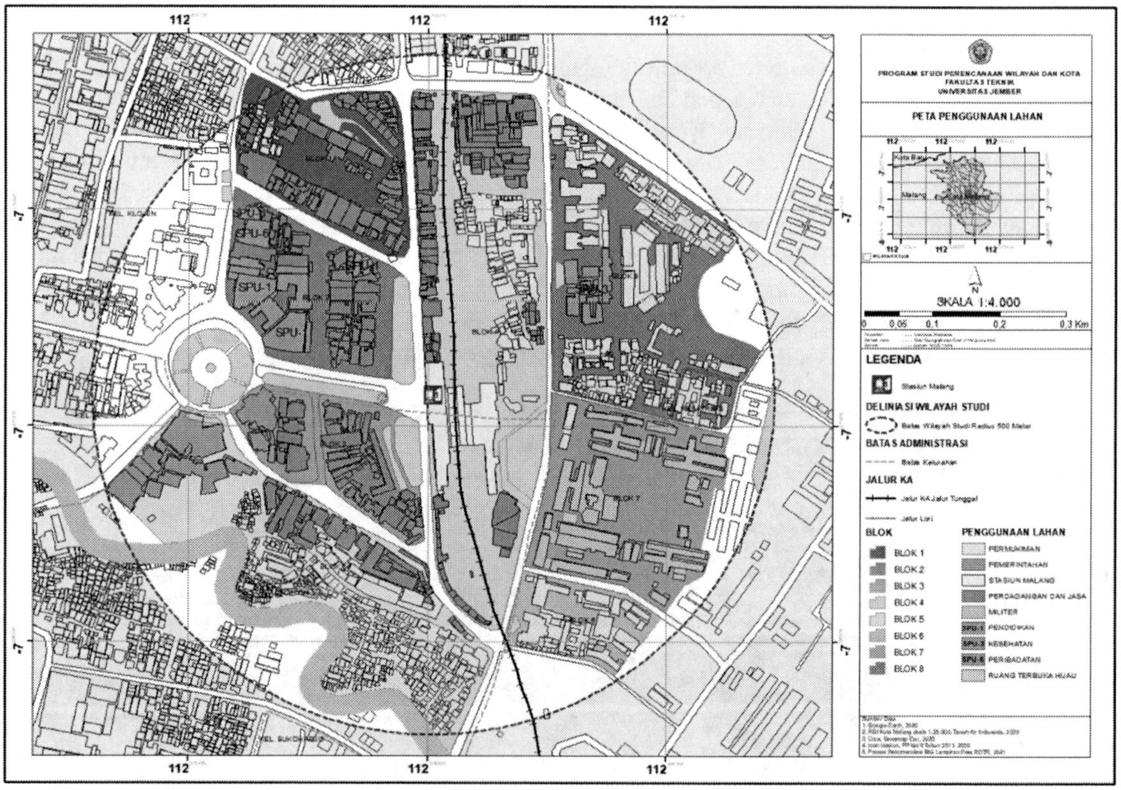

Figure 2. Interpretation of diversity map

The results of the analysis of land-use diversity in the research area show that half of the research area is functioned as residential buildings, with a proportion of 55%. Parameters of commercial buildings and offices with a proportion of 43% meet the specified parameters, which are 30%-70%. The only type of land use that does not match the parameters is Green Open Space, with a proportion of only 2% of the parameters of 5%-15%.

3.1.3. Design. There are four variables in the design indicator, namely: pedestrians, crossing facilities, bicycle lanes, and transit points. Pedestrians in the research location area are located on the main road, and have completeness in the form of tactile paving for people with disabilities. The pedestrian dimensions have met the parameters, which have a width of 2 to 3 meters. Although the main route in the research location area has pedestrians that meet the standards, several areas do not meet the standards, such as the width of fewer than 2 meters and the unavailability of facilities for persons with disabilities.

There are only two zebra crossings complete at the research site. Both locations are in front of Malang Kota Baru Station. Pedestrian-prone points such as schools, offices, government centers, and shopping areas are still not found in the study location area.

Bicycle lanes are one of the necessary instruments in the development of transit-based areas. This is under one of the objectives of implementing the TOD concept, namely to reduce the use of motorized vehicles, as well as to create a comfortable area for pedestrians and cyclists. In the research area, there were no bicycle lanes along the road, so there was no separation between bicycle users and other motor vehicle users.

There are three transit points at the research location, one of which is Malang Kota Baru Station. This train station serves road trips with local routes as well as medium and long-distance routes. While the other transit points are bus stops. The primary survey was carried out on the parties around the bus stop. The results of the interpretation obtained information for the bus stop that was actively used only the Sriwijaya Bus Stop. This bus stop is located in front of Malang Kota Baru Station.

3.2. Priority of development.

The priority of developing the transit area of Malang Kota Baru Station is determined from the results of the AHP analysis. Respondents who become objects are all relevant stakeholders, in this case, the respondents involved are parties who have a background in urban development and transportation. Seven respondents participated, they came from various agencies such as government officials, lecturers, and DAOP 8 employees. The survey results were processed using the AHP method based on the criteria for the predetermined variables. The results of the AHP analysis output obtained an AHP output diagram based on the TOD principle approach as shown in Figure 3.

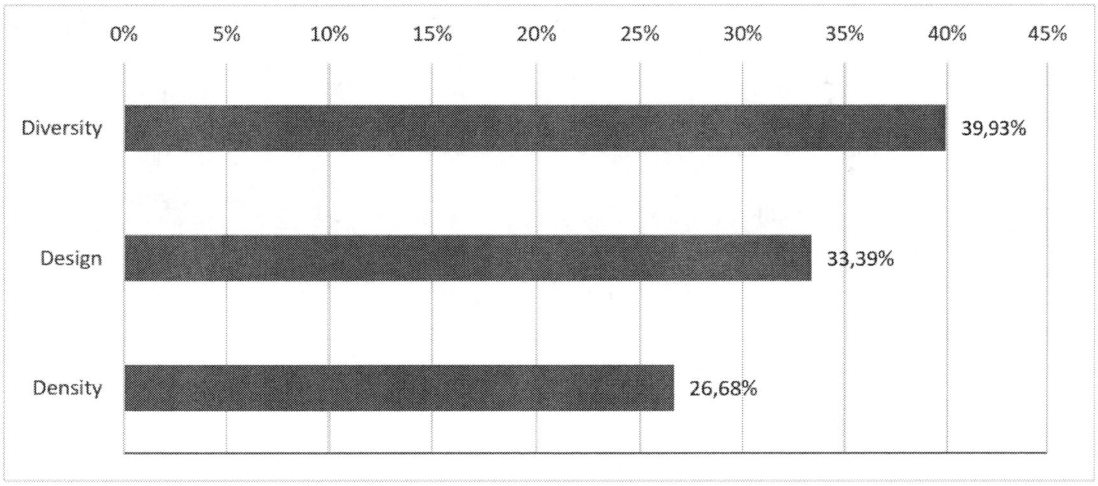

Figure 3. AHP analysis output diagram based on the TOD principle approach

The development priorities on indicators and research variables based on the results of the AHP analysis are obtained:

1. Diversity, with an assessment result of 39.93%. The order of priority of the components is as follows:
   a. Availability of pedestrian paths (22.11%);
   b. Pedestrian connectivity (21.13%);
   c. Availability of road crossing facilities (19.18%);
   d. Availability of bicycle lane facilities (18.82%); and

e. Dimensions of the pedestrian path (18.76%).

2. Design, with 33.39% assessment results. The order of priority of the components is as follows:
   a. Trade and services (27.27%);
   b. Offices (26.05%);
   c. Public Space (23.94%); and
   d. Residential (22.74%).
3. Density, with a calculation result of 26.68%. The order of priority of the components is as follows:
   a. Building Density (48.1%);
   b. Basic Building Coefficient (KDB) (25.95%); and
   c. Building Floor Coefficient (KLB) (25.94%).

3.3. Area development strategy

The strategy for developing the Malang Kota Baru Station area using the transit principle approach (TOD) is obtained through a series of SWOT analysis stages. Internal and external factors were identified based on the results of the conformity analysis and AHP analysis that had been carried out previously. Subsequently, the Internal Factors Analysis Strategic (IFAS) Matrix and the External Factors Analysis Strategic (EFAS) Matrix were prepared. Weights and ratings are determined based on development priorities based on the results of AHP analysis for each component of internal and external factors. IFAS matrix analysis results are shown in Table 3.

Table 3. Matrix of Internal Factors Analysis Strategic (IFAS)

No.	Internal Factor	Weight	Rating	Score	Remark
A.	Strengths				Rating Scale 1-4. Score = Weight*Rating Value meaning: • A positive sign is a strength. • A negative sign is a weakness.
1.	There are various land uses in the research area.	9.5%	3	0.285	
2.	Has a commercial activity center.	9.5%	4	0.380	
3.	It is the location of one of the tourist attractions of Malang City, namely Jodipan Village.	9.5%	2	0.190	
4.	It is the central government area.	9.5%	4	0.380	
5.	It has complete public facilities.	7.0%	2	0.140	
	Amount:	45%		1.375	
B.	Weaknesses				
1.	The need for public space is not fulfilled according to the rules.	7.0%	2	-0.140	
2.	Has a poor level of pedestrian service.	9.5%	4	-0.380	
3.	The small dimensions of the pedestrian path in some areas.	9.5%	3	-0.285	
4.	The lack of pedestrian path facilities is under standards.	9.5%	3	-0.285	
5.	Does not have a bike path.	9.5%	4	-0.380	
6.	Has a low level of accessibility for non-motorized vehicle users.	10.0%	4	-0.400	
	Amount:	55.0%		-1.870	
	Total	100.0%		-0.495	

Based on table 3, the Strength score is +1.375 on the internal factor. Meanwhile, the Weakness score is -1.87. The total score on the internal factor is -0.495, where the SWOT analysis quadrant is more directed at Weakness. Meanwhile, the results of the EFAS matrix are shown in table 4.

Table 4. Matrix of Eksternal Factors Analysis Strategic (EFAS)

No.	External Factor	Weight	Rating	Score	Remark
A.	Opportunities				Rating Scale 1-4. Score = Weight*Rating Value meaning: • A positive sign is an opportunity. • A negative sign is a threat.
1.	RTRW Malang City and RDTR Centre Malang have development plans that are in line with the TOD concept.	40,0%	3	1,2	
2.	The research area has a generation in the form of commercial, educational, office, government, and tourism areas which are one of the goals of the community in their activities.	20,0%	2	0,4	
	Amount:	60%		1,6	
B.	Threats				
1.	The level of discipline of traders in the research area is still low, so many of them sell in the pedestrian area.	20,0%	2	-0,4	
2.	There are many city public transportations and online taxis that park inappropriately, especially around public facilities while waiting for passengers.	20,0%	1	-0,2	
	Amount:	40%		-0,6	
	Total	100%		1	

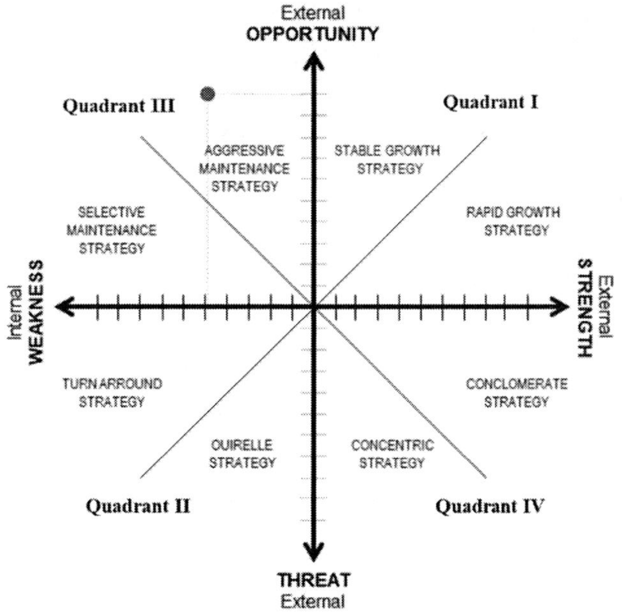

Figure 4. Matriks of analysis strategy quadrant of IFAS-EFAS

Based on table 4, the Opportunity score is +1.60 on the external factor. Meanwhile, the Threat score is -0.60. The total score on the external factor is +1.00, where the SWOT analysis quadrant is more directed to Opportunity. Based on the analysis of the IFAS Matrix and the EFAS Matrix in table 3 and table 4, the recommended strategy can be obtained, namely the aggressive maintenance strategy, where the analysis results show that it is in quadrant III (see Figure 4).

Aggressive maintenance strategy on the development of the Malang Kota Baru Station Area is carried out by prioritizing implementing the Weakness-Opportunity Strategy (W-O Strategy). Strategies that can be done are:

1. Enforcement of building intensity can be adjusted to the rules of the Malang City spatial policy and the provision of incentives and disincentives to the intensity of buildings that are not appropriate.
2. In line with the enforcement of building intensity, enforcement of regulations related to Green Open Space can also be carried out by implementing incentives and disincentives.
3. The construction of pedestrian and cyclist facilities is needed to facilitate the use of non-motorized vehicles and public transportation. In the concept of a transit-based area, the availability of pedestrian and bicycle facilities is required 100% within the area.

4. Conclusions

The suitability analysis in the Malang Kota Baru Station area shows that the existing conditions are not suitable. Of the nine variables used (building density, Basic Building Coefficient (KDB), Building Floor Coefficient (KLB), residential, non-residential, pedestrian availability [7], crossing facilities availability, bicycle lane availability, and transit points), there is no match between the conditions existing with predefined parameters.

Nine variables are used in the AHP analysis, and the order of priority and the results of the assessment of the TOD indicators are:

- First, diversity of 39.93% with the priority order of components: (i) availability of pedestrian paths, (ii) connectivity of pedestrian paths, (iii) availability of road crossing facilities, (iv) availability of bicycle lanes, and (v) dimensions of lanes. pedestrian.
- Second, the design is 33.39% with the components in order of priority: (i) trade and services, (ii) offices, (iii) public spaces, and (iv) settlements.
- Third, density is 26.68% in order of priority of components: (i) building density, (ii) Building Base Coefficient (KDB), and (iii) Building Floor Coefficient (KLB).

The regional development strategy at Malang Kota Baru Station with the TOD principle approach can be carried out with an aggressive maintenance strategy. The results of the SWOT analysis give the results being in quadrant three with negative IFAS and positive EFAS values. The W-O strategy must be carried out in the development area by maximizing various opportunities, to resolve or minimize internal weaknesses that occur.

References

[1] Tamin, O.Z. (1999). Concept Of Transportation Needs Management As An Alternative For Solving Urban Transportation Problems in DKI. ITB Urban And Regional Planning Journal. Volumes 10 (1).
[2] Institute for Transportation and Development Policy (ITDP) 2017, TOD STANDARD, New York.
[3] BPS, 2019
[4] Minister of Agrarian Affairs and Spatial Planning (2017), Minister of Agrarian Affairs and Spatial Planning Number 16 of 2017 concerning Guidelines for the Development of Transit-Oriented Areas.
[5] Treasure Coast Regional Planning Council (2012), Florida TOD Guidebook.
[6] Saaty, Thomas L.1993. The Analytical Hierarchy Process: Planning, Priority Setting, Resource Allocation. Pittsburgh: University of Pittsburgh Pers.

IOP Conf. Series: Earth and Environmental Science 1000 (2022) 012026 doi:10.1088/1755-1315/1000/1/012026

[7] Ministry of Public Works and Public Housing, Number 02/SE/M/201. Technical Planning of Pedestrian Facilities. 26 February 2018.

IOP Conf. Series: Earth and Environmental Science 1000 (2022) 012027 doi:10.1088/1755-1315/1000/1/012027

A Comparison Analysis on Car User Decision When Faced with Different Congestion Pricing Policy (Case Study: Jakarta Metropolitan Area)

Alvinsyah[1] and Muhammad Fathurrizqi[1]

[1]Civil Engineering Department, University of Indonesia, Depok Indonesia

Alvinsyah2004@gmail.com

Abstract. This research aims to analyze the car user's decision in their mode choice when faced with two different congestion pricing, namely Road Pricing (RP) and Parking Pricing (P2) policy scheme. The comparison analysis is conducted through the developed binomial logit model both for RP and P2 policy schemes. Data is collected by utilizing a stated preference survey, where the car user is asked their preference towards the mode choice on a given set of price and timesaving combination for both policies. Then the utility function for each policy is established by conducting some statistical procedures to have a feasible and reasonable model. Having set the utility functions, the validity test is carried out to the developed model using a different set of data from the survey. Further analysis is done to select the model that satisfies the statistical feasibility and the validity threshold number. Comparison to both different choice models yields different decisions represented in the form of shifting mode percentages. The research results show that the RP policy scheme tends to shift the car user higher than the P2 policy scheme at the same total additional charging fare.

1. Introduction

Traffic congestion in Jakarta is a severe problem and is unlikely to be solved by adding more road capacity. Due to spatial limitations in the most congested areas and latent demand induced by the added capacity, the Government needs to shift its focus from the supply side to the demand side for tackling traffic congestion. Road Pricing (RP) or Parking Pricing (P2) can form part of a traffic demand management strategy [1] to provide an efficient, equitable and flexible solution to handle traffic congestion problems in the long term. A detailed explanation regarding congestion pricing (or often called road pricing) studies and application can be found in many works of literature [2, 3, 4, 5, 6, 7]. Meanwhile, previous research extensively describes parking pricing issues [5, 8, 9, 10, 11, 12].

Although parking pricing is part of the congestion pricing [1], the Government of Jakarta recently started considering this policy as a traffic restraint instrument [13]; after it has been treated as a source of government revenue for decades. While, on the other hand, road pricing has long been discussed, planned, and even tried to be implemented [14] by the Jakarta Government as a traffic restraint tool. Unfortunately, due to several constraints that occurred, this policy still cannot be implemented yet. Ideally, these two TDM schemes can be applied together to obtain optimal traffic control within the city, but sometimes many factors can be constrained for such policies to be implemented together or individually. While many studies on ERP for Jakarta have been done [15, 16, 17, 18], only a few have been done for parking pricing as a traffic restraint instrument [13, 19]. However, on the other hand, applying P2 is considered by some to be the second-best alternative to RP [20]. Furthermore, many studies on people's travel behaviour have been done for RP [21] and P2 [22]. However, studies that compare the impacts of these two policies are rare [23]. Therefore, this research tries to observe the impact on car users if these two pricing policies are implemented. The car user perception will be analyzed through their decision on the mode choice if they are faced with different charging fare and timesaving options for both RP and P2 policy schemes and if they are implemented individually or separately. Considering that congestion pricing schemes potentially can improve environment quality [24, 25, 26], this research can be helpful for further research on the impact of these policies on the reduction of congestion and the improvement of environmental quality. The following section will discuss the research methodology, data collection and model development, research results and discussion, and the final section will be the research conclusion.

2. Research Methodology

Since the analysis will heavily focus on the private car user response to the offered congestion (pricing) policies, the research's main steps are data collection and analysis, model development, and comparison analysis through the developed model. Schematically the research flow is represented in Figure 1.

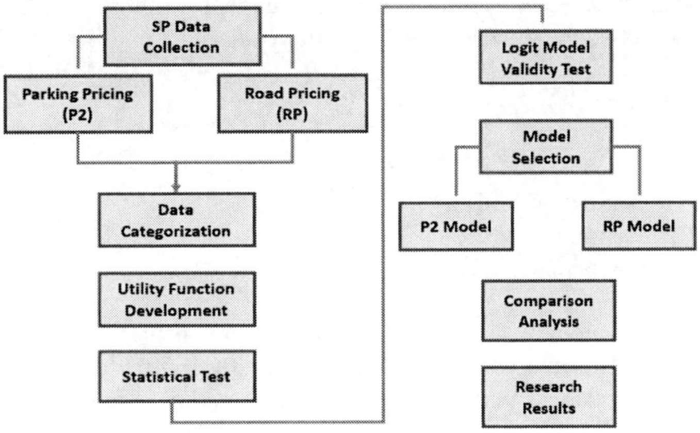

Figure 1. Research Framework

A stated preference (SP) survey form for RP and P2 policies is prepared before data collection. The primary information collected from the target sample (respondent) are socio-economic characteristics of the respondent, trip purpose, trip O-D, travel attributes such as travel time and travel cost, and respondent decision on the mode choice for a given set of prices and time saving. During the survey, the respondent will be asked their preference to both RP and P2 policy scheme, so the hypothetical condition play a significant role. The most crucial aspect in the hypothetical condition is the assumption that the total additional cost due to either RP scheme or P2 scheme is the same regardless of the pricing mechanism offered in the SP form. Referring to the previous study, four options can be selected by the private car users when faced with such an RP policy scheme [27], but a recent study [28] shows that most private car users prefer to shift their mode of travel to public transport compared with other options. Therefore, in this research, the option given to the private car user for their decision is public transport only. In the hypothetical condition, the public transport option is assumed the same as the current situation: service and fare.

Since the data used in this study is obtained from an SP survey, in which the respondents had to choose between discrete alternatives, the preferred modelling framework is a discrete choice [29]. In this research, a binary logit model, a specific form of multinomial logit model [30, 31] is used and shown in Equation (1) is utilized;

$$P = \frac{e^{U_{ii}}}{1 + e^{U_{ii}}} \quad (1)$$

The primary assumption is that each decision-maker seeks to maximize his utility and chooses the alternative with the highest utility for him. The utility of an alternative *i* for decision-maker *n* is defined by its utility function with a deterministic part V_i and a random part $\mathcal{E}_i$ [29]:

$$U_{in} = V_{in} + \mathcal{E}_{in} = \beta\, x_{in} + \mathcal{E}_{in} \quad (2)$$

The deterministic utility can be described by a vector of unknown taste parameters to be estimated and a vector x_{in} containing the alternative's attributes and the decision-makers socio-economic characteristics. The assumed distribution of the random error term defines the model structure and, thereby, the functional form of the choice probabilities.

Due to the dependent variable characteristics is a dichotomic condition and recent similar research found a nonlinearity relationship between dependent and independent variable [19, 28, 32, 33], the binary logistic regression method is adopted to develop the utility functions in this research [34];

$$Y = \beta_0 + \beta_1 X_1 + \ldots\ldots + \beta_n X_n \quad (3)$$

where,
X_i, X_n = Independent variables
β_0 = Regression Constant
β_1, β_n = Regression Coefficent

Before developing a utility function, the collected data is cleaned by using box plot analysis, so the outliers could be excluded in the analysis. Then a correlation test by the rank spearman method [35] is carried out to determine independent variables that should be included in the utility function. Once the independent variables that have a high correlation with the dependent variable are obtained, the next step is to conduct goodness of fit tests to the predeveloped utility functions represented by Hosmer and Lemeshow and Omnibus of Model Coefficient tests, Wald-significant test, -2 log-likelihood test, Nagelkerke R Square, dan Overall Percentage. A detailed explanation of the formulation and how these tests are conducted and interpreted can be found in other relevant literature and research [34, 35, 36, 37, 38]. Besides the statistical test, a validity test is also conducted by imposing the proposed utility function into the binomial logit model and using a different data set from the survey. This test aims to measure the bias level of the model result to the real data represented by an RMSE value. The RMSE calculation is done by using the following [39]:

$$RMSE = \sqrt{\frac{\sum_{t=1}^{n}(A_t - F_t)^2}{n}} \quad (4)$$

where,
At = Observed data
Ft = Model result
n = number of observed data

Once the statistical and the validity tests are done, the utility function that satisfies the standard requirement of both tests is selected for further analysis. Having selected the utility functions, the two functions representing RP and P2 policy will be used for comparison analysis. The analysis will focus on the different car user preferences toward the RP and the P2 scheme offered, represented by the percentage of car users that will shift to public transport. Alternatively, the shifting could be interpreted as the potential number of car reductions.

3. Data Collection

As mentioned previously, that car user preference will be obtained from an SP survey, so some crucial factors in the SP survey will be briefly explained in the following paragraphs, while detail and thorough explanations on this SP method can be found in some literature [40, 41, 42, 43]. Since the respondent will be faced with two different pricing policy schemes (i.e., RP and P2 schemes) in the survey, some essential hypothetical conditions informed to the respondent are;

- The pricing policy of both RP and P2 schemes is applied only in the designated area [44] as shown in Figure 2.
- The survey simulates the pre-pandemic condition.
- Odd-Even Plate Number Policy scheme is still in operation for the P2 policy scheme.
- The total extra charge or fare that must be paid due to the applied RP or P2 scheme will be the same.
- The total parking duration is assumed to be 8 hours/working day
- The additional parking charge (i.e., P2 scheme) is set on an hourly basis and is based on the official regulation [45, 46]
- The parking payment mechanism is kept as it is (i.e., hourly basis)
- When the RP charge is applied, the current parking charge still prevail (i.e., must be paid)
- The RP charge is paid when entering or crossing the designated area
- The RP charge is set the same as the difference between the totally new and the current parking charge
- The RP scheme is applied from 5.30 AM to 9.30 AM only
- The public transport service and the fare is as the current situation

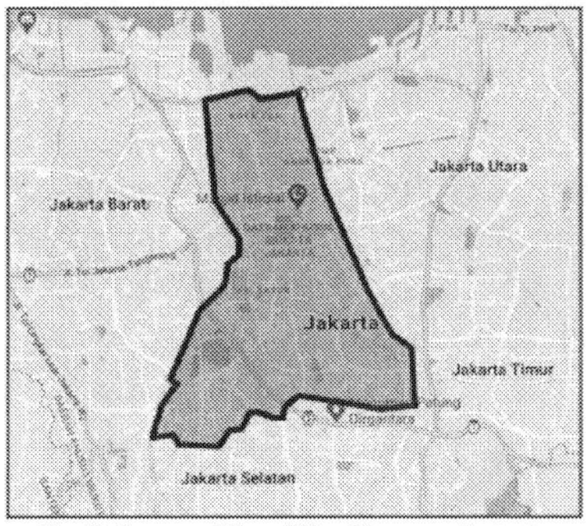

Figure 2. Jakarta Traffic Restraint Area [44]

Due to pandemic conditions, the survey is carried out both online and offline. Therefore, especially for the online method, some critical screening parameters in the digital survey form should be carefully prepared and designed to obtain proper respondents. The following parameters are set as the screening parameters in the survey form:

- The target sample is the car users which is selected randomly
- The trip destination should be within the designated restraint area as in Figure 2.
- Their expenses should bear all transport costs; and
- Park their car in the official parking space

Regarding the SP questions in the survey form, the pricing scenario offered to the respondents is summarized in Table 1. These pricing scenarios are combined with the assumed travel time saving from 10 minutes to 40 minutes with 10 minutes increment [32, 33].

Table 1. Pricing Scenario for RP and P2 Policy

Pricing ID	Additional P2 Charge per hour (IDR)	RP Charge per entry (IDR)
1	1.000,00	8.000,00
2	2.000,00	16.000,00
3	3.000,00	24.000,00
4	4.000,00	32.000,00
5	5.000,00	40.000,00
6	6.000,00	48.000,00
7	7.000,00	56.000,00

The total valid samples collected during the survey is 100 respondents and the trip purpose 64% of them is working purposes.

4. Model Development

Referring to the recent research findings, the working purpose trip sample group yields a better statistical test result in the model development process [32, 33, 47]. Therefore, in the utility function development, the collected sample will be categorized into two groups, namely the all-purpose (AP) trip group, which represents all sample data, and the working purpose (WP) trip group, which represents working trip purpose only (see Figure 3). This categorization is applied for both predefined pricing policies (i.e., RP and P2 policy). Therefore, the proposed utility function in the RP scheme will consist of RP-AP and RP-WP, while in the P2 scheme, the group will also consist of P2-AP and P2-WP.

The first step in the utility function development is to observe the relationship level between the respondent's decision (dependent variable) and the influencing factors to his/her decision (independent variable), representing personal characteristics and travel characteristics by applying the rank spearman correlation test. From eight independent variables tested, only RP or P2 fare (or additional charging) variable, denoted as X7, has a significant correlation with the dependent variable, ranging from 0.384 to 0.472, as summarized in Table 2.

Table 2. Rank Spearman Correlation Test

	Category			
	RP-AP	RP-WP	P2-AP	P2-WP
Fare (X_7)	0.432	0.401	0.474	0.384

Based on this correlation test, the statistical test is conducted to evaluate the feasibility of the four predeveloped utility functions, as summarized in Table 3 for the RP scheme category and Table 4 for the P2 scheme category. Besides the statistical test, a model validity (RMSE) test is also conducted by incorporating all four predeveloped utility functions into the binary logit model as in Equation (1) using a different sample data set.

Table 3. Statistical Test for RP Scheme Category

	Utility function	Omnibus Test	Hosmer Test	-2 Log Likelihood	Nagelkerke R Square	Overall Prcntge (%)
RP-AP	$U = 0.0172 + 0.907X_7$	0.000	0.082	12544.44[a] 917.458[b]	0.354	85
RP-WP	$U = 0.2588 + 0.916X_7$	0.000	0.073	703.782[a] 521.319[b]	0.334	88

[a]Innitial value
[b]Final value

Table 4. Statistical Test for P2 Scheme Category

	Utility function	Omnibus Test	Hosmer Test	-2 Log Likelihood	Nagelkerke R Square	Overall Prcntge (%)
P2-AP	$U = 0.9886 + 0.593X_7$	0.000	0.299	1966.163[a] 1595.827[b]	0.299	74
P2-WP	$U = 0.5340 + 0.462X_7$	0.000	0.806	1197.390[a] 1048.197[b]	0.403	81

[a]Innitial value
[b]Final value

This test, represented by the RMSE value, is carried out to observe the level conformity of model result with the actual data collected from the field, and the test result is shown in Table 5.

Table 5. Validity (RMSE) Test

	Category			
	RP-AP	RP-WP	P2-AP	P2-WP
RMSE (%)	14.68	7.05	18.71	9.95

5. Analysis and Discussion

Referring to the statistical test results as indicated in Table 3 and Table 4 and looking at the Nagelkerke R Square and Overall Percentage parameters in those Tables, the utility function formed by the working purpose (WP) data group for both RP and P2 schemes yields a better result. Furthermore, based on the validity test as indicated in Table 4, the statistical test result is confirmed by the RMSE value, which is less than 10% [39] for the utility function formed by the WP data group. Therefore, the utility function formed by the WP data group as shown in Table 6, is selected as the representative model for further analysis.

Table 6. Selected Model

	Utility function
RP-WP	$U = 0.2588 + 0.916X_7$
P2-WP	$U = 0.5340 + 0.462X_7$

The binary logit model with the selected utility function for RP and P2 schemes is shown in Equation (5) and Equation (6).

$$P_{(RP)} = \frac{e^{(0.2558 + 0.916\,XX7)}}{1 + e^{(0.2558 + 0.916\,XX7)}} \quad (5)$$

$$P_{(P2)} = \frac{e^{(-0.5340\ +\ 0.462\ XX7)}}{1 +\ e^{(-0.5340 + 0.462\ XX7)}} \qquad (6)$$

A graphical representation of the developed logit model is established both for RP and P2 logit model by imposing variety fare (additional charging) values into Equation (5) and Equation (6) as represented in Figure 3. Meanwhile, the numerical representation of these fare values is shown in Table 7. It is important to note that the curves in Figure 3 and figures in Table 7 are based on the fares (or additional charging) utilized in the survey form, although any fare values can be exercised by using the developed logit model.

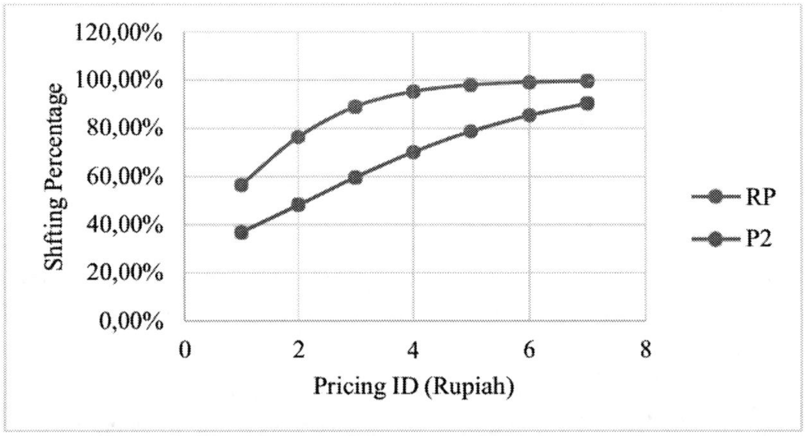

Figure 3. Willingness to shift curves

Referring to the figures in Table 7, it is interesting to observe that the respondents react differently when they are faced with the same amounts of additional Charge imposed by RP and P2 schemes. The figures in Table 7, show that the respondents seem more sensitive to the RP fares than P2, which is indicated by the higher percentage shifting (to the alternative mode) values for all additional charges. The difference is quite significant for each charged fare, ranging from 9.31% to 29.37% and with an average of 20.63%. While, looking at the form of curves for both policy schemes in Figure 3, the first four RP fare increase significantly impacts the respondent compared with those of P2.

Table 7. Willingness to Shift Probability

Pricing ID	Total Pricing Value (in Rupiahs)	Shifting percentage (%)		Different ((%)
		RP-Scheme	P2-Scheme	
1	40.000,00	56.43	36.96	19.47
2	48.000,00	76.40	48.20	28.20
3	56.000,00	89.00	59.63	29.37
4	64.000,00	95.29	70.11	25.18
5	72.000,00	98.06	78.83	19.23
6	80.000,00	99.21	85.53	13.68
7	88.000,00	99.68	90.37	9.31

The P2 fares increase tends to form a relative linear curve which can be interpreted that the respondent still has a higher willingness to pay the additional parking fee. From these results, it seems that the respondent psychologically is highly affected by the magnitude of the pricing charge rather than the total charge they should spend. Referring to similar studies conducted in other countries [48, 49, 50, 51], it is found that a similar phenomenon also occurs. Unfortunately, an apple-to-apple comparison cannot be made since those studies technically have slightly different objectives and approaches.

Considering the actual situation and the result of this research, the RP policy is better implemented if the Government only focuses on relieving congestion. On the other hand, the P2 policy would be the better option if the government policy also keens to gain additional revenue. For instance, if 60% of car users need to be shifted to public transport, the total cost of RP and the existing parking fee that a car user should pay would be IDR 41,307 -. Meanwhile, the total cost of P2 (the existing and additional parking fee) that a car user should pay would be IDR 48,033.

Since the results of this study and several other studies show higher levels of public acceptance compared to RP policies [48, 49, 50, 51], the implementation of the P2 policy should be seriously considered by the Government, especially with the situation only few cities have succeeded in implementing the RP policy [20], the failure of the Jakarta Government to implement ERP [14].

Various studies show that the congestion pricing scheme can potentially reduce environmental deterioration due to the reduction of vehicle emissions [24, 25, 26]. Therefore, to have a stronger justification for implementing the P2 policy in Jakarta, it is necessary to link it with other policies related to environmental quality improvement [52, 53]. Consequently, if P2 policy is properly implemented, various benefits such as traffic congestion level reduction, additional revenue, and environmental quality improvement could be gained.

6. Conclusion

An analysis of car user preference when they are faced with two different congestion pricing policy schemes, namely Road Pricing (RP) and Parking Pricing (P2P has been conducted. It is found that the main factor affecting the car user preference is the pricing fare. A separate logit binomial model based on the stated preference survey data is developed for both policy schemes. A probability shifting mode curve related to various pricing fares is developed for comparative analysis based on these two models. The analysis shows that for the same total additional charging fare, the RP policy scheme gives a higher impact to the car user, reflected in a higher probability of shifting to the alternative mode than that of the P2 policy Scheme. This result also indicates that car users psychologically have more attention or concern with the direct charging fares applied by these two policy schemes rather than the total amount paid due to these additional charging fares. Referring to this research result, the Government has an opportunity to determine and choose whether the pricing policy scheme is focused on reducing the congestion only, or both are reducing the congestion and gaining more revenue at the same time. Therefore, implementing RP or P2 policy will yield multiple benefits, namely congestion level reduction, additional revenue, and environmental quality improvement.

7. References

[1] Gomez-Ibanez J, and Small, K 1994 NCHRP synthesis 210 of highway practice*: road pricing for congestion management: a survey of international practice*, Report, National Research Council, Washington, D.C.

[2] Croci E 2016 Urban Road Pricing: a comparative study on the experiences of London, Stockholm, and Milan. *Transportation Research Procedia*, **14**, 253-262

[3] Seik F T 2000 *An Advanced Demand Management Instrument in Urban Transport: Electronic Road Pricing in Singapore*. Volume **17**(1), Pergamon

[4] Niskanen E and Nash C 2008 Road pricing in Europe - a review of research and practice. *Advances in Spatial Science*, 55, 5–27.

[5] Washbrook K, Haider W, Jaccard M 2006. Estimating Commuter Mode Choice: A Discrete Choice Analysis of the Impact of Road Pricing and Parking Charges. Springer, *Transportation, Volume* **33**, pp. 621–639

[6] Phang S Y and Toh R S 2004 Road congestion pricing in Singapore: 1975 to 2003. *Transportation Journal*, **43**(2), 16–25

[7] Nourinejad M & Roorda M J 2017 Impact of hourly parking pricing on travel demand. *Transportation Research Part A: Policy and Practice*, **98**, 28–45

[8] Bernstein A 2010 Parking Rates Go Up, Cities Make Bucks: Nobody Likes Paying for Parking, But with City Budgets Tightening More Municipalities Are Eying the Parking Meter as a Source of New Funds. Retrieved from Marketplace: http://marketplace.publicradio.org/display/web/2010/05/04/pm-cities-raise-parking-rates-for revenue

[9] Broaddus A, Litman T and Menon G 2009 *Transportation Demand Management.* Eschborn: GTZ.

[10] Litman T 2018 *Parking Pricing Implementation Guidelines. How More Efficient Parking Pricing Can Help Solve Parking and Traffic Problems, Increase revenue, and Achieve Other Planning Objectives*, pp. 1-35.

[11] Litman T 2016 *Parking Management: Strategies, Evaluation and Planning.* Victoria: Victoria Transport Policy Institute.

[12] Saleh W and Sammer G 2009 *Travel Demand Management and Road User Pricing.* Farnham: Ashgate Publishing Limited

[13] DKI Jakarta 2019 *Studi Kajian Penerapan Tarif Parkir Tinggi*, Laporan Akhir, UPT Perparkiran, Dinas Pehubungan DKI Jakarta

[14] Akbar J 2020 PTUN Jakarta Minta Anies Lanjutkan Lelang ERP yang Sebelumnya Dibatalkan. https://kumparan.com/kumparannews/ptun-jakarta-minta-anies-lanjutkan-lelang-erp-yang-sebelumnya-dibatalkan-1sy685W85bp/full, diakses pada 6 Juli 2021 Pukul 21.39

[15] JETRO 2008 *The Study on Jakarta Road Pricing in the Republic of Indonesia*, Final Report, Japan External Trade Organization.

[16] CTS-UI 2006 *Studi Penerapan Kebijakan Pembatasan Lalu lintas di DKI Jakarta*, Laporan Akhir, Center for Transport Studies, Universitas Indonesia

[17] Rizki M, et al. 2016 Route Divert Behavior in Jakarta Electronic Road Pricing Policy Implementation, *International Journal of Technology*, **4**: 571-580

[18] Sunitiyoso Y, et al 2020 Road Pricing in Indonesia: How Will Public Respond? *Transportation Research Procedia*, **47**, 123–130

[19] Bala F 2019 *Analisis Dampak Penerapan Kebijakan Biaya dan Ruang Parkir Terhadap Pengurangan Penggunaan Mobil Pribadi*, Skripsi Sarjana Strata-1, Departemen Teknik Sipil Universitas Indonesia, tidak dipublikasikan

[20] Miller S and Wilson R 2015 *Parking Taxes as a Second-Best Congestion Pricing Mechanism*, Inter-American Development Bank, IDB Working Paper Series Nº IDB-WP-614

[21] Chiou Y C, Fu C 2017 Responses of drivers and motorcyclists to congestion charge, *Transportation Research Procedia* **25**, 2957–2969

[22] Mei Z, et al. 2020 Assessment of Different Parking Pricing Strategies: A Simulation-based Analysis, *Sustainability* **12**, 2056

[23] Glavića D, Simićevića J, Milenkovića M 2020 Parking versus Congestion Pricing: Comparative Analysis, *Journal of Road and Traffic Engineering*, **LXVI**, **3**, 11-16

[24] Baghestani A, Tayarani M, Allahviranloo M and Gao H O 2020 Evaluating the Traffic and Emissions Impacts of Congestion Pricing in New York City, *Sustainability* **12**, 3655

[25] Daniel J I and Bekka K 2000, The Environmental Impact of Highway Congestion Pricing, *Journal of Urban Economics* **47**, 180-215

[26] Santos G, Rojey L and Newbery D 2000 *The Environmental Benefits from Road Pricing*, DAE Working Paper 0020, Department of Applied Economics, University of Cambridge.

[27] Wheway J and Cheuk K 1999 Implementation of Road Pricing Model with The Emme/2 Macro Language, *Proceeding on 1st Asian EMME/2 Users Conference Shanghai*

[28] Aditya F 2019 *Analisis Dampak Penerapan Kebijakan Road Pricing Terhadap Pengurangan Penggunaan Kendaraan Pribadi*, Skripsi Sarjana Strata-1, Departemen Teknik Sipil Universitas Indonesia, tidak dipublikasikan

[29] Domencich T A and McFadden D 1975 *Urban Travel Demand: A Behavioral Analysis.* Amsterdam: North Holland Publishing Company.
[30] McFadden D 1974 *Conditional logit analysis of qualitative choice-behaviour.* In: Zarembka, P. (Ed.), Frontiers in Econometrics. Academic Press, New York, pp. 105-142
[31] Ben-Akiva M E and Lerman S R 1985 *Discrete Choice Analysis*: Theory and Application to Travel Demand. MIT Press, Cambridge.
[32] Franssius E *2020 Analisis Potensi Perpindahan Moda Bagi Pengguna Transportasi Umum Akibat Pengoperasian Layanan LRT Di Jakarta*, Skripsi Sarjana Strata-1, Departemen Teknik Sipil Universitas Indonesia, tidak dipublikasikan
[33] Christian K L 2020 *Analisis Willingness to Pay dan Willingness to Shift Pengguna Kendaraan Pribadi Untuk Layanan LRT Jakarta*, Skripsi Sarjana Strata-1, Departemen Teknik Sipil Universitas Indonesia, tidak dipublikasikan
[34] Hosmer D and Lemeshow S 2000 *Applied Logistic Regressions.* USA: John Wiley & Sons.
[35] Santoso S 2014 *Statistik Non Parametrik.* Jakarta: PT Elex Media Komputindo
[36] Draper N and Smith H 1998 *Applied Regression Analysis.* New York: John Wiley and Sons Inc.
[37] Freedman D A 2009 *Statistical Models: Theory and Practice.* Cambridge: Cambridge University Press.
[38] Gelman A and Hill J 2007 *Data Analysis Using Regression and Multilevel/Hierarchical Models.* Cambridge: Cambridge University Press.
[39] Tamin O Z 2000 *Perencanaan & Pemodelan Transportasi.* Intitut Teknologi Bandung.
[40] Aizaki H, Nakatani T and Sato K 2015 *Stated Preference Methods Using R.* Boca Raton: Taylor & Francis Group, LLC
[41] Sanko N 2001 *Guidelines for Stated Preference Experiment Design.* Leiden: Ecole Nationale des Ponts et Chassees.
[42] Hensher D A 1994 Stated Preference Analysis of choices: the State of Practice. *Transportation,* **21**, pp. 107-133
[43] Pearmain D and Kroes E P 1990 *Stated Preference Techniques: A Guide to Practice.* Den Haag: Steer Davies & Gleave
[44] Pemerintah Provinsi DKI Jakarta 2012 *Peraturan Daerah Provinsi Daerah Khusus Ibukota Jakarta No. 1 Tahun 2012 Tentang Rencana Tata Ruang Wilayah 2030*
[45] Pemerintah Provinsi DKI Jakarta 2017 *Peraturan Gubernur Provinsi DKI Jakarta No. 31 Tahun 2017 Tentang Tarif Layanan Parkir, Denda Pelanggaran Transaksi dan Biaya Penderekan/Pemindahan Kendaraan Bermotor*
[46] Pemerintah Provinsi DKI Jakarta 2013 *Peraturan Gubernur Provinsi DKI Jakarta Nomor 179 Tahun 2013 Tentang Tarif Layan Parkir*
[47] Athira I C, et al. 2016 Estimation of Value of Travel Time for Work Trips. *Transportation Research Procedia* **17**, pp. 116-123.
[48] Albert G and, Mahalel D 2006 Congestion tolls and parking fees: A comparison of the potential effect on travel behaviour, *Transport Policy* **13**, 496–502
[49] Feng S W and Ye J J 2008 A Comparative Study of Parking and Congestion Charge Policies based on Transport Mode Choice Estimation, Proceedings of the 11th International IEEE Conference on Intelligent Transportation Systems Beijing, China, October 12-15
[50] Azari K A, Arintono S, Hamid H, Rahmat R A O K, 2013 Modelling Demand Under Parking and Cordon Pricing Policy, *Transport Policy* **25**, 1–9
[51] Shiftan Y., Golani A. 2005 Effect of auto restraint policies on travel behavior, Transportation Research Record: *Journal of the Transportation Research Board,* **Vol. 1932**, Transportation Research Board of the National Academies, Washington, pp.156-163
[52] Republik Indonesia 2011 *Peraturan Presiden Republik Indonesia Nomor 61 Tahun 2011 Tentang Rencana Aksi Nasional Penurunan Emisi Gas Rumah Kaca*
[53] Pemerintah Provinsi DKI Jakarta 2005 *Peraturan Daerah Provinsi Daerah Khusus Ibukota Jakarta Nomor 2 Tahun 2005 Tentang Pengendalian Pencemaran Udara*

Study of travel shuttle mode in supporting connectivity between strategic tourist attractions in South Lampung Regency

[a]Muhammad Zainal Ibad, [a]Destri Amanda, [b]Rahayu Sulistyorini, [b,c]Reza Asriandi Ekaputra, [a]Zenia F Saraswati, [b]Muhammad Alfat Rizki Pratama, [a]Salwa Nabilla Antiqasari

[a]Departement of Urban and Regional Planning, Institut Teknologi Sumatra, Jalan Terusan Ryacudu Nomor 1, Kabupaten Lampung Selatan, Provinsi Lampung
[b]Departement of Civil Engineering, Institut Teknologi Sumatera, Jalan Terusan Ryacudu Nomor 1, Kabupaten Lampung Selatan, Provinsi Lampung
[c]Department of ICT Integrated Safe Ocean Smart Cities, Dong-A University, Busan, Republic of Korea

zainal.ibad@pwk.itera.ac.id

Abstract: The development of the tourism sector depends a lot on the availability of transportation. The advancement of transportation facilities will drive the progress of the tourism sector and vice versa. The formulation of the problem in this study is how the study of tourist shuttle mode in supporting connectivity between the leading tourist attractions in South Lampung Regency to review the mode of shuttle tourism in support of connectivity between the leading tourist attractions in South Lampung Regency. This study uses descriptive statistical methods, trip distribution methods, and analysis of travel shuttle plans. To support the potential - a potential tourist attraction in South Lampung Regency needed a mode of transportation that can connect the location of one tourist attraction with the location of other tourist attractions so that the public is easier and not only dependent on private transportation. Based on the research, the planned mode of the tourist shuttle will connect six tourist attraction locations with a considerable demand for tourists among other tourist attractions in South Lampung Regency. So the result of this study is formed travel patterns and travel shuttle transportation planning to support connectivity between tourist attractions.
Keywords: Tourism Connectivity, Travel Shuttle, Tourist Attraction, South Lampung.

1. Introduction

Tourism is one of the sectors that play an important role in improving the economy of a country. Tourism is also very closely related to tourist activities. According to the World Tourism Organization (WTO) and The Caribbean Tourism Organization (CTO) travelers are people who travel and stay outside their neighborhood for no more than a year but more than 24 hours. There are many factors supporting tourism, one of which is transportation and road facilities available and quality to facilitate tourists who will come to a tourism area. The development of the tourism sector depends a lot on the availability of transportation. Distance and time factors greatly influence people's desire to travel. The existence of various transportation options today causes the growth of tourism to progress very rapidly. The advancement of transportation facilities will drive the progress of the tourism sector and vice versa. Based on data from the Central Bureau of Statistics, eleven provinces in Indonesia that are most visited by tourists are Bali, DKI Jakarta, Special Region of Yogyakarta, East Java, West Java, North Sumatra, Lampung, South Sulawesi, South Sumatra, Banten, and West Sumatra [1].

Lampung Province is one of the provinces in Indonesia that has very promising tourism potential. From the results, there are 50 national tourism destinations, one of which is Krakatau-Ujung Kulon destination which has seven Tourism Development Areas in Lampung Province, with two areas located in the south Lampung regency, namely Kalianda and surrounding areas and Krakatau-Sunda Strait and surrounding areas [2]. Tourism potential in South Lampung Regency is supported because of the natural wealth in the form of the beauty of the beach and the culture that exists. The tourism potential of the South Lampung Regency can support the strengthening of competitiveness and have the support of accessibility networks and infrastructure that supports the movement of tourists and tourism activities. In the Regional Regulation of South Lampung the development of tourism activities based on the potential ofnatural tourism [3]. One of the development strategies is to ensure smooth access that can support the formation of movement of tourist routes.

From various tourist attractions in South Lampung Regency, six top tourist attractions are most visited by tourists both Indonesian and foreign tourists according to data from the Dinas Pariwisata dan Budaya of South Lampung Regency, namely Dermaga Bom Kalianda which is also a fish auction place, Kalinda Resort (Grand Elty), Embe Beach, Kahai Beach, Pemandian Air Panas Way Belerang, and Makam Pahlawan Radin Inten II. From the various tourist attractions available in the tourism area of South Lampung Regency the provision of public transportation facilities is still minimal, tourists must use private vehicles or use motorcycle taxis to get to existing tourist attractions, it takes connectivity between tourist attractions by providing good facilities for tourists visiting in the form of tourist shuttles.

2. Theory

In Undang-Undang Nomor 22 Tahun 2009 that the transportation of people for tourism purposes should be used for tourism services where the implementation of people's transportation for tourism purposes must use public passenger cars and public bus cars with special signs and is not allowed to use public motor vehicles in trays, except in areas that are not yet available special transportation for tourism. In the implementation of a system of public transportation facilities, several aspects are reviewed [4]:

- Load factor: Is the amount that states the level of tightness (saturation of the number of passengers) in public transportation in certain zones.
- Cyclical time: The length of time the vehicle starts waiting at the terminal until it arrives back at the same terminal. The length of cycle time is largely determined by the length of the track, the speed of the vehicle when operating, dwelling time, and layover time.
- Headway: The time distance between vehicles on the path of the same road, the smaller the value of the headway indicates the frequency of the vehicle is higher.

Characteristics of tourists are knowledge of how to meet the needs and desires of each person either viewed individually or in groups related to the activities of purchasing, using, and disposal of goods, services, ideas, and experiences [5]. Efforts to be able to maintain and improve the quality of service for tourism industry players can be seen from the point of view of tourists, especially about travel decisions seen from tourist behavior. Travel pattern or travel pattern is designed according to the characteristics of each region so that it can provide an overview of the superior attractions of an area whose results canbe a guideline for the creation of tour packages following the needs of the tourist market. Travel Patternformed must provide many choices of tour packages to tourists, so that creative and innovative idea areneeded in their preparation [6]. Transportation connectivity in tourism areas encourages an increase in thenumber of tourists. Ease to tourist attractions with other tourist attractions becomes one of the factors that support the progress of tourism in a region. In the Government Regulation of Number 50/2011 aboutRencana Induk Pembangunan Kepariwisataan Nasional 2010 – 2025. The direction of the policy of providing and developing transportation facilities includes the development and improvement of ease of access and movement of tourists to the destination and the development and improvement of the comfort and security of the movement of tourists to the destination [7].

IOP Conf. Series: Earth and Environmental Science 1000 (2022) 012028 doi:10.1088/1755-1315/1000/1/012028

3. Research methodology

The data collection methodology in this study includes primary and secondary data collection. The collection of primary and secondary data from this study through literature studies to find out the development of tourist shuttle modes in support of connectivity between the leading tourist attractions in the South Lampung Regency. Primary and secondary data collection is also conducted to determine the number of tourists visiting various tourist attractions that are the focus of research. The sampling technique used in this study is to use a purposive sampling approach. Purposive sampling is one of the non-random sampling techniques where researchers determine sampling by setting specific characteristics that are following the purpose of the study so that it is expected to answer research problems [8]. This research conducted three analyses, namely analysis tourist travel characteristics, analysis of tourist travel patterns, and analysis of tourist shuttle plans [9]. This can be described on the following flow chart:

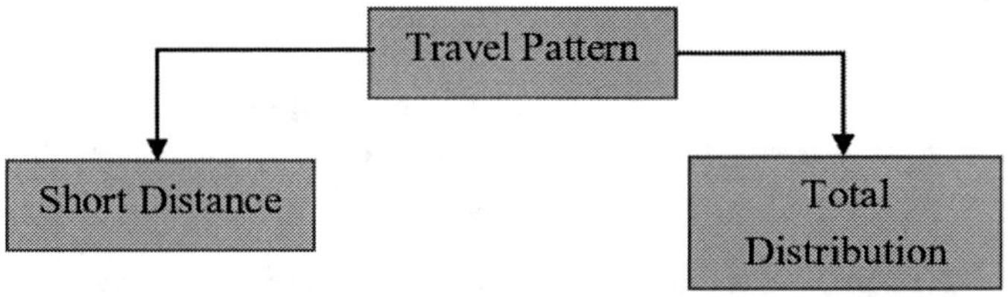

Figure 1. Tourist Travel Pattern Analysis

3.1 Method of Travel Patterns

From the questionnaire results, namely the mode of transportation used by respondents to the location of tourist attraction, in this analysis, the data is processed into a passenger car unit (pcu) so that it can be seen the total rise and pull of each tourist attraction. A passenger car unit is a unit of the vehicle in the flow of traffic equivalent to a light vehicle/passenger car where the amount of pcu is influenced by the type/type of moving vehicle. Below is a table of passenger car units commonly used in Indonesia sourced from Indonesia's road capacity manual [10].

Table 1. Standard Passenger Car Unit

No.	Vehicle Type	Passenger Car Unit
1	Motorcycle	0.25
2	Car	1.00
3	Light Truck	1.20
4	Medium Truck	2.50
5	Bus	1.30
6	Heavy Truck	3.00

Source: MKJI, 1997.

3.2 Travel Shuttle Planning Analysis

This analysis is a step used until the formation of a tour shuttle plan. The tour shuttle plan will connect the tourist sites of Kalianda Bomb Pier which is also a fish auction place, Kalianda Resort, Pantai Embe, Pantai Kahai, Pemandian Air Panas Way Belerang, and Makam Raden Inten II. The planning of the operational system of tourist transportation in this study is as follows [11]:

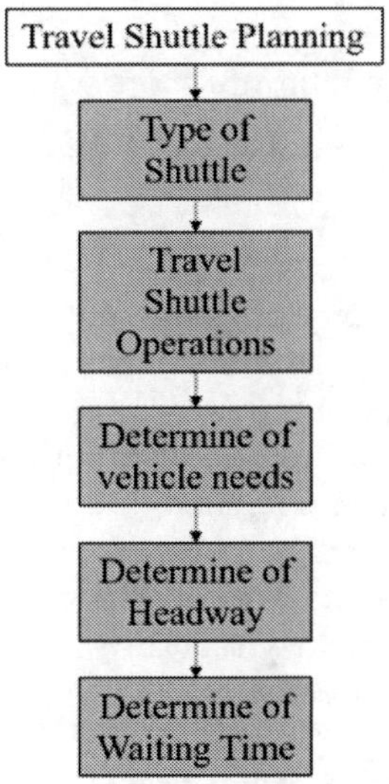

Figure 2. Tourist Travel Shuttle Planning

1. Type of Shuttle, using minibus-type vehicles, the carrying capacity of vehicles in serving the route is 19 passengers.

Table 2. Passenger Capacity

No	Vehicle Type	Seat capacity	Up Capacity	Total Capacity
1	Public transport	8	-	8
2	Small Bus	19	-	19
3	Big Bus	20	10	30
4	Single Floor Big Bus	49	30	79
5	Double Floor Big Bus	85	35	120

Source: Direktorat Jenderal Perhubungan Darat (2002)

In this study, the tourist shuttle is a small bus-shaped mode of transportation which means the passenger capacity of this tour shuttle is 19 passengers under the regulation of the [12].

2. Travel Shuttle Operations, shuttle tours are operational by moving regularly in trays during an operational time (assuming 8 hours/day).
3. Determine of Vehicle Needs, the determination of the number of vehicle to be provided can be determined using the following equation:
The operation of the 8-hour shuttle tour is converted into 480 minutes.

$$Total\ rit/day = \frac{480}{travel\ time\ in\ rit} \tag{1}$$

4. Determine of Headway, headway is the time interval between one vehicle and another vehicle that must be provided determined using the following equations:

$$h = \frac{time\ travel\ in\ one\ rit}{N} \tag{2}$$

N = total vehicle
1 rit = travel from the point of departure until returning to the point of departure
h = *headway* (minute)

5. Determine of Waiting Time, waiting time is the stop time of public transportation at the origin or destination. Calculation of public transport waiting time can be measured from half the headway [13].

4. Research result

4.1 Travel Pattern Analysis

Tourism in South Lampung Regency is very potential, unfortunately as explained earlier that no mode of transportation can connect between tourist attractions. This analysis identifies how tourist routes in South Lampung Regency and especially travel patterns are tried to be realized in this study. The method used is the descriptive method of analysis and trip distribution with data collection techniques through online observation, online questionnaires, and literature studies. From the results of the study, it is known that some of the leading tourist attractions based on the largest number of visitors from the data of the Tourism and Culture Office of South Lampung Regency, namely Dermaga Bom Kalianda which is also a fish auction place, Kalianda Resort (Grand Elty), Embe Beach, Kahai Beach, Pemandian Air Panas Way Belerang, and Radin Inten II Cemetery.

Table 3. Total Trip Generation

Tourist Attractions	Trip Production (pcu)	Trip Attraction (pcu)	Total (pcu)
Dermaga Bom	6	42.25	48.25
Grand Elty Krakatoa	39.95	59.4	99.35
Embe Beach	26.15	36.4	62.55
Kahai Beach	2.5	25	27.5
Pemandian Air Panas Way Belerang	3	11.4	14.4
Makam Pahlawan Raden Intan II	3.5	6.5	10

Source: Research Result, 2020

From the processing of data results of online questionnaires obtained total trips in six tourist attraction locations from vehicles used by tourists to go to the tourist attraction location converted into a passenger car unit to be attached in the attachment. From the total results of the trip obtained total rise and pull from each tourist attraction with the largest attraction, grand Elty Krakatoa Kalianda 99.35 pcu/day. In planning a tourist transportation service, one of the important things that need to be done is to plan the route that will be crossed by the transportation and to determine the trajectory that will be traversed by the tourist transportation in question using the approach manually and according to the data analyzed in the second target. This approach is done by connecting the location of tourist attractions with the location of other tourist attractions. Based on the results of the analysis of the second target on the map of tourist travel patterns, it can be determined the trajectory that is passed to connect the location of tourist attractions with each other.

Table 4. Plan Route Length Table

	Route	Length of route (km)
1	Grand Elty - Pantai Embe	1,8
2	Pantai Embe – Dermaga Bom Kalianda	13,2
3	Dermaga Bom Kalianda – Pemandian Air Panas Way Belerang	3
4	Air Panas Way Belerang – Pantai Kahai	21,7
5	Pantai Kahai – Makam Pahlawan Raden Intan II	11,1
6	Makam Raden Intan II – Grand Elty Krakatoa	25,9
	Total length of the route	76,7

Source: Research Result, 2020

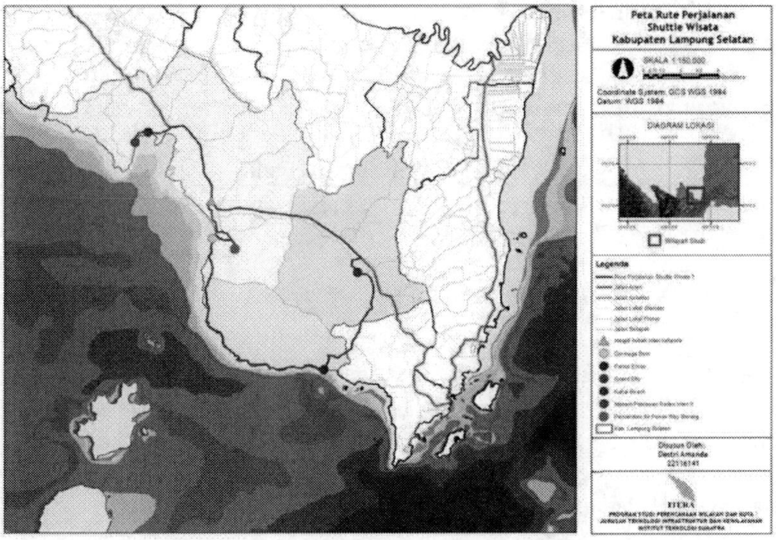

Figure 3. Mapping Route Travel Shuttle in South Lampung Regency
Source: Processing Results by ArcGis 10.3, 2020.

After making the route obtained from the total trip overlay results can be seen the largest total trip is in the tourist attraction Grand Elty Krakatoa so that the first route that became the starting point is Grand Elty Krakatoa - Embe Merak Belantung Beach – Dermaga Bom - Pemandian Air Panas Way Belerang - Kahai Beach - Makam Pahlawan Radin Inten II and back again to Grand Elty Krakatoa then obtained the results of the length of the route passed by the tourist shuttle is 76.7 km.

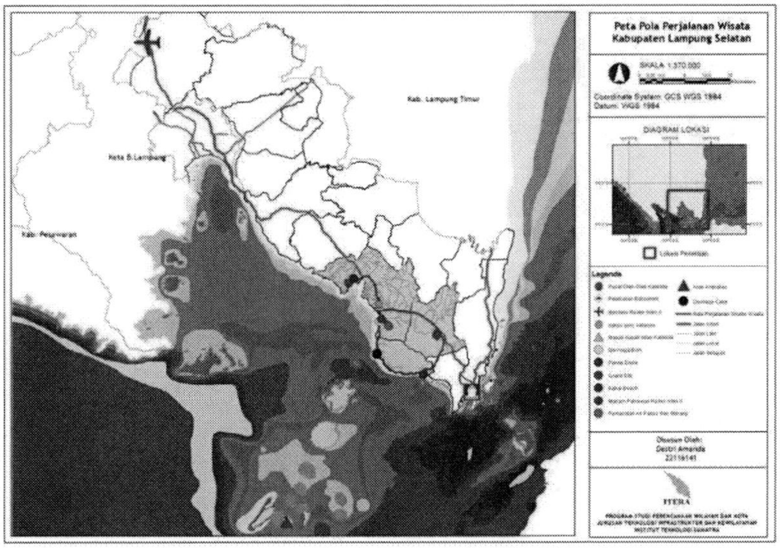

Figure 4. Mapping Travel Pattern in South Lampung Regency
Source: Processing Results by ArcGis 10.3, 2020.

From the map of tourist patterns/travel patterns can be seen that six locations of the top tourist attractions in South Lampung Regency are near the port of Bakauheni so tourists from outside Lampung Province get easy access to tourist attractions in South Lampung Regency.

4.2 Travel Shuttle Plan Analysis

The tour shuttle plan will connect the tourist sites of Dermaga Bom Kalianda, Kalianda Resort, Embe Beach, Kahai Beach, Pemandian Air Panas Way Belerang, and Raden Inten II Cemetery are top tourist attractions from South Lampung Regency. There are several stages of planning, namely planning tourist routes, vehicle operational time, speed of plan, travel time, number of vehicle needs, headway, and waiting time.

Table 5. Travel Time Table

	Route	Length of route (km)	Speed (km/hour)	Travel time (minute)	Maneuver Time (minute)	Travel time (minute)
1	Grand Elty - Pantai Embe	1.8	40	2.7	0.27	2.97
2	Pantai Embe – Dermaga Bom Kalianda	13.2	40	19.8	1.98	21.78
3	Dermaga Bom Kalianda – Pemandian Air Panas Way Belerang	3	40	4.5	0.45	4.95
4	Air Panas Way Belerang – Pantai Kahai	21.7	40	32.55	3.255	35.805
5	Pantai Kahai – Makam Pahlawan Raden Intan II	11.1	40	16.65	1.665	18.315
6	Makam Raden Intan II Grand Elty Krakatoa	25.9	40	38.85	3.885	42.735
	Total	76.7		115.05	11.505	126.555

Source: Research Result, 2020

From the analysis produced the length of the route that started from Grand Elty Krakatoa and ended back at Grand Elty Krakatoa which is 76.7 km with a planned speed of 40 km / h, the total travel time is 126.55 minutes or 2.1 hours.

Table 6. Number of Travel Shuttle Needs

Route	Operational Time (minute)	Time Travel/rit (Minute)	Total Rit (rit/day)	Demand/ tourist(person/day)	Vehicle Capacity (Passenger)	Total Trip Shuttle	Total Vehicle Need
Grand Elty Krakatoa - Pantai Embe - Dermaga Bom - Pemandian Air Panas Way Belerang - Pantai Kahai - Makam Pahlawan Raden Intan II - Grand Elty Krataoa	480	126.55	4	486	19	25	7

Source: Research Result, 2020

The determination of the number of vehicles is influenced by several factors, namely the operational time of the fleet, the travel time in one rit, the potential number of passengers obtained from the number of tourists in each tourist attraction in question, and the capacity of the vehicle from the operational vehicle. On the planned route the total number of shuttle tours needed as many as 7 vehicles. The calculation of the above needs does not take into account the presence of spare vehicles.

Table 7. Headway

Route	Time Travel/rit (minute)	Total Vehicle Capacity	Headway (minute)
Grand Elty Krakatoa - Pantai Embe - Makam Pahlawan Raden Intan II - Pantai Kahai - Dermaga Bom Kalianda - Pemandian Air Panas Way Belerang - Grand Elty Krataoa	126.55	7	18

Source: Research Result, 2020

From the formula above, the headway is generated for the planned route with a travel time of 126.55 minutes and a total of 7 vehicles, the resulting headway is 18 minutes which means the departure distance between the shuttle tour one with the other is 18 minutes.

Table 8. Travel Shuttle Waiting Time Calculation Table

	Route	Headway (minute)
1	Grand Elty - Pantai Embe	9
2	Pantai Embe – Dermaga Bom Kalianda	9
3	Dermaga Bom Kalianda – Pemandian Air Panas Way Belerang	9
4	Air Panas Way Belerang – Pantai Kahai	9
5	Pantai Kahai – Makam Pahlawan Raden Intan II	9
6	Makam Raden Intan II – Grand Elty Krakatoa	9
	Total Waiting Time in 1 Rit	54

Source: Research Result, 2020

From the results of the analysis obtained the results of the operational plan of shuttle tours with a route length of 76.7 km using the speed of the plan based on Government Regulation No. 79 of 2013 on Traffic And Road Transport Network is 40 km / h with travel time added headway and waiting time is 198.5 minutes or the equivalent of 3.3, an hour in one go. With the route that has been formed in the second target and the shuttle tour plan, it can improve connectivity between the leading tourist attractions referred to in the study so that tourists can more easily visit six excellent tourist attractions and it is expected that there is an increase in tourists because of the youthfulness of accessing each of these tourist attractions.

5. Conclusion

Based on the existing problem that no mode of transportation supports tourism activities in South Lampung Regency planned route based on the analysis results, the starting point of the route is in Grand Elty Krakatoa because it has the highest total trip. The length of the route from Grand Elty Krakatoa – Embe Merak Belantung Beach – Dermaga Bom – Pemandian Air Panas Way Belerang – Kahai Beach – Raden Intan II Heroes Cemetery and back to Grand Elty Krakatoa then obtained the results of the long route that the shuttle tour traveled is 76.7 km reached with a travel time of 2.1 hours with a headway of 18 minutes and waiting time in each tourist attraction is 9 minutes. For the number of tourist shuttle needs from the calculation that has been done that with operating hours 8 hours a day and the demand of tourists based on the average visits per day, it takes 7 shuttle tours for this research plan.

6. References

[1] Peraturan Daerah Kabupaten Lampung Selatan Nomor 15 Tahun 2012 Tentang Rencana Tata Ruang Wilayah Kabupaten Lampung Selatan Tahun 2011-2031
[2] Peraturan Pemerintah Republik Indonesia Nomor 50 Tahun 2011 Tentang Rencana Induk Pembangunan Kepariwisataan Nasional Tahun 2010 – 2025.
[3] Peraturan Pemerintah Daerah Provinsi Lampung Nomor 6 Tahun 2012 Tentang Rencana Induk Pembangunan Kepariwisataan Daerah Provinsi Lampung.
[4] Undang-undang Republik Indonesia Nomor 22 tahun 2009 Tentang Lalu Lintas dan Angkutan Jalan.
[5] Kotler dan Keller. 2009. "*Manajemen Pemasaran*". Jilid 1. Jakarta: Erlangga
[6] Ahmad, Rimba. 2015. "*Kajian Teori Pariwisata Segmentasi Pasar Wisatawan*". Denpasar: Fakultas Pariwisata Universitas Udayana.
[7] Kotler. 2002. "*Pemasaran Perhotelan dan Pariwisata*" . Jakarta: PT. Prenhallindo.

IOP Conf. Series: Earth and Environmental Science 1000 (2022) 012028 doi:10.1088/1755-1315/1000/1/012028

[8] Sugiyono. 2007. "*Metode Penelitian Kuantitatif Kualitatif dan R&D*". Bandung: Alfabeta.
[9] Tamin, Ofyar Z. 2000. "*Perencanaan dan Pemodelan Transportasi*". Edisi Kedua. Bandung: Penerbit ITB.
[10] Direktorat Jenderal Bina Marga. 1997. "*Manual Kapasitas Jalan Indonesia*" Jakarta: Kementerian Pekerjaan Umum.
[11] Studio Perencanaan Transportasi. "*Pengembangan Konektivitas Transportasi Kawasan Wisata di Kabupaten Pangandaran*" . Magister Perencanaan Wilayah dan Kota Institut Tekonologi Bandung. Bandung.
[12] Harun, Hermawan dan Rudi. 2001. "*Dasar-dasar Transportasi*". Bandung: ITB.
[13] Marsudi, 2005. "*Analisis Kinerja Mobil Penumpang Umum (MPU) dan Sistem Jaringan Trayek di Kota Salatiga* ". Semarang: Magister Teknik Sipil Universitas Diponegoro.

IOP Conf. Series: Earth and Environmental Science 1000 (2022) 012029 doi:10.1088/1755-1315/1000/1/012029

Dynamics of Supply-Demand Online Motorcycle Taxis in Urban Area

Adi Subandi[1,2], Rudy Hermawan Karsaman[1], Harun Al Rasyid Lubis[1]

[1]*Civil Engineering Department, Faculty of Civil and Environmental Engineering, Bandung Institute of Technology - Indonesia.*
[2]*Civil Engineering Department, Faculty of Engineering, University of Subang - Indonesia.*

E-mail : subandiadi@yahoo.com.

Abstract : In Indonesia's urban area, online motorcycle taxis "Ojol" have grown significantly, especially for support mobilization and other activities. Currently, it was considered "oversupply" indicated by not accepting new registrations for a new driver and decreasing the existing driver incomes. With the proposed development and modification model for controlling online motorcycle taxis numbers in urban areas, it is hoped that the equilibrium point for the provision of online motorcycle taxis numbers can be optimal, not only impacting partners' welfare but a more comprehensive urban transportation system. Based on a pilot survey with data ranging from 50 respondents, each for passengers and drivers, with SEM models, it was indicated that level of user satisfaction, which was affected by income level has a higher influence (-0.039) than movement characteristics (0.011), while at consistency level analysis based on driver's perception indicates that safety aspect has a higher effect (-0.288) than income level (0.251). Output analysis is still provisional, more data is needed to represent a more comprehensive output.

1. Introduction

Significant growth of online motorcycle taxis from start launching in Indonesian region since 2015 with a total of 30,000 partners/drivers until November 2019 has reached more than 2 million or in other words, the growth rate is calculated to reach ± 190% per year, it's equal to ± 1% of the total population of Indonesia, which as of 21 November 2019 has reached 271 million (BBC News Indonesia, 23/11/2019). This raises concerns that implementation of public transport in urban areas will worsen and has contributed to the growth rate of national vehicles too, especially motorbikes, which reached 6.6% over the last 5 years with an average nominal increase of ± 7 million motorbikes per year (Source: National Statistics Agency, 2019).

Several studies have confirmed that travel behavior and improvement and online motorcycle taxis as part of the ride-sourcing system are considered to have been able to provide service resolutions that were not provided by conventional modes before (Mendez 2017; Creutzig 2019), also discussed aspects of the impact of ride-sourcing (online motorcycle taxis) which are considered disruptive innovations that disrupt existing public transportation system (Kumar 2020; Nurhidayah and Alkarim 2017; Wang 2018), likewise, the ride-sourcing app has increased vehicle kilometers traveled (Henao 2017; Lavieri 2020), and discuss regarding technical and non-technical aspects of the implementation of this ride-sourcing, so that new model can compete with the previous model (Irawan et al. 2020; Lee 2017).

The government has made efforts to control the growth of online motorcycle taxis, with the enactment of Protection of the safety of motorbike users used for benefit of community and enactment of lower and upper limit service fees and minimum service fees determined based on zoning scheme for online motorcycle taxis operation area so that it affects the level of demand for online motorcycle taxi services which also affects the number of orders and level of partner income, these conditions have an impact on changes in equilibrium in the performance of online motorcycle taxis. This is a motivation for conducting research that will focus on proposals related to rationalization of the need for online motorcycle taxi quota for urban transportation, which is expected to become a preference for related stakeholders in determining sustainable policies regarding the implementation of transportation in urban areas.

2. Method

Based on objectives formulation in research, to identify potential requests for online motorcycle taxi services which are influenced by tariff based on satisfaction level for user's perspective and estimate supply which is reviewed partner consistency level for driver's perspective by considering income level. The research hypothesis predicts that the tariff has an influence on online motorcycle taxi potential demand and the income level which is a motivation to remain consistent as partners will affect online motorcycle taxi drivers operating number in urban areas. For modeling, based on heterogeneous characteristics of data, the model is to be constructed in the SEM model. Furthermore, for predicting needs of online motorcycle taxis number, it is used with the optimization equation by considering partner's income level.

Using models to support analysis, with consideration of the complexity of data, the researcher uses the SEM model to accommodate these conditions. Where according to the designation of the model, the SEM model will be intended to evaluate existing conditions, to predict and identify variables and indicators that are considered to affect online motorcycle taxis operations.

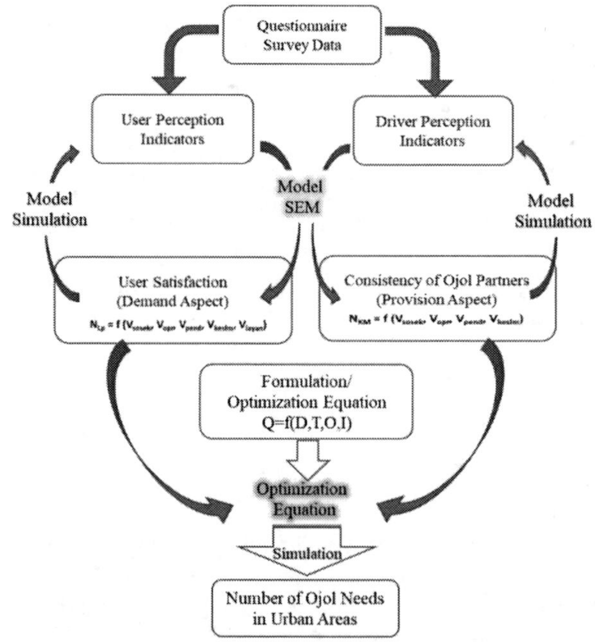

Figure 1. The Flow of Using SEM Models and Optimation Formulation in Research

By considering quite complex characters which have multi-implications potential on factors relationship that influence for determination of quota requirement estimated, this research will be simulated through an optimization equation with the partner's income level constraint. The model simulation process will also consider SEM model output values that have been converted into percentage units to be calculated for determining online motorcycle taxis needs number as an output of this research.

2.1 SEM Model Preparation

Modification of SEM model and optimization equation is considering each characteristic of these models, where SEM model with evaluative descriptive characteristics is used for analysis and parameter estimate indicators and variables choice that influence (based on user and driver perceptions) to identify aspects of user satisfaction (demand potential) and partner consistency (supply). For identifying parameters that are considered quite complex and difficult to assume, for easier calculation prosses, the function is often represented as linear parameters. For SEM model structure that related to determining user satisfaction level is built by several qualitative variables that are considered to affect user satisfaction in determining the choice of mode, this equation is developed as the following equation :

$$\eta_{satisfact} = (\gamma_{sosec}.\xi_{sosec}) + (\gamma_{mob}.\xi_{mob}) + (\gamma_{income}.\xi_{income}) + (\gamma_{safe}.\xi_{safe}) + (\gamma_{serv}.\xi_{serv}) + \zeta_{satisfact} \quad (1)$$

where :

$\eta_{satisfact}$ = Satisfaction level of online motorcycle taxi users (Endogenous Variable).
ξ_{sosec} = Exogenous variable for user's socio-economic aspects
ξ_{mob} = Exogenous variable for user's movement characteristic aspect
ξ_{income} = Exogenous variable for user's income level aspect
ξ_{safe} = Exogenous variable for user's safety aspect
ξ_{serv} = Exogenous variable for service level scenarios of users aspect
γ_i = Parameters for each exogenous variables were reviewed.
$\zeta_{satisfact}$ = Residual error / vector of the satisfaction model.

Meanwhile, the SEM model structure in determining for partner consistency level is based on the driver's perception which is built by several qualitative variables, for construct model can be seen in the following equation:

$$\eta_{consist} = (\gamma_{sosec}.\xi_{sosec}) + (\gamma_{opr}.\xi_{opr}) + (\gamma_{income}.\xi_{income}) + (\gamma_{safe}.\xi_{safe}) + \zeta_{consist} \quad (2)$$

where :

$\eta_{consist}$ = Consistency level of online motorcycle taxi drivers (Endogenous Variable).
ξ_{sosec} = Exogenous variable for driver's socio-economic aspects
ξ_{mob} = Exogenous variable for driver's movement characteristic aspect
ξ_{income} = Exogenous variable for driver's income level aspect
ξ_{safe} = Exogenous variable for driver's safety aspect
γ_i = Parameters for each exogenous variables were reviewed.
$\zeta_{concsist}$ = Residual error / vector of the consistency model.

2.2 Formulation Of Optimization Equation

Furthermore, in optimization equation formulation, for identifying factors that are considered to affect supply aspect, where estimate quota requirement linearly is a representation for requests divided the number by average order capacity, or in other words for requests number of quota requirements number is the multiplication. For average order capacity of online motorcycle taxis, needs a number, which can be seen in the following equation.

$$D = BO \times Q \quad (3)$$

where :

D = User demand/level of demand for online motorcycle taxi services (User per day)
BO = Average order capacity (range 5 s/d 25 order per hari)
Q = Online motorcycle taxi needs number (Mitra)

Formulation concept for developing an optimization model for online motorcycle taxi quota needs with several considerations and assumptions that are deemed necessary, including:

- Considering online motorcycle taxi users' number who tend to increase with time will affect for quota requirement at the same time, where this limitation is oriented to determine an optimal amount of quota requirements for a specified period time taking into account order capacity and partner income.
- According to the explanation of equation (3), assuming that in certain conditions where demand reaches at maximum point (which is considered as the total order capacity for partners), while the trend of partners increases linearly number, so that increase in partners will experience a "crash" when approaching a maximum point of order capacity. This condition will lead to the trend of partner increase, which was originally linear to become logarithmic.
- Equations are formulated for each aspect (Demand - Supply) by considering all component data characteristics aspects that are easily obtained from related sources.
  - Supply aspects component consider to:
    - Order capacity per day: is the maximum number of orders on average that can be served by partners as online motorcycle taxis (range between 5 to 25 orders per day based on survey data obtained or determined based on the ratio of population density / 500 >> with notes a more accurate estimation is needed in determining the density of urban areas.
    - Partner Consistency Value (NKm): is the value obtained from SEM simulation modeling results based on driver's perceptions.
  - Demand aspect components consider to:
    - User Satisfaction Value (NLp): is the value obtained from SEM simulation modeling results based on user perceptions or practically is a predictive value of potential online motorcycle taxi users percentage.
    - Potential demand (user/day): obtained from the simulation results of a graphical model that considers the order capacity per partner day with a rate of 10,000 Rp. per order (amount of average rate based on the tariff).
- The formulation proposed in determining numbers of requests (as a function of total quota) is based on considerations of the above aspects as follows:

$$D_R = \left(\left(\text{C1 x Ln}(Q_o + \text{C2})\right) - \text{C3}\right) \text{ x FR, or}$$
$$Q_o = \text{EXP}(((D_R/\text{FR}) + \text{C3})/\text{C1}) - \text{C2} \tag{4}$$

where :
D_R = Demand estimate number per day
Q_o = Urban online motorcycle taxi needs number
FR = Ratio Factor (NLp : NKm)
NKm = Value of partners consistency
NLp = Value of user satisfaction
C1, C2, C3 = Equation constants based on the base order value (BO)
BO = Base order per day.

Table 1. Constant Value for Logaritmic Equation

Base Order per Day	C1	C2	C3
5 Order	7.541	302	43.073
10 Order	15.083	302	86.147
15 Order	22.624	302	129.220
20 Order	30.165	302	172.294
25 Order	37.706	302	215.367

According to the equation above, assuming of partner consistency and user satisfaction value at maximum conditions, as simulated in following graphical form in figure 2.a. Likewise, in figure 2. b with a condition that takes into account the NLp and NKm values, a graphical model can be done by determining demand user as D*NLp and for base order: BO * NKm. Furthermore, by considering that income level ≥ threshold value (UMR), for optimum amount needs estimate is determined based on equation below:

$$Partner\ Income = \left(\frac{D_R}{Qo}\right) x\ TOx\ Hx\ FKp \tag{5}$$

where :

D_R = Demand estimate number per day
Q_o = Urban online motorcycle taxi needs number
TO = Average Tarrif per order (determined 10.000 Rp. per order)
H = Operating day number in 1 month (determined 28 day/month)
FKp = Correction income number is partner's revenue multiplier after deducting for operator discount fee of 20% per order

Based on this equation, it can be simulated in a graphical form as in the following figure:

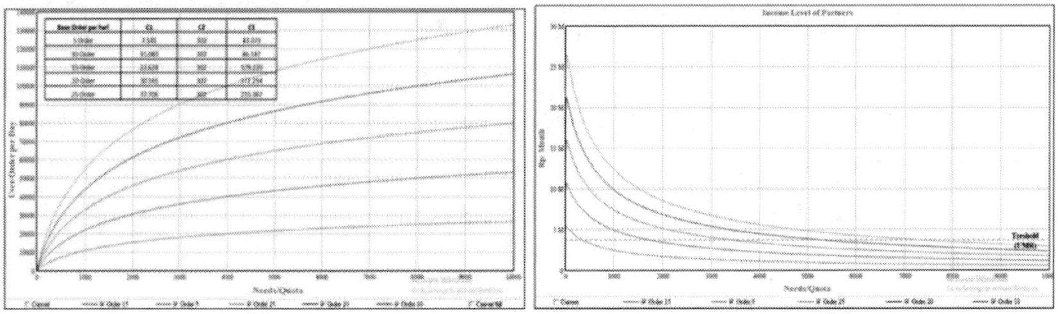

(a) (b)

Figure 2. (a). Chart of Partner Requirements Numbers Estimate for Each Base Order & (b). Chart of Partner Income Estimate for Each Base Order

From the graphical form above, it can be determined the needed number of based on the potential demand of online motorcycle taxi users in urban areas.

3. Result And Discuss

3.1 Indicator and Variable Identification

Several variables and indicators that will be proposed in this study will be reviewed based on the perspective of both user and driver. This is done to estimate characteristics and potential of demand from identification results of user's perspective, while in driver's perspective is directed to identify the consistency of partner as a driver based on aspects proposed in options offered. Variable and indicator data inventory used as in matrix below:

Table 2. Variables and Indicators Model Based on User Perspectives

No.	Variable		Indicator	Symbol	Source
1	Socio-Economic	ξ_{sosek}	Age	SE 1	$X_{SE1} = \lambda_{SE1}.\xi_{sosek} + \delta_{SE1}$
			Gender	SE 2	$X_{SE2} = \lambda_{SE2}.\xi_{sosek} + \delta_{SE2}$
			Education	SE 3	$X_{SE3} = \lambda_{SE3}.\xi_{sosek} + \delta_{SE3}$
			Work	SE 4	$X_{SE4} = \lambda_{SE4}.\xi_{sosek} + \delta_{SE4}$
			Vehicle Ownership	SE 5	$X_{SE5} = \lambda_{SE5}.\xi_{sosek} + \delta_{SE5}$
			SIM Ownership	SE 6	$X_{SE6} = \lambda_{SE6}.\xi_{sosek} + \delta_{SE6}$

No.	Variable		Indicator	Symbol	Source
2	Level of Income	ξ_{pend}	Average Monthly Income	TP 1	$X_{TP1} = \lambda_{TP1}.\xi_{pend} + \delta_{TP1}$
			Transportation Expenditures	TP 2	$X_{TP2} = \lambda_{TP2}.\xi_{pend} + \delta_{TP2}$
			Tariff	TP 3	$X_{TP3} = \lambda_{TP3}.\xi_{pend} + \delta_{TP3}$
			Travel Costs	TP 4	$X_{TP4} = \lambda_{TP4}.\xi_{pend} + \delta_{TP4}$
			Maintenance Cost	TP 5	$X_{TP4} = \lambda_{TP5}.\xi_{pend} + \delta_{TP5}$
3	Characteristics of Movement	ξ_{perg}	Travel Origin	KP 1	$X_{KP1} = \lambda_{KP1}.\xi_{perg} + \delta_{KP1}$
			Destinations	KP 2	$X_{KP2} = \lambda_{KP2}.\xi_{perg} + \delta_{KP2}$
			Travel Distance	KP 3	$X_{KP3} = \lambda_{KP3}.\xi_{perg} + \delta_{KP3}$
			Waktu PerjalanaTime Travel	KP 4	$X_{KP4} = \lambda_{KP4}.\xi_{perg} + \delta_{KP4}$
			Mode Alternatif	KP 5	$X_{KP5} = \lambda_{KP5}.\xi_{perg} + \delta_{KP5}$
4	Safety Aspects	ξ_{keslm}	Identity Suitability	KS 1	$X_{KS1} = \lambda_{KS1}.\xi_{keslm} + \delta_{KS1}$
			Ideal Speed	KS 2	$X_{KS2} = \lambda_{KS2}.\xi_{keslm} + \delta_{KS2}$
			Violation of APILL	KS 3	$X_{KS3} = \lambda_{KS3}.\xi_{keslm} + \delta_{KS3}$
			Health Protocol	KS 4	$X_{KS4} = \lambda_{KS4}.\xi_{keslm} + \delta_{KS4}$
			Safety Ridding	KS 5	$X_{KS5} = \lambda_{KS5}.\xi_{keslm} + \delta_{KS5}$
5	Service Level Option	ξ_{pel}	Scenario 1	PL 1	$X_{PL1} = \lambda_{PL1}.\xi_{pel} + \delta_{PL1}$
			Scenario 2	PL 2	$X_{PL2} = \lambda_{PL2}.\xi_{pel} + \delta_{PL2}$
			Scenario 3	PL 3	$X_{PL3} = \lambda_{PL3}.\xi_{pel} + \delta_{PL3}$
			Scenario 4	PL 4	$X_{PL4} = \lambda_{PL4}.\xi_{pel} + \delta_{PL4}$
			Scenario 5	PL 5	$X_{PL5} = \lambda_{PL5}.\xi_{pel} + \delta_{PL5}$
			Scenario 6	PL 6	$X_{PL6} = \lambda_{PL6}.\xi_{pel} + \delta_{PL6}$

For purposes of analysis, distribution and model structure schemes from the variables above are constructed like the schematic below.

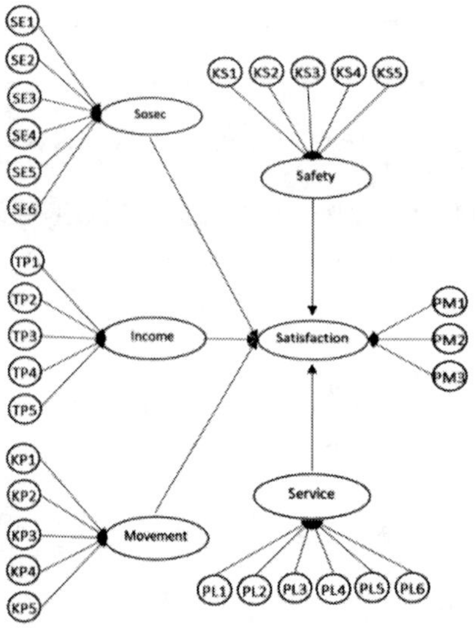

Figure 3. Variable and Indicator Model Structure on MC Taxis Online Users Perspective

Based on the previous explanation, the output of this analysis will be used as a variable for determining estimated characteristics and potential demand of online motorcycle taxi users which will be input in optimization analysis at a later stage.

Therefore, from driver's perspective, analysis orientation is directed at identifying consistency of drivers as online motorcycle taxi partners based on indicators offered that are focused on income level

IOP Conf. Series: Earth and Environmental Science 1000 (2022) 012029 doi:10.1088/1755-1315/1000/1/012029

aspect, so that it will be a consideration in input regarding optimization analysis in estimating the need for online motorcycle taxi quota for urban transportation.

In this study, based on data from a pilot survey conducted, data on perceptions of users and drivers were obtained with a limited number of respondents. However, the researcher conducted this pilot survey sample to re-check the proposed model structure based on input data from the pilot survey, so that it will become a preference for evaluating the structure of the model and questionnaire format distributed to each respondent.

3.2 SEM Modelling

For the SEM modeling process, inputting data has been prepared according to the initial framework of the proposed model, where at this stage SEM model structure is built to accommodate all variables and indicators proposed to identify the influence of variables and indicators on the level of satisfaction of online motorcycle taxi users (Rasyid et al. 2020).

The structural form of the SEM model consists of a structural model built by the relationship between variables and other variables forming a structural model with 6 measurement models. After running the SEM program on the initial structure model, it's indicated that the amount of data input has not met the expected SEM running model, so the next step is to sort variables and indicators that need to be eliminated to get suitability of amount an input data. According to recommendations of SEM model on the number of variables and indicators proposed, several income level variables which are represented by indicators related to financial aspects of user and movement characteristics variables are represented, so that can be shown by SEM model structure such as in the image below.

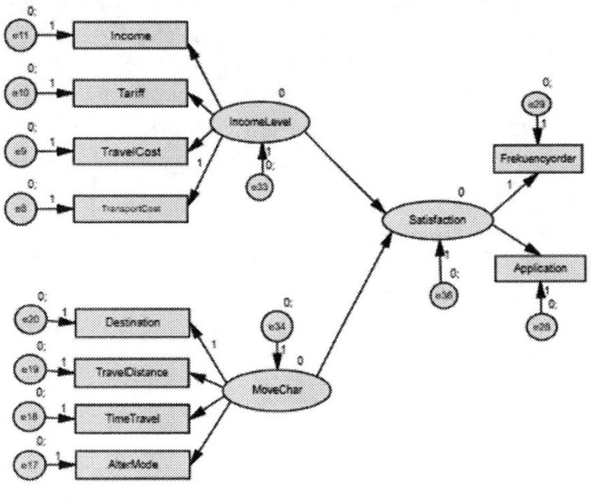

Figure 4. SEM Model Structure Result of Model Iteration Based on User Perception

The model structure shown above which consists of 1 structural and 3 measurement models, SEM program has been able to produce the expected model output, which indicates the influence of variables and indicators that affect the level of user satisfaction to use of online motorcycle taxis as shown in the figure below.

From the output of running SEM model, it's indicated that level of income has a higher effect (-0.039) when compared with movement characteristics (0.011) on level of user satisfaction in utilizing online motorcycle taxis. So that it can be formulated to calculate the amount of user satisfaction based on the following equation:

$$Satisfaction = -0.039 * Income\ Level + 0.011 * Movement\ Characteristics \quad (6)$$

The equation above represented that every 1 increase in value of income level will decrease user satisfaction level by 0.039, and each additional value for movement characteristics of an increase in

IOP Conf. Series: Earth and Environmental Science 1000 (2022) 012029 doi:10.1088/1755-1315/1000/1/012029

satisfaction level by 0.011. Where in determining fixed model used, also necessary to consider fit aspects of the model.

Likewise, stage analysis of model based on driver's perspective to identify the level of consistency as online motorcycle taxi partner, with the same process, SEM model analysis of input data does base on driver's perspective. Description for an explanation, taking into account variables and indicators characteristics of output model, obtained several income level variables represented by indicators related to financial aspects of online motorcycle taxi driver-partners and safety aspect variables represented by safety indicators aspects in online motorcycle taxis operations, in such a way that structural form of SEM model can be represented.

The model structure which consists of 1 structural and 3 measurement models, SEM program produces an output model, which indicates the influence of variables and indicators that affect for consistency of partners level with the result (from default model), that's gained number of Chi-square = 36,787; Degrees of freedom = 33 and Probability level = 0,000 as shown figure above. From SEM output models, indicated that compliance with safety aspects has a higher effect (-0.288) when compared to income levels (0.251) on the consistency of partners as online motorcycle taxis level. So that can be formulated to calculate the level of partner consistency based on the following equation:

$$\textit{Partner Consistency} = 0.251 * \textit{Income Level} - 0.288 * \textit{Safety Aspect} \quad (7)$$

The equation above can be represented that every 1 increase in income level value will increase partner consistency level by 0.251, and each additional value for the safety aspect reduces the level of partner consistency by 0.288. In determining a fixed model to identify partner consistency level that also necessary to consider fit aspects of the model which are part of model output, so that formulation generated from the model structure is a representative output.

After determining each output value based on user perception (level of satisfaction) and driver perception (level of partner consistency) from the SEM model simulation results above, to easily interpret SEM model value results, the next stage is converted to a percentage value.

- Satisfaction levels based on user perceptions
  - From the model simulation & data analysis for a pilot survey conducted, the results showed that online motorcycle taxi users had a satisfaction level of -1,864.37 or in the "Low" category, which was 29.20%, as the following figure;

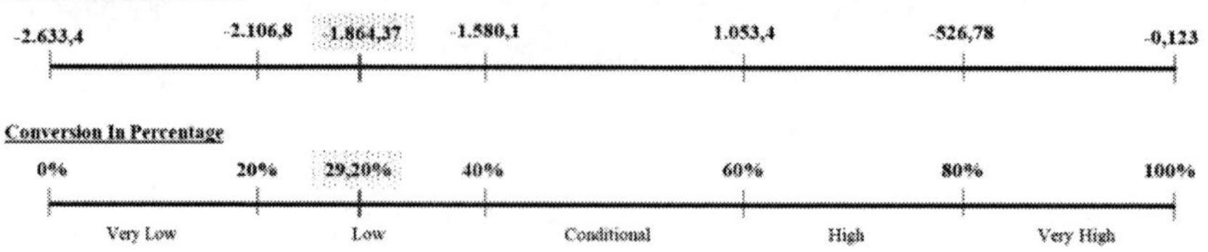

Figure 5. Conversion of User Satisfaction Level Value

  - This condition is predicted because the transportation expenditure indicator has an impact on mode choice options for users so that they tend to choose other options for movement;
  - Indicators of tariffs in the income level aspect equation have a smaller effect than other indicators, this happened because tariff adjustments impact that has been implemented tends to not have a major effect on incidental users.
- The level of partner consistency based on driver's perception
  - For model simulation & pilot survey data analysis results show that online motorcycle taxi partners/ drivers have a consistency level of 968.33 or in the "Conditional" category, which is 54.852% as the following figure;

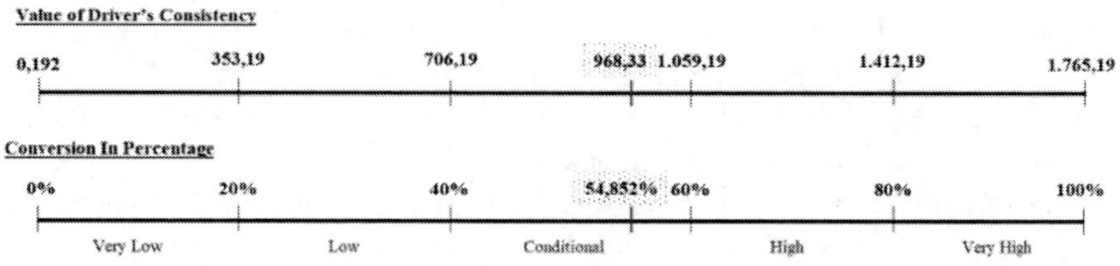

Figure 6. Value Conversion of Driver Partner Consistency Level

- This condition represents that currently partner's motivation to remain consistent as online motorcycle taxis drivers have decreased, this is because income as an online motorcycle taxi driver tends to decrease so that it directly or indirectly affects for consistency level of partners as online motorcycle taxi drivers;
- It is indicated that income indicator from online motorcycle taxis on income level aspect equation has a greater influence than other indicators, this is one of the basic considerations in identifying variables/ indicators to control online motorcycle taxis number.

3.3 Optimization Model Analysis

Based on pilot survey data analysis conducted results, which partners/drivers consistency value was 54.85% and user satisfaction value was 29.20% (from simulation results of SEM model, it was determined that value of FR = 0.53) with a base order of 25 orders per day, then the equation for determining demand number can be determined from a graphical simulation as shown in figure 7.a. and to determine the range for online mc taxis number in urban areas, it can be simulated in figure 7.b.

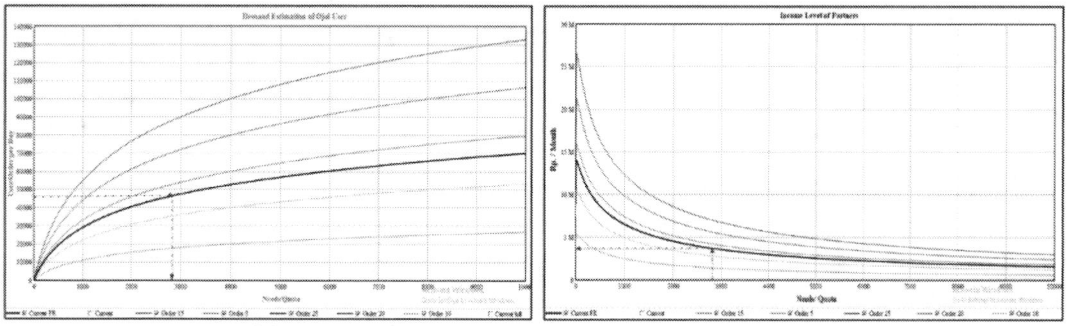

(a) (b)

Figure 7. (a). Partner Requirements Numbers Estimate for 25 Orders per Day & (b). Estimated Income of 25 Orders per Day Based on UMR

For an optimum range of online motorcycle taxi needs with a base order scenario of 25 orders per day, obtained of partners proposed number needs to be in a maximum range of 2,800 partners with income level in the range of Rp. 3.7 million (UMR) to Rp. 14 million per month from the estimated total orders number around 46,304 orders per day.

4. Conclusion

Based on analysis results, the following conclusions are as follows:

1). In this research, an econometric model could be used for analysis and parameter estimation of choice mode utility variables that had an effect (based on user and driver perceptions) in order to identify aspects of user satisfaction (demand) and driver consistency (supply). While SEM model could be used to simulate as well as validate the influence of variables from the previous econometric model for the optimization stage in determining the rationalization of online motorcycle taxi quota requirement for urban transportation.

2). According to SEM model results, user perceptions analysis results indicate that income level has a higher effect (-0.039) than movement characteristics (0.011) on user satisfaction level in utilizing online motorcycle taxis. Meanwhile, based on driver's perception, indicated that safety aspect's compliance has a higher effect (-0.288) than income levels (0.251) on partners consistency level.

3). From optimization equation with income level constraint that exceeds UMR nominal is oriented for the optimum number of partners and partner's welfare level will be more prospective.

4). The proposed equation model is a practical model that is easy to implement as a preference by stakeholders (regulators and operators at the regional level) in formulating online motorcycle taxis number needs in a particular urban area.

5). For the implementation of the fixed model used is expected to be continuous and able to accommodate the potential for growth for a period of at least 3 to 5 years (which is considered as the time period for imposing a limit on the number of online motorcycle taxi quota in urban areas).

6). As for recommendations, where analysis output is still provisional, more data is needed for study are able to represent a more comprehensive output.

5. REFERENCES

[1] Creutzig, Felix. 2019. "On-Demand Motorcycle Taxis Improve Mobility, Not Sustainability." Case Studies on Transport Policy 7(2): 218–29;

[2] Henao, Alejandro. 2017. A Framework for Understanding the Impacts of Ridesourcing on Transportation. Disrupting Mobility (Impacts of Sharing Economy and Innovative Transportation on Cities);

[3] Irawan, Muhammad Zudhy, Prawira Fajarindra Belgiawan, Ari Krisna Mawira Tarigan, and Fajar Wijanarko. 2020. "To Compete or Not Compete: Exploring the Relationships between Motorcycle-Based Ride-Sourcing, Motorcycle Taxis, and Public Transport in the Jakarta Metropolitan Area." Transportation 47(5): 2367–89. https://doi.org/10.1007/s11116-019-10019-5;

[4] Kumar, Soheil Ghili and Vineet. 2020. "Spatial Distribution of Supply and the Role of Market Thickness: Theory and Evidence from Ride Sharing." (2219);

[5] Lavieri, Patrícia S. 2020. 148 Investigating Objective and Subjective Factors Influencing the Adoption, Frequency, and Characteristics of Ride-Hailing Trips. The Hong Kong Polytechnic University, Hung Hom, Kowloon, Hong Kong;

[6] Lee, C. 2017. "Dynamics of Ride Sharing Competition." Economics working paper (July): 2017–5. https://web5.iseas.edu.sg/images/pdf/ISEASEWP2017-05Lee.pdf;

[7] Mendez, Victor M. et al. 2017. 37 Energy Research and Social Science Beyond Traffic: Trends and Choices 2045—A National Dialogue About Future Transportation Opportunities and Challenges. Disrupting Mobility (Impacts of Sharing Economy and Innovative Transportation on Cities);

[8] Nurhidayah, Fitriyah, and Ficky Alkarim. 2017. "Domination Of Transportation Network Companies (Tncs) In Indonesia: An Indonesian Case." International Journal of Business, Economics and Law 12(3): 11–20;

[9] Rasyid, Harun Al et al. 2020. "Micro Studies Related to Engineering and Facility Arrangement in Supporting the Up and Down Activities of Online Ojek Users in the Framework of Education and Policy Studies at an Activity Center, Case Study of the ITB Campus Area." 4(1): 39–49;

[10] Wang, Runyi. 2018. "Supply-Demand Forecasting For a Ride-Hailing System." https://escholarship.org/uc/item/1tr0c2p0. University of California.

IOP Conf. Series: Earth and Environmental Science 1000 (2022) 012030 doi:10.1088/1755-1315/1000/1/012030

Integrated Transport System in Yogyakarta, Indonesia: Aspect Policy

Danny Setiawan[1], Dibyo Susilo[2], Arien Setyadi[3]

[1,2]Department of Civil Engineering, Universitas Teknologi Yogyakarta, Jl. Glagahsari No. 63, Yogyakarta
[3]Dinas PUP-ESDM DIY

danny.setiawan@staff.uty.ac.id

Abstract. The application of an intermodal transportation integration system will make it easier for people to carry out activities, guarantee travel time, optimize the use of public transportation, and reduce the use of private vehicles, which can affect road performance. The policy for implementing the transportation integration system needs to be considered to accommodate travel activities by following regional development conditions. This study aims to determine the management integration and the constraints in implementing the transportation integration system. This study uses a qualitative method by considering the aspects of the policy that involve elements of regulators, operators, and consumers. This research shows that the regulator can manage the transportation integration system by implementing government affairs in the transportation sector; however, there are obstacles in regulatory linkages, coordination, and limited authority. So it is necessary to optimize the role of regulators to coordinate intensely with public transport operators to realize an integrated transportation system management that can meet the community's travel needs.
Keywords: Integration; Policy; Public Transportation; Yogyakarta

1. Introduction

The development of regional transportation, which includes land, sea, air, and rail transportation, is carried out in an integrated intermodal manner, which is realized by optimizing the provision of transportation network systems and services, managing travel needs, and using high technology in transportation development as mention by Governor of Special Region of Yogyakarta [1], research by Jean-Paul Rodrigue [2], Abou Senna, et al. [3], and Ahmad Munawar [4]. The implementation of transportation integration management must involve many cross-sectoral and regional stakeholders, namely the Regional Government and the House of Representatives (DPR) as the Regulator, State-Owned Enterprises (BUMN), Regional-Owned Enterprises (BUMD), and investors as Operators, as well as the public using transportation as consumers. When viewed from the perspective of the urban transportation integration system, there will be more elements in it because it pays attention to aspects of regional spatial planning, parts of transportation systems and techniques, environmental factors, and social and cultural aspects of society.

Yogyakarta is a city of education, tourism, and culture that serves domestic and foreign tourists, so the government provides many transportation nodes, including airports, train stations, bus terminals, and bus stops. In accommodating various transportation nodes, supporting facilities are needed to integrate

the movement patterns of the community and tourists. However, there are transportation system problems in Yogyakarta that have a direct impact on the provision of competent and efficient transportation services, as described by the Indonesian Ministry of Transportation [5] among others: there is still a lack of integration of service networks and road transportation infrastructure networks with other modes, so that partially door-to-door services have not been realized, the unavailability of integration of public transport schedule and tariff services on various modes of transportation, minimal interconnection points / no connection points well-planned, and the absence of an institution that fully coordinates between governmental organizational units in Yogyakarta that can handle programs and activities for the management of the intermodal transportation integration system. To realize an increase in transportation services and an increase in intermodal integration, it is necessary to adapt to economic development, technological progress, spatial planning policies, the environment, and the level of development of a region as described by Errampalli et al. [6].
Seeing the various problems of transportation integration mentioned above, it is necessary to improve the structure of the transportation system and to facilitate the flow of people and goods moving both within cities and between cities; a transportation system is needed that can accommodate and provide certainty of travel time. Thus, the transportation integration system is one of the solutions to reduce the number of congestion, optimize the use of mass transportation, and facilitate the movement of people and goods [7], [8], [9]. For this reason, this research will analyze the integrated management of the transportation integration system in the Province of Yogyakarta Special Region, the obstacles faced in its implementation, and the transportation integration system management solutions.

2. Methods

Based on [10], The National Transportation System (SISTRANAS) has a crucial role in a systemically organized transportation arrangement to serve as a guideline and basis for planning, development, and transportation management to realize the provision of effective and efficient transportation services. SISTRANAS is arranged in an integrated manner and is manifested in the National Transportation Order (TATRANAS), the Regional Transportation Order (TATRAWIL), and the Local Transportation Order (TATRALOK). The development of SISTRANAS needs to be made sustainable, consistent and integrated between modes and other development sectors.
Management of a complex level of transportation services requires the Government and Public Transportation Authorities to innovate in providing transportation user services because innovation is fundamental in achieving sustainable integrated transportation management. GIZ by Federal Ministry for Economic Cooperation and Development Jerman [11] stated that the Public Transportation Authority is needed to coordinate the planning and regulation of the public transportation system through subsidies and integrated transportation; therefore, an independent institution that can coordinate public and private interests is needed. Department of Planning Western Australia [12] mentions that the Integrated Transportation Plan document is a tool to analyze the overall needs of the current and future transportation system in a regional government administrative area or an agency work area with transportation problems. Refers to the integrated transportation planning used (The Australian Department of Transports Metropolitan Transport Strategy) states that an integrated transportation system must have the principles of safety, efficiency, effectiveness, environmental responsibility, social responsibility, and responding to challenges.
One of the parameters in implementing a sustainable transportation system policy is the effectiveness and efficiency of public transportation, as mention by Ahmad Munawar et al. [13]. This research is policy research, namely research on a policy application of the transportation integration system with the dimensions of research relating to: (i). Policy formulation; (ii). Policy implementation; (iii). Policy performance; and (iv). Policy environment as described by Michael Hill [14]. The formal policies discussed are decisions codified in writing and legalized or formalized so that they can take effect in a legal form grouped into three, namely laws, laws, and regulations as mentioned by Riant Nugroho [15].

The method used is a type of qualitative research and a descriptive-analytical approach to analyze formal legal data on regional laws and the main tasks and functions of agencies within the Provincial Government of the Special Region of Yogyakarta (DIY) that support the implementation of regional government affairs related to the transportation system. Literature studies are used to formulate government programs in the management of integrated and sustainable transportation systems, which are then used as a basis for evaluating local laws and regulations and regional apparatus organizations through descriptive analysis and in-depth interviews with local government agency stakeholders, as mentioned in the book written by A. Rofiq Djaelani [16], Jo Moriarty [17], and Hossein Nassaji [18]. Retrieval of data using participatory observation and interviews with regulators, operators, and consumers to find out the integrated management of the transportation integration system in the Province of Yogyakarta Special Region, the obstacles faced in implementing it, and the transportation integration system management solution.

3. Result and Discussion

3.1. Integrated Transportation System in Special Region of Yogyakarta (DIY)

The resulting research by Thierry Vanelslander an Shi, Xiaoning [19] Various forms of transportation system integration have been carried out in various approaches, including through the perspective of service integration, infrastructure investment, or the application of information systems. Seeing the condition of DIY, referring to the division of authority between the State Government, Provincial Government and Regency or City Government as regulated in Law Number 23 of 2014 concerning Regional Government, the DIY Provincial Transportation Service as the organizer of regional government affairs in the field of transportation cannot implement the system. Integrated and sustainable transportation management as a whole. However, the DIY Regional Government is a Regional Apparatus Organization that administers regional government affairs in the fields of: (i). Public works and spatial planning; (ii). Transportation; (iii). Living environment; (iv). Capital investment; and (v). In accordance with the main tasks and functions of the competing agency or agency, tourism can partially complement each other in supporting the management of an integrated and sustainable transportation system.

On the other hand, although there are no regional laws and regulations that have a comprehensive and comprehensive scope for implementing an integrated and sustainable transportation system management program, all program criteria have been partially accommodated within the material for regional regulations related to transportation stipulated in DIY.

3.1.1. Transportation Management Policies are Integrated into Local Regulation

The DIY Regional Government accommodates the implementation of regional government affairs related to integrated transportation management policies into regional regulations as follows:

1. DIY Regional Regulation Number 2 of 2009 concerning the DIY Regional Long-Term Development Plan for 2005 s.d. 2025. It states that the long-term development direction of DIY related to transportation is:Pembangunan dan pelayanan sistem transportasi dan prasarana wilayah.
   a. The creation of efficient and effective transportation integrated to support the economy, education, and tourism.
   b. Acceleration of rural development and small and medium-sized cities to reduce the gap between regions, as mentioned by Governor of Special Region of Yogyakarta [20].
2. DIY Regional Regulation Number 2 of 2010 concerning DIY Regional Spatial Planning for 2009 until 2029. It is stated in Article 11 paragraph (2) that the Regional Infrastructure System Development Plan consists of road networks, railroad networks, marine transportation infrastructure networks, air transportation infrastructure networks, telematics networks, water resources infrastructure, energy networks, and infrastructure. Environment. Further, Article 12 states that the road network development policy is:
   a. Increase accessibility to all Regions and penetrate isolation;

b. Creating maximum integration between various modes of transportation in the Region and cities in the Region;
c. Increase the effectiveness and efficiency of the road, as mention by the Governor of the Special Region of Yogyakarta [21].

3. DIY Regional Regulation Number 8 of 2015 concerning Regional Transportation Development Patterns. It is stated in Chapter II on Regional Transportation Development that the development of regional transportation in the regions is realized by optimizing the provision of transportation network systems and services which include land, sea, air, and rail transportation which is carried out in an integrated and intermodal way [1].

3.2. Constrains on Integrated Transportation System Management
The DIY regional government still faces obstacles in managing an integrated and sustainable transportation system, namely:

3.2.1. The Discontinuity of Local Laws and Regulation
There are three areas of discontinuity of regional laws that are recognized by the Province of Yogyakarta, namely: a) The master planning of national and regional transportation infrastructure networks have not all been accommodated in the DIY RTRW (Regional Spatial Plan) document; b) The DIY RTRW (Regional Spatial Plan) document which is spatial or spatial related to the transportation network is not optimally aligned with the DIY sectoral RPJMD document; c) Medium or long term planning documents: RPJMD and RTRW DIY have not been optimally accommodated in the short term planning documents: DIY RKPD, Work Plan and DPA SKPD.

3.2.2. Limited Authority
Three points become the limitation of authority in the scope of activities under the control of the Central Government based on Law Number 23/2014 concerning Regional Government, including first, the development or provision of infrastructure for rail and air transportation. Second, organizing governmental affairs in the field of aviation sub-affairs. Third, the implementation of operations in government affairs in the transportation sector, sub-railroad affairs.

3.2.3. The Long Span of Control Between Regional Government Agencies in DIY
The other research includes articles on the analysis of transportation planning content in two cities in Canada, namely Toronto and Montreal. This study explores the framework used and the language used in the transportation planning document to address the last mile (LMP) problem. Several policy recommendations expand on three themes drawn from content analysis, emphasizing shared mobility, public-private partnerships, and diversification of land use as a long-range strategy, as described by Justin B. Hollander [22]. This is, of course, different so that these three obstacles are encountered in the field compared to the research results of Bista, Hollander, and Situ. Then the article written by Win Akustia [23] about integration between passenger transportation modes in Gorontalo City, Indonesia, uses three leading indicators (integrated infrastructure, integrated network, and integrated services) which concludes that people prefer to use private vehicles and bentor. In this study, it is suggested to improve intermodal integration at the main node in Gorontalo City, including through the provision of various transfer facilities, increasing the integration of route networks and service systems. Meanwhile, in this study, the authors provide several considerations as an alternative to solving existing constraints.

3.3. Integrated and Sustainable Transportation System Management Mechanism
Forms of integrated transportation system management have been carried out in many countries from regional and national levels, one of which is the Intelligent Transportation System with the TSM & O

(Transportation Systems Management and Operations) as mention by Hunt, K, et al. [24]. Further research [3] offers the planning and design stages of integrating the TSM & O strategy as a routine method in business practice. The mechanism for administering regional government affairs of the DIY provincial government in managing an integrated and sustainable transportation system can at least be optimized through the following considerations:

a. All administering stakeholders (agency or agency) in carrying out their duties and functions remain within the limits, scope, and authority mandated by laws and regulations;
b. Optimizing the mechanism for planning and implementing regional development through strengthening the role of the DIY Regional Government OPD as a solution to the identified weaknesses;
c. Forming a new work unit or management institution in stages according to the needs of the formation process and the actual conditions of transport carrying capacity.

The management of an integrated and sustainable transportation system in DIY can be implemented through the formulation of programs or activities of the proposed local government, namely: Integrated and Sustainable Transportation System Management Program, because it is supported by regional laws and can be implemented by the duties and authorities of 9 (nine) agencies or stakeholder agencies that have the same scope as the program.

The key in implementing an integrated and sustainable transportation system management program is to compile programs and activities into the implementation documents of the RKPD, Renja, and DPA because only with these documents the technical agencies have a legal basis in their implementation.

3.3.1. Conditions for Integrated and Sustainable Transportation System Management

1. Land Transportation Sector, Transportation Agency DIY

   The Department of Transportation carries out its primary duties and functions as limited to the given authority, namely in managing road transportation modes, and does not have the power to manage other transportation modes: rail and air. This makes it challenging to manage integrated transportation.

   There is no law regulating integrated transportation between central and regional as well as between regions. This has resulted in the DIY Transportation Agency's policy of not being able to manage transportation at the district/city level and the policies between Regency / City Governments that are not yet integrated. However, transportation management coordination can emulate cross-regional coordination platforms such as the Yogyakarta - Sleman - Bantul Joint Secretariat (Sekber Kartamantul) or the Regional Spatial Planning Coordinating Board (BKPRD).

   This incompleteness is also evident in the management of road transportation modes, namely: the control of road facilities by the Department of Transportation and the management of road infrastructure by the Public Works Office, where program preparation and implementation are given to each SKPD.

   Integrated transportation management is also influenced by policies to the Regions and DPRD regarding regional development priorities and proportional budgeting in transportation management.

2. Traffic Sector Transportation Agency DIY

   The Transportation Agency only carries out programs and activities that have been compiled in the Regional Government Work Plan (RKPD) document following their main tasks and functions.

   Integrated transportation management is still constrained by the limited authority of the Department of Transportation, which only manages road mode transportation facilities and licensing officers at the district/city level. However, it has been able to provide input on integrating the intermodal and intermodal transportation infrastructure network to managers of other modes of transportation (rail and air) at the national level.

   The range of management coordination is felt to be quite long between the Transportation Agency and the national level transportation managers and other agencies at the DIY regional government level. On the other hand, the proportionality of the transportation management budget is not

IOP Conf. Series: Earth and Environmental Science 1000 (2022) 012030 doi:10.1088/1755-1315/1000/1/012030

balanced between the manager of road transportation facilities (Department of Transportation) and the manager of road transportation infrastructure (Department of Public Works).

3. Spatial Planning and Development Division, DIY Land and Spatial Planning Service
The Department of Land and Spatial Planning has compiled policies, strategies, and plans for urban infrastructure development and integrated intermodal and intermodal integrated transportation infrastructure network development contained in the DIY RTRW (Regional Spatial Plan) Review Document will be stipulated in 2017. RTRW (Regional Spatial Planning) serves as a reference document for the integrated planning of the master plan (compiled by other agencies) to provide a spatial structure for the development of transportation infrastructure networks (road, rail, air, and sea modes), as well as to provide the basis for coordinated implementation among SKPDs that implement integrated transportation systems. In addition, the RTRW Appendix (Regional Spatial Planning) also contains an indication of integrated transportation programs in the implementation of SKPD and the required funding sources.
However, the RTRW document (Regional Spatial Plan) is not in line with the RPJMD document and the DIY Regional Government Work Plan (RKPD), and the SKPD Work Plan (Renja). This occurs because, among other things, the mechanism for the preparation of long-term and medium-term development planning documents (RPJMD and RTRW (Regional Spatial Planning)) is often preceded by short-term development planning documents (RKPD and Renja / Rienstra SKPD) so that there is no continuity.
Until now, the implementation and supervision of regional spatial planning for the implementing SKPD sectors have not been carried out optimally. Likewise, the coordination of the performance and management of the space with the Regency or City Government has not been optimal.
4. Environmental Pollution Sector, DIY Environmental Agency
The Environmental Agency has a role in determining quality standards for exhaust gas emission from motorized vehicles, drafting laws and regulations regarding the testing agency for emissions, noise, vibration, and odor, and preparing ambient air testing of air quality status (only held in 2017). However, because the authority to carry out motor vehicle emission testing activities lies with the Regency / City Government, BLH only encourages its implementation. Moreover, the test costs are borne by vehicle owners, so not many motorized vehicle owners carry out emission tests.
5. Public Work, Department of PUP & ESDM DIY
The PUP & ESDM Office plays a role in compiling local regulations, providing policy recommendations, implementing District Financial Assistance mechanisms for planning and/or building new road networks, and implementing road infrastructure development, regulation, supervision, and guidance following the authority of the DIY Regional Government.
Support for integrated transportation management is tailored to the main tasks and functions of each SKPD, and efforts to integrate programs and activities between SKPDs are left to Bappeda. However, it is still felt that the coordination span is quite long between P2JN (Ministry of Public Works) and the Yogyakarta Regional Government in the development or rehabilitation activities of national roads connected to provincial roads.
In the case of new road network construction, the PUP & ESDM Office gets additional assignments to assess and pay land compensation in land acquisition activities, the authority of the Regional Revenue and Management and Asset Service.
6. Sub Division of Transportation, Development Administration Bureau, DIY Regional Secretariat
The Development Administration Bureau plays a role in monitoring, facilitation, and transportation studies related to the transportation sector, public works, and the environment. As a result, all the implementation of SKPD's powers and functions has been optimal, while in its performance, the leading sector coordination between SKPDs depends on the material discussed. On the other hand, coordination and absorption of the community's aspirations and other stakeholders are available for coordination and routine agendas in the Traffic Forum facilitated by the Transportation Agency.
In the course of implementing integrated transportation management, the obstacles faced include: DPRD political policies can change programs and activities that have been planned; as well as

licensing of land use for transportation infrastructure networks is the authority of the Regency or City Government, so it needs a process and time in its implementation.

7. Facilities and Infrastructure Sector Bappeda DIY
   Bappeda plays a role in integrating various regional infrastructure development plans across sectors and regions and controlling the implementation of regional development through monitoring and evaluation mechanisms. The DIY regional government has carried out all stages of regional planning and development mechanisms and integrated transportation management. The limitation experienced by Bappeda is the limited allocation of funding to carry out studies/studies of integrated transportation management.

3.3.2. Evaluation of The Integrated Transportation System Management of The DIY Local Government

Through understanding the mechanisms for planning and implementing regional development and from the results: literature study, analysis, as well as descriptions and perceptions of the organizers, it is possible to identify several constraints/obstacles/weaknesses that cause less optimal integrated transportation management in DIY, namely as follows:

1. The key to carrying out integrated and sustainable transportation management is to include supporting programs and activities (appropriate functions) into the RKPD, Renja, and DPA documents, because only with these documents can specialized agencies carry out supporting programs and activities (according to their authority). Integrated and sustainable transportation management.
2. RKPD, Renja, and DPA as implementation documents of the RPJPD / RPJMD references, sectoral in the duties and functions of each technical agency. However, the infrastructure development mechanism requires a legal basis for using regional space contained in the RTRW document (Regional Spatial Planning), and if it does not accommodate the spatial program and structure in the related spatial map: (i). Urban System Development Plan; and (ii). Regional Infrastructure System Development Plan (in this case, the infrastructure network and transportation services for all modes), the implementation of the development cannot be carried out in a legal review (legally flawed). Therefore the RTRW document (Regional Spatial Plan) must be in harmony and complement each other with the RPJPD / RPJMD document. Bappeda and the DIY Land and Spatial Planning Agency need to strengthen their coordination in harmonizing the material.
3. The RTRW document (Regional Spatial Planning) has become very important in the implementation of spatial-based infrastructure development so that the integration of various master plans for road, rail, air, and sea transportation infrastructure and service modes must have been accommodated in the RTRW document (Regional Spatial Planning). In this case, the Department of Land and Spatial Planning DIY must be the leading sector that has a high ability in the preparation of RTRW (Regional Spatial Planning) that accommodates various spatial / spatial-based infrastructure development plans.
4. If in the coordination mechanism between: (i). DIY Land and Spatial Planning Agency; (ii). Technical administering stakeholders (national level agencies and DIY Regional Government OPD); Regional planning coordinator (Bappeda and Regional Secretariat DIY); not proactively coordinating in accommodating transportation infrastructure and service network planning, the material in the RTRW document (Regional Spatial Planning) does not optimally support the implementation of transportation management. Furthermore, there will be a gap between the need for transportation management and the planning document that contains SKPD programs and activities.

4. Conclusion

Based on the analysis of the formal legal policies for the management of the transportation integration system, descriptive analysis and stakeholder perspectives on transportation management in DIY, and analysis of the implementation mechanisms and transportation integration system management institutions needed, it is concluded that: integrated transportation management in DIY can implement the scope of the program proposed, namely: Management of an Integrated and Sustainable Transportation System, because it is supported by regional laws and following the primary duties and authorities of the relevant agencies in the DIY Regional Government. Moreover, to overcome obstacles: (i). The discontinuity between regional planning documents; (ii). The limited scope of authority of the Central Government; and (iii). With a long span of coordination control, the mechanism and the establishment of the proposed transportation management unit and/or agency can be applied.

The keys to implementing an integrated and sustainable transportation system management are: (i). Making master planning for integrated transportation infrastructure and service networks legal basis, and (ii). Ability to translate it into development documents of RKPD, Renja, and DPA supporting agencies. Thus, the proposed program needs to be continued until the formulation of technical activities to integrate infrastructure networks and integrated transportation services. Incorporated transportation technical planning documents should be included in regional legislation as an implementable legal basis for local governments. Regional policymakers must establish policies according to local conditions and wisdom in dealing with transportation problems closely related to the community's socio-culture and restricted vision.

Acknowledgments

The author would like to thank the Ministry of Education and Culture of the Republic of Indonesia for providing the opportunity and financial assistance to be able to carry out this research.

References

[1] Governor of Special Region of Yogyakarta. 2015. *Peraturan Daerah Daerah Istimewa Yogyakarta Nomor 8 Tahun 2015 Tentang Pola Pengembangan Transportasi Wilayah*. Yogyakarta.

[2] Rodrigue, Jean-paul. 2006. "Intermodal Transportation and Integrated Transport Systems : Spaces, Networks Intermodal Transportation and Integrated Transport Systems : Spaces, Networks and Flows." *Intermodal Transportation and Integrated Transport Systems*, 2–25.

[3] Abou-senna, Hatem, Essam Radwan, and Alexander Navarro. 2018a. "Integrating Transportation Systems Management and Operations into the Project Life Cycle from Planning to Construction : A Synthesis of Best Practices." *Journal of Traffic and Transportation Engineering (English Edition)* 5 (1): 44–55. https://doi.org/10.1016/j.jtte.2017.04.006.

[4] Munawar, Ahmad. 2007. "Public Transport Reform in Indonesia, A Case Study in the City of Yogyakarta." *World Academy of Science, Engineering, and Technology* 28: 39–44.

[5] Badan Penelitian dan Pengembangan, Sekretariat Badan. 2012. *Studi Tinjau Ulang Tataran Transportasi Wilayah Provinsi DIY*. Jakarta: Kementerian Perhubungan Republik Indonesia.

[6] Errampalli, Madhu, K S Patil, and C S R K Prasad. 2020. "Evaluation of Integration between Public Transportation Modes by Developing Sustainability Index for Indian Cities." *Case Studies on Transport Policy* 8 (1): 180–87. https://doi.org/10.1016/j.cstp.2018.09.005.

[7] Segola, Motshidisi, and Adewole S Oladele. 2016. "Traffic Congestion and Mobility Solutions for Francistown Road Transportation Network Systems." *BIE Journal of Engineering and Applied Sciences* 6 (2).

[8] Radwan, Ahmed Hosney. 2015. "Intelligent Transportation System as a Tool for Solving Cairo' s Transportation Problems." *International Journal of Scientific and Engineering Research* 6 (11). https://doi.org/10.14299/ijser.2015.11.001.

[9] Cheng, Zhi Aaron, Min-Seok Pang, and Paul A Pavlou. 2016. "On Intelligent Transportation Systems and Road Congestion." In *Thirty Seventh International Conference on Information Systems*, 1–19. Dublin.

[10] Menteri Perhubungan, 2005. Peraturan Menteri Perhubungan No. KM 49 Tahun 2005 Tentang

Sistem Transportasi Nasional (SISTRANAS), Jakarta

[11] GIZ. 2004. *Sustainable Urban Transport Improvement Project - 10 Principles for Sustainable Urban Transport*. Jerman: Federal Ministry for Economic Cooperation and Development.

[12] Department of Planning, Western Australia. 2012. *Guidelines for Preparation of Integrated Tansport Plans*. Australia: Western Australian Planning Commision.

[13] Munawar, Ahmad., Muchlisin, Sebhatu, and Samuel Petros. 2013. "The Role of New Transport Policy on Creating Sustainable and Integrated Public Transit System in Jakarta (Case Study: Transjakarta, Indonesia And Freiburg, Germany)." Karslad University.

[14] Hill, Michael. 2005. *The Public Policy Process*. 4th editio. London: Pearson-Longman.

[15] Nugroho, Riant. 2013. *Metode Penelitian Kebijakan*. Yogyakarta: Pustaka Pelajar.

[16] Djaelani, A. Rofiq. 2013. "Teknik Pengumpulan Data Dalam Penelitian Kualitatif." *Majalah Ilmiah Pawiyatan*, 2013.

[17] Moriarty, Jo. 2011. *Qualitative Methods Overview*. London: School for Social Care Research

[18] Nassaji, Hossein. 2015. "Qualitative and Descriptive Research : Data Type versus Data Analysis Qualitative and Descriptive Research : Data Type versus Data Analysis." *Language Teaching Research2* 19 (2). https://doi.org/10.1177/1362168815572747.

[19] Shi, Xiaoning, and Thierry Vanelslander. 2010. "Design and Evaluation of Transportation Networks : Constructing Transportation Networks from Perspectives of Service Integration , Infrastructure Investment and Information System Implementation." *Journal of Economic Research and Electronic Networking* 11: 1–4. https://doi.org/10.1007/s11066-010-9053-2.

[20] Governor of Special Region of Yogyakarta, 2009. *Rencana Pembangunan Jangka Panjang Daerah Tahun 2005 – 2025*. Yogyakarta: Peraturan Daerah DIY.

[21] Governor of Special Region of Yogyakarta. 2010. Rencana Tata Ruang Wilayah Provinsi Daerah Istimewa Yogyakarta. Yogyakarta.

[22] Bista, Shabnam, Justin B. Hollander, and Minyu Situ. 2020. "A Content Analysis of Transportation Planning Documents in Toronto and Montreal." *Journal of Case Studies on Transport Policy* 8 (2). https://www.sciencedirect.com/journal/case-studies-on-transport-policy/vol/8/issue/2.

[23] Akustia, Win. 2016. "Evaluasi Keterpaduan Antarmoda Transportasi Di Kota Gorontalo." *Jurnal PenelitianTransportasi Multimoda* 14 (1): 31–40. https://doi.org/10.25104/mtm.v14i1.82.

[24] Atkinson, J., Bauer, J., Hunt, K., et al. 2013. *Designing for Transportation Management and Operations*. Reston: Science Applications International Corporation.

Road Infrastructure Deficiency and Road Safety Audit at Black Spot Area in Rural Road

G Sugiyanto[1], R Suciningtyas[1], E W Indriyati[1], Yanto[1], B Mulyono[1] and M Y Santi[2]

[1]Jenderal Soedirman University, Department of Civil Engineering, Purbalingga, Central Java, Indonesia
[2]Health Polytechnic Ministry of Health of Yogyakarta, Yogyakarta, Indonesia

gito.sugiyanto@unsoed.ac.id

Abstract. One of the factors that caused traffic accidents is road infrastructure. Strategies to minimize the road deficiency infrastructure is implementation of the forgiving road, self-explaining road, and self-regulating road. The purpose of this study was analyzing the deficiency of road infrastructure and implementing the road safety audit at black spot areas in rural areas. Study location in Bojongsari Street, Purbalingga. Parameters that are analyzed in deficiency of road infrastructure include the road geometric condition, road pavement performance, and road equipment facilities. Parameters that analyzed in road geometric condition, namely stopping and passing sight distance, lane width of road, and road shoulder width. The results of this study show that the highest passing and stopping sight distance of all vehicles was motorcycles at 304.48 m and 64.67 m. The road pavement performance based on pavement condition index for the longitudinal/transverse cracking conditions is 94 and for the lane or shoulder drop-off condition is 77. Recommendations given based on road safety audit results for road geometric is to improve the road shoulder, for pavement condition improves shoulder drop-off and longitudinal/transverse cracking. For the road equipment facilities are to install the maximum speed limit sign of 40 km/h and install the warning sign.

1. Introduction

One of the most important measures for reducing fatalities and minimizing the severity of traffic accident victims is safe road infrastructure design. Strategies to minimize the deficiency of road infrastructure, first is forgiving road (roads that are able to minimize the severity of accident victims when a collision), second is self-explaining road (roads that are able to explain the purpose without "communication"), and third is self-regulating road (roads that are able to create compliance without warning) [1]. One of the factors that caused traffic accidents is road infrastructure including the geometric design, road pavement [2], side friction, and environment. One of the methods to analyze the infrastructure deficiency is road safety audit. Road safety audit reports on the potential road safety issues and identifies opportunities for improvements in traffic safety for all road users [3]. Road safety audit is one of the approaches to improve the traffic safety and reduce the number of traffic accidents [4-5]. Driving speeds affect the risk of being involved in a crash and the severity of injury. The main risk factor for the occurrence of accidents in road traffic is speed [6]. The strategies to improve road safety by applying the safe road infrastructure designs, determining the speed limit of vehicles, system theory, improved the pavement material [7-8] and assessment [9].

The purpose of this study is to analyze the road infrastructure deficiency black spot area in rural areas with a case study in Bojongsari Street, Purbalingga. Bojongsari Street is the highest ranked road with traffic accidents in Purbalingga District with 20 cases of the accident, 5 deaths and 57 slightly-injured people [10]. One of the methods that can be used to determine road pavement performance based on road damage type using pavement condition index (PCI). PCI is a numerical index between 0 to 100 [11]. The PCI rating range and scoring scale can be seen in Figure 1.

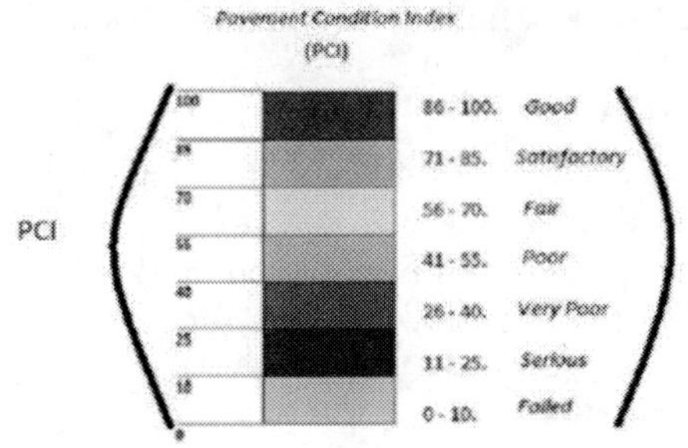

Figure 1. Scoring scale of pavement condition index [11].

2. Method

2.1. Location of the study

The location of the study was in Bojongsari Street, Purbalingga precisely in the connecting line between Purbalingga and Bobotsari. This road included collector road functions. In this street, the location of the black spot is located in front of Vocational High School or SMK N 1 Bojongsari.

2.2. Data collection

The number of victims and traffic accident data in Purbalingga District from 1st January 2016 to 31st December 2018 were obtained from the Purbalingga Police [10]. Based on the number of traffic accident data and number of traffic accidents victims then used to determine the black spot location based on the equivalent accident number (EAN) and upper control limit (UCL) method [12-13]. The weight of the EAN based on Directorate General of Highways Republic of Indonesia [14] is weight value 12 for fatality, weight value 3 for a severe-injury and for minor-injuries, weight value 1 for property damaged only. Road geometric and asphalt pavement conditions were acquired based on field observation. Speed gun Bushnell is used to obtain the vehicle's speed. The passing and stopping sight distance is measured based on the design speed, PIEV time, gravitation acceleration, and the friction coefficient between tires and road surface.

2.3. Analysis approach

2.3.1. Stopping sight distance

According to the AASHTO (American Association of State Highway and Transportation Officials), "stopping sight distance (SSD) reflects a distance within which a driver can effectively see an object in the roadway and stop their vehicle before colliding with the object" [15]. The stopping sight distance declared in meter [16] can be determined by referring to Equation (1).

$$SSD = \frac{V_R}{3.6}T + \frac{\left(\frac{V_R}{3.6}\right)^2}{2gf} \quad (1)$$

with:
V_R is design speed in km/h, T is perception, identification, emotion, and volition (PIEV) time (2.5 second), g is gravitation acceleration with a value of 9.8 m/s^2, and F is coefficient of friction between tires and road surface for flexible pavement type 0.35 to 0.55.

2.3.2. Passing sight distance

According to the AASHTO, "passing sight distance (PSD) is the distance that drivers must be able to see along the road ahead to safely and efficiently initiate and complete passing maneuvers of slower vehicles on two-lane, two-way highways using the lane normally reserved for opposing traffic" [15].

"PSD is a consideration along two-lane roads on which drivers may need to assess whether to initiate, continue, and complete or abort passing maneuvers" [17]. Provision of PSD would need a clear area inside each curve that would extend beyond the normal right of way line [18-19]. Factors that influence the passing sight distance were PIEV time and speed of vehicle. There is a relationship vehicle speed and passing sight distance, higher speed more passing sight distance.

2.3.3. Longitudinal/transverse cracking

Longitudinal/transverse cracking occurs in single or parallel road pavements. The number of total longitudinal crack length and the width crack was used to classify the severity level. The value of PCI for longitudinal transverse cracking are determined based on the distress density value for longitudinal and transverse cracking in percent (%), the deduct value for longitudinal transverse cracking, the total deduct value, the corrected deduct value (CDV) and the PCI refer to Equation (2).

$$PCI = 100 - CDV \qquad (2)$$

2.3.4. Lane or shoulder drop-off

Lane or shoulder drop-off is the difference of elevation between pavement edge and road shoulder. The value of lane or shoulder drop-off is based on the position of road shoulder elevation toward pavement edge elevation on the right side and the left side then classified as a low, medium, or high level. The PCI values for shoulder drop-off are determined based on the distress density value for lane or shoulder drop-off in percent (%), the deduct value for lane or shoulder drop-off, the total deduct value, the corrected deduct value and the pavement condition index or PCI using the Equation (2).

2.3.5. Road equipment facilities

There are six parameters that are analyzed in road equipment facilities, namely number and condition of speed limit sign, curve direction sign, warning sign, traffic signals, road marking, and the lightning condition. The conditions of road markings according to the Ministry of Transportation standard of road marking PM Number 67, 2018 [20]. Traffic signals, curve direction and warning signs according to standard signs of Ministry of Transportation PM Number 13, 2014 [21].

3. Result and discussion

3.1 Condition road geometric and speed of vehicle

3.1.1 Condition of road geometric

Bojongsari Street Purbalingga, Central Java is a collector road with two lanes two way without median or undivided (2/2 UD). Road width is 8.0 m (2 x 4.0 m) with the road shoulder width of 100 cm. The road shoulder of the side from Bobotsari direction has a width of 2.5 m while for the side of the direction of Purbalingga the road width is 2.9 m. But from the road shoulder width, only 1.0 m can be used because of the side obstacles or hazards in the form of quite a lot of trees and street vendors. Bojongsari Street does not have sidewalks and road medians. The type of pavement is flexible pavement. Road markings are in good condition. Land use around the road in the form of houses and residents' shops and shops. Furthermore, the difference between elevation of pavement edge and road shoulder is 13 cm on the right side and 3 cm on the left side. The standard of road shoulder width is minimum 150 cm and width of road is 600 cm [22].

3.1.2 Speed of vehicle, passing and stop sight distance

Vehicles speed data was distributed into seven types of vehicles. Passing and stopping sight distance of each vehicle were measured based on the design speed of the road and vehicle's maximum speed [23]. Total vehicles taken in the field survey is 215 vehicles, with an S-curve of vehicle speed can be seen in Figure 2.

Based on Figure 2, 90% of motorcycles, 76% of passenger cars (PC), 50% of large trucks (LT), 40% of pick-up, 30% of large bus (LB), 20% of micro bus (MB) and 20% of light truck (LT) exceed the maximum speed limit in the field as many as 40 km/h. The higher speed the more accidents [23-24]. Woolley *et al.* [25] and Qu *et al.* [26] discuss impact of lower speed limit in fuel consumption.

IOP Conf. Series: Earth and Environmental Science 1000 (2022) 012031 doi:10.1088/1755-1315/1000/1/012031

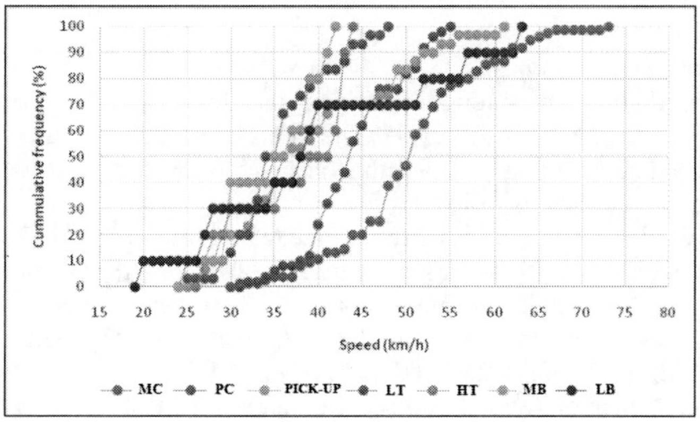

Figure 2. S-curve of vehicle speed and the speed limit in Bojongsari Street.

The highest speed of all vehicles was motorcycle at 73 km/h. The maximum speed of each vehicle was large bus at 63 km/h, pick-ups at 61 km/h, passenger cars at 55 km/h, light trucks at 48 km/h, heavy trucks at 44 km/h, and micro bus at 44 km/h. The maximum speed for all type vehicles in Bojongsari Street is 73 km/h. Based on a speed survey in the field using speed gun Bushnell, the average speed of motorcycle at 51 km/h, passenger car at 44 km/h, pick up and large bus at 40 km/h, heavy truck at 38 km/h, light truck at 36 km/h, and microbus at 35 km/h. Statistical analysis of vehicle speeds results, include the mean of speed, mode of speed, median of speed, variance of speed, a standard deviation of speed, the amount of data, and 15th, 50th, and 85th percentiles for each type of vehicles in Bojongsari Street is shown in Table 1. Passing and stopping sight distance for each vehicle type in Bojongsari Street can be seen in Table 2.

Table 1. Statistical analysis of vehicle speed in Bojongsari Street

Analysis of statistical		Motorcycles	Passenger cars	Pick-ups	Light trucks	Heavy trucks	Micro bus	Large bus
Mean of speed (km/h)		51	44	40	36	38	35	40
Modus of speed (km/h)		48	40	29	34	43	30	32
Median of speed (km/h)		51	44	37	35	41	36	39
Variance of speed (km/h)		65	29	91	29	46	33	89
Standard deviation (km/h)		8	5	10	5	7	6	14
Amount of data (n)		75	50	30	30	10	10	10
Minimum speed (km/h)		31	32	26	25	27	25	20
Maximum speed (km/h)		73	55	61	48	44	42	63
Percentile	15th	43	39	28	30	27	29	26
(km/h)	50th	51	44	40	36	38	35	40
	85th	58	51	50	42	42	40	56

Based on Table 2, the highest passing and stopping sight distance of all vehicles was motorcycles at 304.48 m and 64.67 m. The lowest passing and stopping sight distance of all vehicles was microbus at 214.80 m and 38.08 m.

Table 2. Stopping and passing sight distance in Bojongsari Street

Type of vehicle	Stopping sight distance/SSD (m)	Passing sight distance/PSD (m)
Motorcycles	64.67	304.48
Passenger cars	52.33	265.24
Pick-up	45.77	242.83
Micro bus	38.08	214.80
Large bus	45.77	242.83
Light trucks	39.58	220.41
Heavy trucks	42.63	231.62

3.2 Condition of road pavement

3.2.1 Longitudinal/transverse cracking

Along 350 m, total longitudinal crack length in Bojongsari Street was 45 m with the width crack < 5 mm, which was in low severity level (L level). The Bojongsari Street width is 8.0 m. Based on the total longitudinal crack length 45 m and width crack is <5 m, the value of PCI for longitudinal transverse cracking are determined as follows:

a. The distress density value for longitudinal/transverse cracking is {(45)/(8x350)}x 100% = 1.607%.
b. Based on Figure 3, with the distress density value is 1.607% and the width of cracks < 5 mm (low severity level or L level), the deduct value for longitudinal transverse cracking is 5.
c. Along the 350 m road section that wasn't divided into several unit segments, total deduct value 5.
d. Based on Figure 4, the CDV with the total deduct value for longitudinal/transverse cracking is 5 and the road section that is not divided into several unit segments or q = 1 is 6.
e. The pavement condition index or PCI = 100 - CDV = 100 - 6 = 94. The PCI for the longitudinal/transverse cracking in Bojongsari Street of 94, included in good condition (86-100).

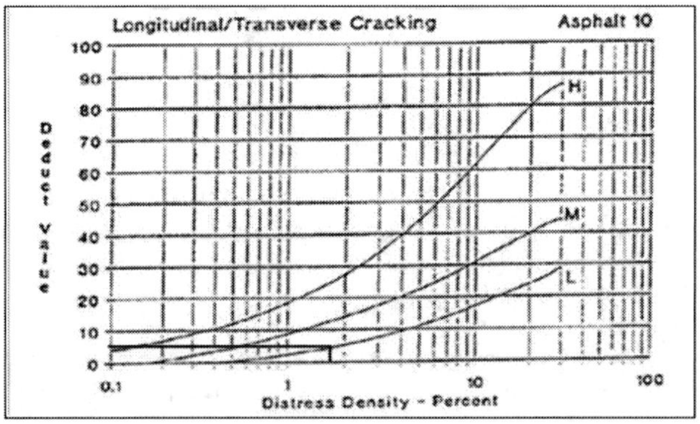

Figure 3. Relationship distress density and the deduct value for longitudinal transverse cracking [11].

3.2.2 Lane or shoulder drop-off

In Bojongsari Street, the position of road shoulder elevation toward pavement edge elevation is 13 cm on the right side, which is classified as medium level. The shoulder drop-off on the left side of the road is 3 cm. This happens because the pavement is overlay while the road shoulder elevation is still constant. The difference of elevation between pavement edge and road shoulder (shoulder drop-off) in Bojongsari Street can be seen in Figure 5.

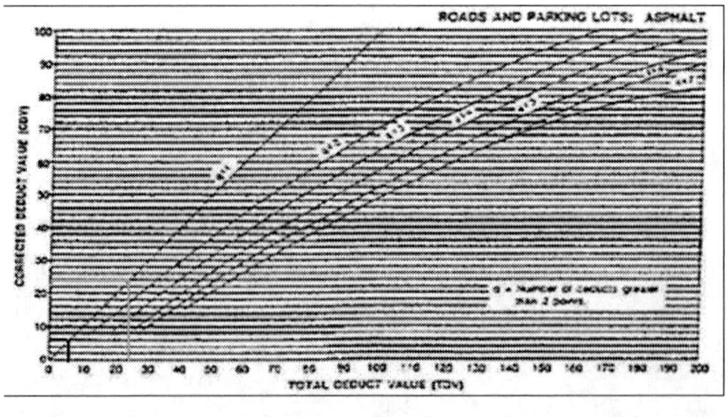

Figure 4. Total deduct value and corrected deduct value for roads and parking lots: asphalt [11].

Figure 5. Shoulder drop-off in Bojongsari Street, Purbalingga.

The PCI values for shoulder drop-off in Bojongsari Street are determined as follows:

a. The distress density value for lane or shoulder drop-off is {(350) / (8.0 x 350)} x 100% = 12.50%.
b. Based on Figure 6, the distress density value is 12.50 % and the different elevation of pavement edge and road shoulder is 13 cm which is classified as medium severity or M level, the deduct value for lane or shoulder drop-off is 23.
c. Along the 350 m road section Bojongsari Street not divided into unit segments or q = 1, the total deduct value is the same as the deduct value is 23.
d. Based on Figure 4, the corrected deduct value (CDV) with the total deduct value is 23 and the road section reviewed not divided into several unit segments or q = 1 is 23.
e. Pavement condition index or PCI = 100 - CDV = 100 - 23 = 77. The PCI value for the lane or shoulder drop-off condition in Bojongsari Street is 77, included in satisfactory condition (71-85).

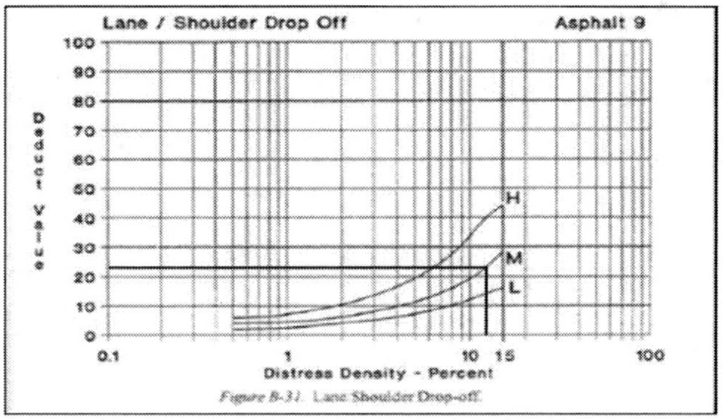

Figure 6. Relationship distress density and deducts value for lane or shoulder drop-off [11].

3.3 Road equipment facilities

The conditions of road markings on Bojongsari Street are quite good according to the Ministry of Transportation standard of road marking PM Number 67, 2018 [20]. Lighting of streets in the field is sufficient with the average distance between lighting lamps is 50 m, not in accordance with the standard requirements is 48 m. Traffic signals, curve direction and warning signs in the field are very lacking with standard signs of Ministry of Transportation PM Number 13, 2014 [21].

3.4 Road safety

In this study, there are three parameters that are analyzed include condition of road geometric, condition of road pavement and harmonization of road equipment facilities. Parameters that analyzed in road geometric condition, namely stopping and passing sight distance, lane width of road, and road shoulder width [27]. Analysis of road infrastructure deficiencies for the pavement condition covers two indicators namely longitudinal/transverse cracking and the difference between elevation of pavement edge and road shoulder (lane or shoulder drop-off). The standard for lane or shoulder drop-off is determined using two values, based on pavement condition index in the amount of 85 and based on the difference between elevation of pavement edge and road shoulder < 1 cm.

Parameters that analyzed in road equipment facilities includes six aspects namely number and the condition of speed limit sign, number and the condition of curve direction sign, number and the condition of warning sign, the availability of traffic signal sign, the availability and condition of road markings, and road lightning condition and distance between the road lightning. Three categories of victims are fatality, severe injured, and slightly injured [28]. Based on the data on the causes of traffic accidents, it is found that the parameters that cause the victim to die are stopping sight distance, passing sight distance, road shoulder width, longitudinal and transverse cracking, lane or shoulder drop-off, and road equipment facilities (speed limit sign, warning sign, and traffic signal sign).

The measurement results of three parameters and the severity rates of casualties in Bojongsari Street shown in Table 3. RSA results include the probability value, severity level, risk valuation and the recommendations to increased traffic safety shown in Table 4.

Table 3. Analysis of infrastructure deficiency and severity rates of casualties in Bojongsari Street

No.	Parameter and criteria (unit)	Standard	Measurement results	Deviation (%)	Fatality	Severe injured	Minor injured
I.	**Road geometric condition**						
1.	**Stopping sight distance (SSD)**						
	SSD of motorcycles (m)	75	64.67	13.37	1	0	4
	SSD of passenger cars (m)	75	52.33	30.23	0	0	2
	SSD of pick-up (m)	75	45.77	38.97	0	0	0
	SSD of microbus (m)	75	38.08	49.22	0	0	1
	SSD of large bus (m)	75	45.77	38.97	1	0	3
	SSD of light truck (m)	75	39.58	47.23	0	0	1
	SSD of heavy truck (m)	75	42.63	43.16	0	0	1
2.	**Passing sight distance (PSD)**						
	PSD of motorcycles (m)	350	304.48	13.01	1	0	5
	PSD of passenger cars (m)	350	265.24	24.22	1	0	3
	PSD of pick-up (m)	350	242.83	30.62	0	0	2
	PSD of micro bus (m)	350	214.80	38.63	0	0	1
	PSD of large bus (m)	350	242.83	30.62	1	0	2
	PSD of light truck (m)	350	220.41	37.03	0	0	1
	PSD of heavy truck (m)	350	231.62	33.83	0	0	1
3.	Road lane width (m)	3.00	4.00	-33.33	0	0	0
4.	Road shoulder width (m)	1.50	1.00	33.33	1	0	0
II.	**Road pavement performance**						
1.	Longitudinal and transverse cracking	85	94	-10.59	1	0	1
2.	Lane or shoulder drop-off (PCI)	85	77	9.41	2	0	1
	Lane or shoulder drop-off (cm)	< 1 cm	13 cm	-1200			
III.	**Road equipment facilities**						
1.	Number of speed limit sign[1)]	Min. 1	0	-100	2	0	4
	Condition of Speed limit sign (%)	100	0	-100			
2.	Number of curve direction sign	Min. 3	0	-100	0	0	4
	Condition of curve direction sign (%)	100	0	-100			
3.	Number of warning sign	Min. 1	0	-100	1	0	3
	Condition of warning sign (%)	100	0	-100			
4.	Availability of traffic signal sign	Available	No	-100	1	0	1
5.	Availability of road markings[2)]	Available	Available	0	0	0	1
	Condition of road markings (%)	100	85	-15			
6.	Distance between the road lightning (m)	Min. 48	50	-4.17	0	0	1
	Condition of road lightning (%)	100	100	0			

[1)]: Ministry of Transportation Republic of Indonesia, PM Number 13, 2014 [21].
[2)]: Ministry of Transportation Republic of Indonesia, PM Number 67, 2018 [20].

Table 4. Road Safety Audit Result and Recommendation in Bojongsari Street, Purbalingga

No.	Parameter	Probability value	Severity level	Risk valuation	Risk category	Recommendations to improve road safety
I.	**Road geometric condition**					
1.	Stopping sight distance	2	100	200	Medium	Passive response
2.	Passing sight distance	2	100	200	Medium	Passive response
3.	Road lane width	0	0	0	Negligible	Passive response
4.	Road shoulder width	2	100	200	Medium	Improve shoulder to 150 cm wide (increased 50 cm).
II.	**Road pavement performance**					
1.	Longitudinal or transverse cracking	0	100	0	Negligible	Passive response
2.	Shoulder drop-off	5	100	500	Extreme	Immediate response. Improve the road shoulder construction and increase the construction thickness of the shoulder parallel to the road pavement elevation.
III.	**Road equipment facilities**					
1.	Speed limit sign	5	100	500	Extreme	Immediate response. Install the maximum speed limit sign 40 km/h
2.	Curve direction sign	5	10	50	Low	Monitoring. Install the curve direction sign and guardrail along the curve.
3.	Warning sign	5	100	500	Extreme	Immediate response. Install the warning sign along with black spot location.
4.	Traffic signal sign	5	100	500	Extreme	Immediate response. Install the warning light sign.
5.	Road marking	1	10	10	Negligible	Passive response
6.	Road lightning	1	10	10	Negligible	Passive response

The analysis result of road infrastructure deficiency and RSA in Bojongsari Street as follows:

a. Road geometric infrastructure deficiencies. The stopping and passing sight distance is in the medium risk category with risk valuation value is 200 and passive response. Road lane width is in the negligible category. Road shoulder width in the fair risk category with the risk valuation value is 200. The recommendation to improve road safety is to increase the road shoulder to150 cm width (increased 50 cm) along Bojongsari Street.

b. Road pavement infrastructure deficiencies. The shoulder drop-off entering into the extreme risk category with the risk valuation is 500. The recommendation is to increase the construction thickness parallel to the pavement.

c. Road equipment facilities. Three parameters or criterias categorized in very dangerous or extreme risk i.e.: the warning sign, the speed limit and traffic signals signs. The recommendation to improve road safety is install the maximum speed limit sign of 40 km/h to guide the road user, install the warning sign along with black site in Bojongsari Street and install the traffic signal sign (install the warning light one phase or two phases). The road marking and road lightning entering in negligible risk category or passive response.

Sight distance is one of the important areas in highway geometric design [17]. The capacity of a two-lane, two-way road is increased if a large percentage of the roadway's length can be used for passing maneuvers [29-31]. Based on the research Yang *et al.* in 2015 [32] and Sugiyanto *et al.* [33-34], road users evaluate their travel cost in terms of travel time, crash risk and speeding. Traffic safety and security is very important in infrastructure development [35]. High speeds and speeding trigger crash frequency [36]. The other study, speeding increases the risk of crash occurrence and severity of traffic accident victims [37]. Installing the speed camera can decrease exceeding the speed limit because the driver views on the speed and enforcement [38]. In the other study by Illahi *et al.* in 2020 [39] that utilizes the Geographic Information System tools and extraction of a map delineating the high-risk priority zones. A majority of the drivers considered breaking the speed limit as a way to reduce their travel time [40].

4 Conclusion and further research

Based on the results of road infrastructure deficiency in Bojongsari Street, the following conclusion can be drawn: the highest speed of all vehicles was motorcycle at 73 km/h, the highest passing and stopping sight distance of all vehicles was motorcycle at 304.48 m and 64.67 m. The PCI for the longitudinal/transverse cracking conditions is 94 and for the lane/shoulder drop-off condition is 77.

The further research is focused on determining the maximum speed limit value of the vehicle. Vehicle speed limit is determined based on vehicle type and land use, such as educational areas, residential areas, industrial areas and central business district. The maximum speed limit values are differentiated for 2-wheeled vehicles and 4-wheeled vehicles or more.

Acknowledgments
"The authors fully acknowledged the Ministry of Education, Culture, Research and Technology Republic of Indonesia for the approved fund of Basic Research".

References
[1] Directorate General of Highways Republic of Indonesia 2006 *Kajian Kebutuhan Pelaksanaan Keselamatan Jalan di Indonesia* (Jakarta: Ministry of Public Works Republic of Indonesia).
[2] Sugiyanto G 2017a Marshall test characteristics of asphalt concrete mixture with scrapped tire rubber as a fine aggregate *J. Teknol.* **79**(2), 55-64. https://doi.org/10.11113/jt.v79.6965.
[3] Federal Highway Administration (FHA) 2018 *Road Safety Audit (RSA)*. https://safety.fhwa.dot.gov/rsa/.
[4] Sugiyanto G, Jajang and Santi M Y 2019a The impact of lowering speed limit on mobility and the environment *AIP Conf. Proc.* **2094**(1) 020019: 1-8. https://doi.org/10.1063/1.5097488.
[5] Sugiyanto G, Fadli A and Santi M Y 2020 Strategies for handling black spot area to increased road safety *ARPN J. Eng. Applied Sci.* **15**(9), 1101-1110. http://arpnjournals.org/jeas/research_papers/rp_2020/jeas_0520_8204.pdf.
[6] Sugiyanto G, Fadli A, Suciningtyas R, Indriyati E W and Santi M Y 2019b Road safety audit at black spot area (case study in Tlahab Lor, Karangreja, Purbalingga) *AIP Conf. Proc.* **2094**(1) 020020, 1-10. https://doi.org/10.1063/1.5097489.
[7] Sugiyanto G 2016 The impact of congestion pricing scheme on the generalized cost and speed of motorcycle to the City of Yogyakarta, Indonesia *J. Eng. Applied Sci.* **11**(8), 1740-1746. http://medwelljournals.com/ abstract/?doi=jeasci.2016.1740.1746.
[8] Sugiyanto G 2018 The effect of congestion pricing scheme on the generalized cost and speed of motorcycle Walailak J. Sci. & Tech. (WJST) **15**(1), 95-106. http://wjst.wu.ac.th/index.php/wjst/article/view/2347.
[9] Mohammad S, Siang T C, Osman S, Jamaluddin N Y, Alfu N A M and Huei L Y 2019 A proposed heutagogy framework for structural steel design in civil engineering curriculum. *Int. J. Emerg. Technol. Learn.* **14**(24), 96-105. https://doi.org/10.3991/ijet.v14i24.12091.
[10] Purbalingga Police Precinct 2019 Traffic Accident in Purbalingga in 2018.
[11] Shahin M Y 1994 Pavement Management for Airports, Roads, and Parking Lots (New York: Chapman and Hall).
[12] Sugiyanto G 2017b The cost of traffic accident and equivalent accident number in developing countries (case study in Indonesia) *ARPN J. Eng. Applied Sci.* **12**(2), 389-397. http://www.arpnjournals.org/jeas/research_papers/rp_2017/jeas_0117_5631.pdf.
[13] Sugiyanto G and Santi M Y 2017 Road traffic accident cost using human capital method (case study in Purbalingga, Central Java, Indonesia) *J. Teknol.* **79**(2), 107-116. https://doi.org/10.11113/jt.v79.5375.
[14] Directorate General of Highways Republic of Indonesia 2004 *Penanganan Lokasi Rawan Kecelakaan Lalu Lintas: Pd.T-09-2004-B* (Jakarta: Ministry of Public Works Republic of Indonesia).
[15] AASHTO 2018 A Policy on Geometric Design of Highways and Streets 7th Edition, The American Association of State Highway and Transportation Officials, Washington DC.
[16] Roes R P, Prassas E S and McShane W R 1998 *Traffic Engineering* (New Jersey: Prentice Hall)
[17] Abdulhafedh A 2020 Highway stopping sight distance, decision sight distance, and passing sight distance based on AASHTO models. O. A. Lib. J. **7**(3), 1-24. https://doi.org/10.4236/oalib.1106095.

[18] Berbel D C, Castro M, Medina L C and Maria S P G 2014 Sight distance studies on roads: influence of digital elevation models and roadside elements *Procedia Soc. Behav. Sci.* **160**, 449-458. https://doi.org/10.1016/j.sbspro.2014.12.157.

[19] Castro M, Iglesias L, Rodríguez-Solano R and Sánchez J A 2006 Geometric Modelling of Highways Using Global Positioning System (GPS) Data and Spline Approximation *Transp. Res. Part C Emerg. Technol.* **14**, 233-243. https://doi.org/10.1016/j.trc.2006.06.00.

[20] Ministry of Transportation Republic of Indonesia 2018 *Peraturan Menteri Perhubungan Republik Indonesia Nomor PM 67 Tahun 2018 tentang Perubahan atas Peraturan Menteri Perhubungan Nomor PM 34 Tahun 2014 tentang Marka Jalan* (Jakarta: Ministry of Transportation Republic of Indonesia).

[21] Ministry of Transportation Republic of Indonesia 2014 *Peraturan Menteri Perhubungan Republik Indonesia Nomor PM 13 Tahun 2014 tentang Rambu Lalu Lintas* (Jakarta: Ministry of Transportation).

[22] Directorate General of Highways Republic of Indonesia 1997 *Tata Cara Perencanaan Geometrik Jalan Antar Kota* (Jakarta: Ministry of Public Works Republic of Indonesia).

[23] Sugiyanto G and Malkhamah S 2018 Determining the maximum speed limit in urban road to increase traffic safety *J. Teknol.* **80**(5), 67-77. https://doi.org/10.11113/jt.v80.10489.

[24] Taylor M C, Lynam D A and Baruya A 2000 *The effects of drivers' speed on the frequency of road accidents*. Transport Research Laboratory Report 421, Road Safety Division, Department of the Environment, Transport and Regions.

[25] Woolley JE, Zito R, Dyson C B, Stazic B and Taylor M A P 2002 Impacts of lower speed limits in South Australia *IATSS Res.* **26**(2), 6-17. https://doi.org/10.1016/S0386-1112(14)60038-8.

[26] Qu X, Meng Q and Liu Z 2013 Estimation of number of fatalities caused by toxic gases due to fire in road tunnels *Accid. Anal. Prev.* **50**, 616-621. https://doi.org/10.1016/j.aap.2012.06.010

[27] Sugiyanto G, Fadli A and Santi M Y 2017 Identification of black spot and equivalent accident number using upper control limit method *ARPN J. Eng. Applied Sci.* **12**(2), 528-535. http://www.arpnjournals.org/jeas/research_papers/rp_2017/jeas_0117_5650.pdf.

[28] Ministry of Transportation Republic of Indonesia 2009 *Indonesian Law No. 22 of 2009 on Road Transport and Traffic*.

[29] Hassan Y, Easa S M and Abd El Halim A O 1996 Passing sight distance on two lane highways: review and revision *Transp. Res. Part A Policy Pract.* **30**, 453-467.https://doi.org/10.1016/0965-8564(95)00032-1

[30] Glennon J C 1998 New and improved model of passing sight distance on two-lane highways *Transp. Res. Rec.* **1195** TRB, National Research Council, Washington DC.

[31] Harwood D W, Gilmore D K, Richard K R, Dunn J M and Sun C 2008 Passing Sight Distance Criteria, NCHRP Report 605, *Transp. Res. Board.*

[32] Yang H, Ye H, Li X and Zhao B 2015 Speed limits, speed selection and network equilibrium. *Transp. Res. Part C Emerg. Technol.* **51**, 260-273. https://doi.org/10.1016/j.trc.2014.12.002.

[33] Sugiyanto G, Santosa P B, Wibowo A and Santi M Y 2015 Analysis of hub-and-spoke airport networks in Java Island, Indonesia based on cargo volume and freight ratio *Procedia Eng.*, **125**, 556-563. https://doi.org/10.1016/j.proeng.2015.11.061.

[34] Sugiyanto G, Santosa P B, Jajang, Fadli A and Santi M Y 2018 Evaluation of hub-spoke airport networks in Sumatra Island, Indonesia to increase efficiency of air transportation *MATEC Web Conf.* **195**(04009), pp. 1-9. https://doi.org/10.1051/matecconf/201819504009.

[35] Vedhathiri T 2018 Critical reviews of selected postgraduate programs in transportation engineering against the needs of infrastructure development J. Eng. Educ. Transform. **31**(4), 5-14. https://doi.org/10.16920/jeet/2018/v31i4/125198.

[36] Imprialou M I M, Quddus M, Pitfield D E and Lord D 2016 Re-visiting crash-speed relationships: A new perspective in crash modeling *Accid. Anal. Prev.* **86**(1), 173-185. https://doi.org/10.1016/j.aap.2015.10.001.

[37] Akpa N A E E, Booysen M J and Sinclair M 2016 A comparative evaluation of the impact of average speed enforcement (ASE) on passenger and minibus taxi vehicle drivers on the R61 in South Africa. *S Afr. Inst. Civ. Eng.* **58**(4), 2-10. https://doi.org/10.17159/2309-8775/2016/v58n4a1.

[38] Schechtman E, Bar-Gera H and Musicant O 2016 Driver views on speed and enforcement *Accid. Anal. Prev.* **89**, 9-21. https://doi.org/10.1016/j.aap.2015.12.028.

[39] Illahi U, Tabbussum R, Wafa B and Mohiuddin I 2020 Identification of high-risk road traffic crash zones for spatial allocation and distribution of proximate health-care facilities: an application of GIS tools *Int. J. Emerg. Technol.* **11**(4), 17-22.

[40] Dinh D D and Kubota H 2013 Drivers' perceptions regarding speeding and driving on urban residential streets with a 30 km/h speed limit *IATSS Res.* **37**, 30-38. https://doi.org/10.1016/j.iatssr.2012.12.001.

IOP Conf. Series: Earth and Environmental Science 1000 (2022) 012032 doi:10.1088/1755-1315/1000/1/012032

Design of climbing lane on provincial road study case in Magetan Districts East Java

V P Arpriyanita, T Tjahjono

Civil Engineering Department, Faculty of Engineering, University Indonesia, UI Depok's New Campus, West Java, 16424, Indonesia

E-mail: putrivenda03@gmail.com

Abstract. The roads from Magetan Districts (East Java) to Surakarta Districts (Central Java) have high climbing conditions. This is because the location is in the mountains. This study, discusses the design of then climbing lane on road Magetan Districts, precisely on Tawangmangu-Plaosan. A climbing lane is a path that is used as an additional route added to a single or multiple traffic lane which serves to increase capacity and/or safety due to a steep gradient. The method of collecting data is by conducting a field survey to review vehicle speed, vehicle volume, road dimensions, and elevation. The results of the study were used to determine the exact location of the climbing lane, to design the climbing lane using the England Standard concept combined with literature studies.

1. Preliminary

1.1. Background.

In an area of course have a plan in the provision of road facilities. Design geometrics is used to obtain safety and comfort results for road users. Topography is also an influencing factor in planning road design. Topography and physical conditions are the basis for planning where the embankment or excavation will be carried out according to the height elevation.

Based on the Regional Spatial Plan (RTRW) of East Java Province, the function plan Magetan Districts in the development of infrastructure is by improvement of potential access roads, development of irrigation, and improvement of ring roads.

In the 2018-2023 Strategic Plan (RENSTRA) of the Public Works and Arrangement Service the space for road network plans on provincial roads is in the form of road development primary collector of Maospati Road – Magetan – Cemoro Sewu. One of these road development is useful for facilitating connections between regions. Sarangan Highway to Tawangmangu-Plaosan Highway is used as an alternative road that connects the region of East Java with Central Java. Tawangmangu-Plaosan Highway is used by motorcycles, cars, heavy vehicles such as trucks and buses to shorten the distance to Central Java. Due to a large number of a vehicle that crossing, it is necessary to add a special lane for heavy vehicle were useful for reducing the level of lag due to decreased performance of heavy vehicle such as buses and trucks.

In the case study conducted, there are two places long the Magetan Districts road until Tawang Mangu Road (Central Java) is used. That road is on Sarangan Highway with a length of 3.4 km and Tawangmangu-Plaosan Highway with a length of 2.4 km.

1.2. Formulation of the problem.
1) Where is the right location in designing the climbing lane in Magetan Districts East Java, which considers several aspects such as traffic (speed, vehicle volume, and road geometry), environment, and ease of manufacture?
2) How is the engineering for the design of the climbing lane in Magetan Districts East Java?

1.3. Purpose of Writing Study
1) Determine the exact location of the climbing lane in Magetan Districts East Java.
2) Designing a climbing lane engineering in Magetan Districts East Java.

1.4. Theoretical Framework
A climbing lane is a special lane provided on the section of the road that exceeds the critical length of the incline to accommodate heavy vehicle when climbing (Guidelines for IKJ of the Directorate General of Highways, 2012).

1.4.1 Indonesian Standard Climbing Lane
The rules governing climbing lanes in Indonesia use the basic design from the Ministry of PUPR 2005. There are conditions used in the availability of climbing lanes including:
1) Climbing lanes must be provided on roads that have a large, continuous slope and a relatively dense traffic volume.
2) Placement of climbing lanes must be carried out with the following conditions:
   a) Provided on arterial or collector roads.
   b) If the critical length is exceeded, the road has a Design Daily Traffic Volume > 15%.
3) The width of the climbing lane is the same as the width of the planned lane.
4) The climbing lane starts 30 m from the beginning of the slope change with a 45 m incline and ends 50 m after the peak of the slope with a 45 m slope.
5) The minimum distance between 2 climbing lanes is 1.5 m.

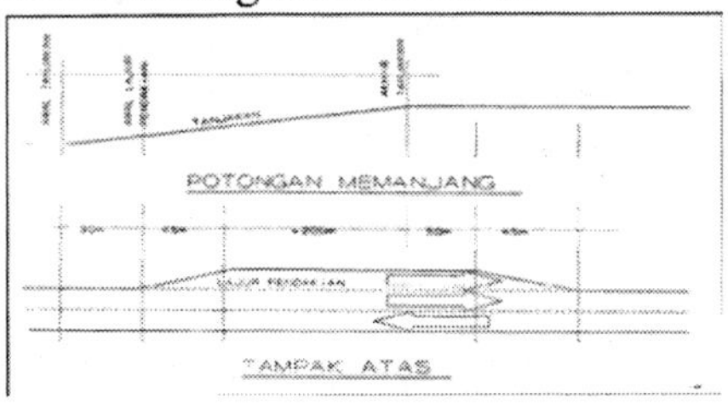

Figure 1. Typical Climbing Lane

1.4.2 American Association of Stae Highway and Transportation (AASHTO) Standard Climbing Lane
In AASHTO, the climbing lane is useful as a lane provider for vehicle moving uphill slowly so that other vehicle using the main lane experience delays. Separate dedicated climbing lanes for slower moving vehicle than adding additional lanes for mixed traffic the addition of climbing lanes also offsets the decrease in operating traffic levels caused by the effects of slope, traffic volume, and heavy vehicle passing by.
In the climbing lane, a 2+1 configuration can be used which can be applied to locations where environmental or fiscal constraints make the provincial of four-lane facilities impractical. The design of the 2+1 road configuration should generally not be considered if the current or projected flow rate exceeds 1200 vehicle/h in one direction of travel. Road 2+1 should only be used on flat or hilly terrain whereas on used terrain and isolated steep inclines it is usually more appropriate to introduce a

climbing lane on an increase. The transition tapers at each end of the auxiliary lane section shall be designed to promote efficient operation and reduce the occurrence of accidents.
In the design of the climbing lane using AASHTO, it can be seen that the length of the tapper used is between 15 m – 30 m. To be able to be more helpful in determining the length of the tapper, can see the table below for the length:

Table 1. Minimum Value of Taper

Metric		U.S. Customary	
Approach Speed (km/h)	Minimum Length (m)[a]	Approach Speed (mph)	Minimum Length (ft)[a]
30	60	20	200
40	60	30	200
50	65	40	300
60	85	45	350
70	105	50	450
80	135	55	550
90	170	60	600
100	185		

[a] Maximum length should be 185 m (600 ft) to avoid use of the turnout as a passing lane.

1.4.3 England Standard Climbing Lane

Because the climbing lane is not written explicitly in the Ministry of Public Works Standards, this study will use England Standards. The England Standard used is the Design Manual for Roads and Bridges CD109: Highway Link Design Revision 1 March 2020. For single trails, hiking trails may be considered if they can be justified on hills with a gradient of more than 2% and longer than 500 m.
The layout at the beginning of the climbing lane: the full width of the climbing lane must be provided at a point 100 m uphill from the 2% curve, and preceded by a taper minimum of 100 m. alignment at the start of the climbing lane will encourage the driver to follow the close lane unless ready. Tapers should provide smooth transitions, taking advantage of the curvature of the road to building up extra width, if possible.
The layout at the end of the trail: the full width of the trail must be maintained up or down the slope to point F, 220 m beyond the end of 2% of the top curve. Once at point F a taper between a minimum of 100 m is provided to narrow the width of the traffic lane from the offside thus eliminating the extra width that allows for the provision of climbing lanes.

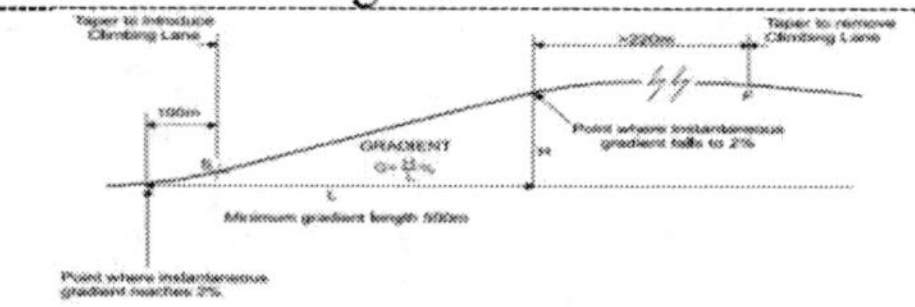

Figure 2. The Layout of Extended Climbing Lane

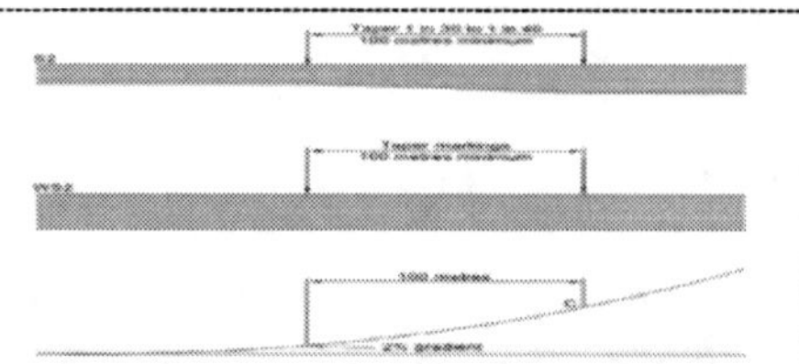

Figure 3. The Layout at the Start of Climbing Lane

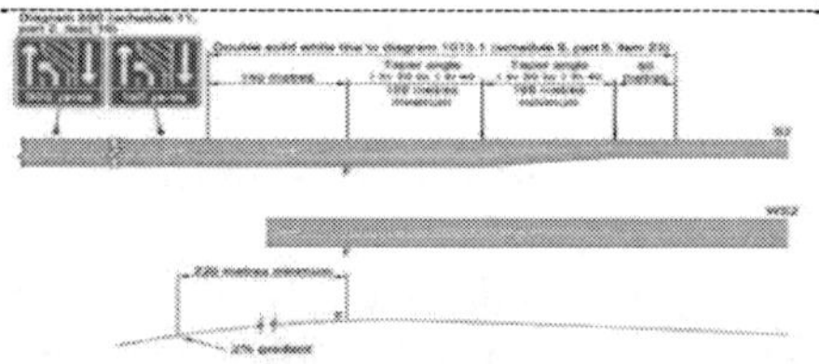

Figure 4. The Layout at the End of Climbing Lane

1.4.4 Traffic Simulation Software PTV Vissim

Vissim is software that is used to analyze detailed and detailed traffic simulations. Vissim is an output software PTV from Germany. The abbreviation for Vissim is Verkehr In Staten Simulations Model. The vissim software contains several features including:

1) A simple comparison of alternative designs of signs, markings, and intersection control equipment.

2) Operational and capacity analysis in a complex situation (such as terminals and stations).
3) Evaluation and optimization of traffic operation (actual traffic coordinates and signals).
4) Evaluation and set according to standard.
5) Pedestrian route.

2. Study Methodology

The writing system of this study refers to the rules and Indonesia Standard applicable in Indonesia. In addition, the design of the climbing lane also uses design standards from England with the combination of literary studies as a reference for the design of the climbing lane on the Magetan Districts road East Java. This study was conducted in Magetan District. In the study conducted in designing climbing lanes, researchers used a study method that was useful as a workflow in this research. The use of the research method is so that the writing of the study can take place properly and efficiently following the planned planning.

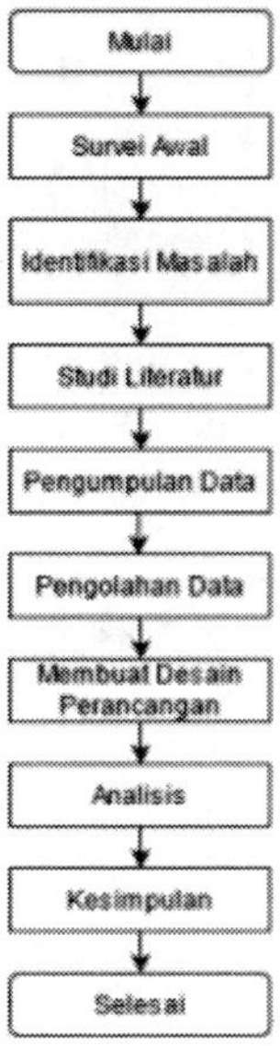

Figure 5. Systematic Flow Chart of Writing Studies

2.1. Data Obtained

In data collection, it will be divided for each activity include:

1) Preliminary survey
    - Determine the location of the climbing lane
    - Existing road conditions
    - Speed of heavy vehicle such as trucks and buses
    - The volume of vehicle that pass through the road segment
    - Road geometry
    - Number of accidents or incidents
2) Doing the design
    - Data obtained from the initial survey
    - Consideration in several aspects including traffic (speed, vehicle volume, and road geometry), environment, and ease of making factors included in road safety.

3. Discussion

3.1. Introduction

This chapter will discuss the processes in data collection and processing that took place during the research study. The first step is to conduct an initial site survey to determine the design. After that, identify the problem to find out the problems that exist in the research location. After that obtaining the data will be used as a basis for calculations. Data processing that is carried out after data collection is useful as input data in the modeling. Next, you can do the design on the climbing lane based on the standards used.

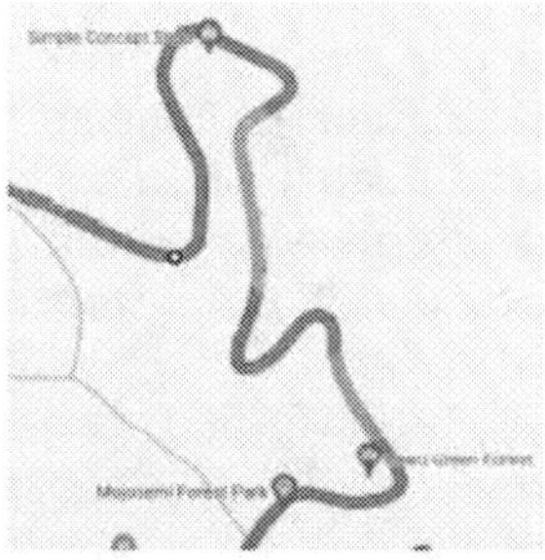

Figure 6. Location for Climbing Lane

3.2. Discussion

In the selected area there is a blue color change that then turns orange which means the influence of existing traffic conditions. So from the map, it can be seen that there is congestion at the location. Therefore, the author chose the location is Tawangmangu-Plaosan Roads which has congestion conditions.

In the existing condition of the road, the location survey is obtained for the number of vehicle/hour, 282 vehicle/h for the east (left lane), and 275 vehicle/h for the west (west lane) with a field speed of 19 km/h. when modeling on vissim can be seen that the volume accommodated is 284 vehicle/h with the speed of 30 km/h.

In the modeling software using Indonesian Standards, the design is carried out with a road length of 2061.4 m with a length of 272.8 m for the initial slope change. Then for the transition/tapper length, which is 45.4 m. for the length of the climbing lane itself has a length of 1521 m, and end at s length of 55.1 m. after that there is a transition lane/final tapper which has a length of 55.9 m. after the final tapper, the vehicle can enter the main lane. For the movement of vehicle, buses, and trucks moving to the left of the road. Then at the end of the tapper, the bus and truck must move to the right to enter the main lane. The volume that can be accommodated on roads with Indonesian Standards is 293 vehicle/h where for speed is 36 km/h.

Figure 7. Simulation-based on Indonesian Standard

In the design of the climbing lane using AASHTO, the length of the road is 2068.3 m with a tapper length of 34 m. then for the length of the climbing lane using a length of 1537 m. after passing the climbing lane before returning to the normal lane, the climbing lane stops at a suffix length of 50.4 m before the final tapper. The final tapper has a length of 34.1 m before entering the main lane so that the vehicle can be prepared to move to the right. For the movement of vehicle, buses, and trucks moving to the left of the road. Then at the end of the tapper, the bus and truck must move to the right to enter the main lane. The volume that can be accommodated on roads with Indonesian Standards is 291 vehicle/h where for speed is 36 km/h.

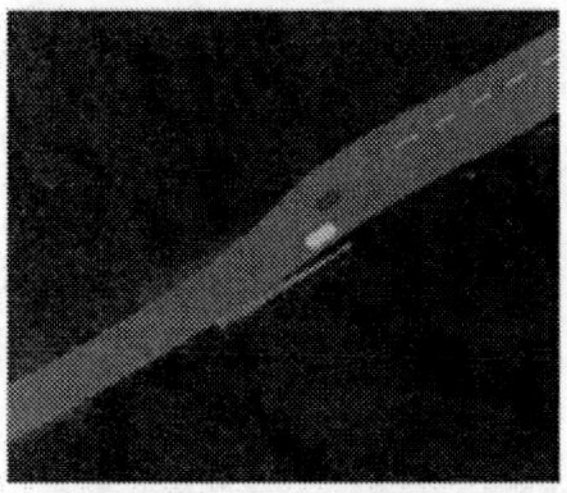

Figure 8. Simulation-based on AASHTO

In the design of the climbing lane using British Standards, the length of the road is 2091.4 m with the length before the tapper is 317.4 m the tapper length used is 101.4 m, then for the length of the climbing lane is 1180 m. the additional length before entering the tapper is 241 m. then for the final tapper, which has a length of 101.3 m. The length of the road where the vehicle has not been able to overtake is 100.5 m. the results of running can be seen in the actual volume that can be accommodated from the design of the climbing lane design. Then the volume of vehicle that can pass is obtained, which is 303 vehicle/h. with a speed of 39 km/h.

In the design of the climbing lane with British Standards with tappers length of 101.4 m and 100.5 m, vehicle can to enter the climbing lane get a longer time to enter the main lane. By providing a climbing lane, apart from providing a special lane for heavy vehicle, it can also be used for overtaking. In environmental conditions such as in mountainous terrain, climbing lanes can also be used to help light vehicle such as cars or other vehicle to overtake heavy vehicle such as trucks and buses.

In British Standards the movement of heavy vehicle such as trucks and buses remains on the left and does not move. In British Standards, the movement to the right is vehicle other than trucks and buses. In the movement enters the initial tapper, which has a gradient value of 2.204% where this value is still included in the existing regulations.

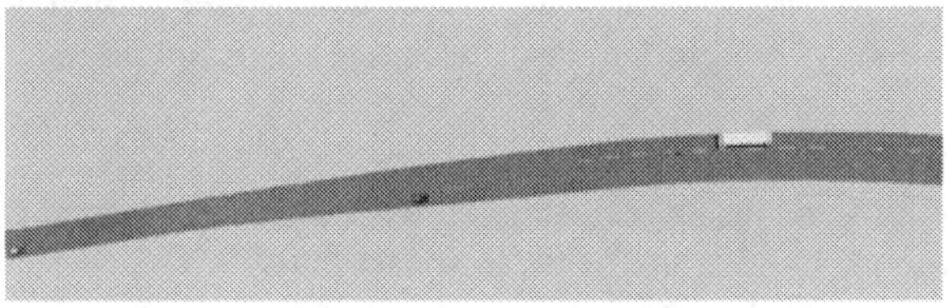

Figure 9. Simulation-based on British Standard

While to show the elevation difference, the author uses drawing software in the form of AutoCAD to show the elevation difference. Here's a picture of the design

Figure 10. The Layout of the Climbing Lane

In addition, there is also a scheme for how the vehicle moves when passing the climbing lane. Below is an overview of the movement of the vehicle. In this schematic image, it is explained that for vehicle traveling from east to west or from East Java to Central Java there is a tapper as a vehicle transition road so that vehicle can pass or overtake vehicle on the left. Then when you enter the climbing lane, it is divided into 3 lanes where 2 left lanes go to Central Java and 1 lane goes to East Java.

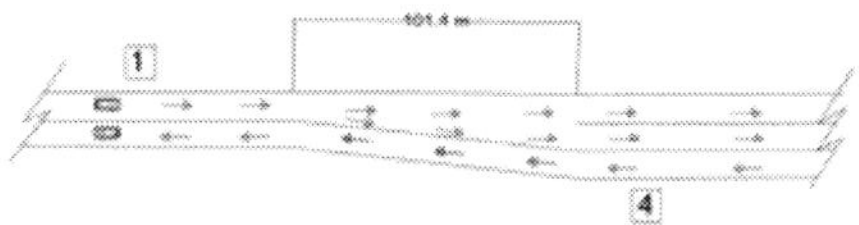

Figure 11. Movement scheme at the start

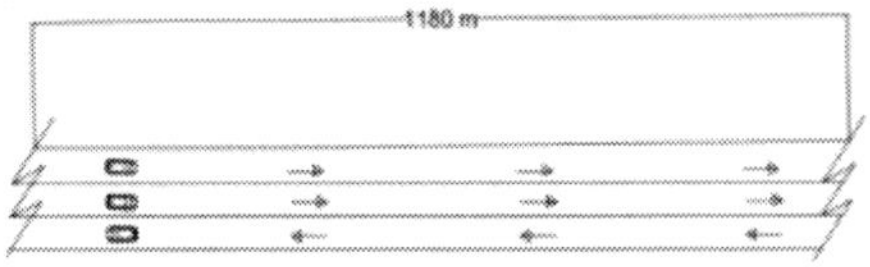

Figure 12. Movement scheme in the climbing lane

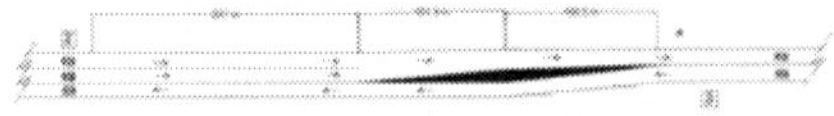

Figure 13. Movement scheme at the end

Then, for the GEH validation test value at AASHTO, which is 0.53, Indonesian Standard is 0.65 and British Standard is 1.1, this value is below the GEH value of 5, then the conditions are met and there are no problems.

4. Conclusions and Suggestions

4.1. Conclusions

Based on the results of the design of the climbing lane on the provincial road, the case study in Magetan Districts, East Java. However, to reduce the risk of danger to road users, additional climbing lanes can also be used.

1) Location for climbing lane
After surveying in two locations then the author has chosen the location in the design of the climbing lane. In selecting the location, the author also considers several aspects such as the environment, vehicle volume, vehicle speed, geometric, and ease of making. Then the author determines the location according to the influencing aspect, on Tawangmangu-Plaosan Road with a climbing lane length of 1180 m. the Tawangmangu-Plaosan Road has a shoulder width of between 0.4 m to 1.2 m, has a lane width of 3.5 m each, a slope of 2.204%, for an altitude between 1527-1676 MASL, is located far from residential areas, there are many tourist attractions, and many heavy vehicle (trucks, buses, etc) pass as the access road to Surakarta, Central Java.
2) Design of the climbing lane
The design goes through various stages in the study, the data obtained are in the form of existing conditions, road geometric conditions, vehicle speeds, and traffic that is interconnected, so a climbing lane plan design will be obtained following British Standards with a combination of rules and standards and applicable climbing lanes in Indonesia in ensuring the safety and comfort of road users. Based on the three existing standards, Indonesian Standards, AASHTO, and British Standard, several comparisons were obtained, including speed and volume.
From each comparison these results are obtained, among others are:

Table 2. Result of the design planning based on the standard

	Indonesian Standard	AASHTO	British Standard
Vol (vehicle/h)	293	291	303
Speed (km/h)	36	36	39

From the results of the same input volume in the software, the best value is using the British Standard. With a movement where vehicle that have low speeds move on the left or remain in the main lane and light vehicle moving on the right make congestion levels decrease problems with traffic conditions in the area.

4.2. Suggestions

Based on the design that has been made regarding the climbing lane on the Tawangmangu-Plaosam Road, there are suggestions including:

1) Based on the design that has been made, the author suggests that in the construction of the climbing lane, British Standards can be used but can still be combined with Indonesian Standards. Because of the design on British Standards, it can help in increasing the volume of passing vehicle. Then, for the movement of heavy vehicle such as buses and trucks, the congestion level is also lower and can even help in reducing congestion, compared to the current condition where there is no climbing lane, the vehicle that will overtake have difficulty and have to adjust their speed to the vehicle in front of them. Then this will be very dangerous.
2) It is necessary to add special regulations regarding traffic signs and road markings for climbing lanes. So that it can provide convenience in organizing and simplifying use for road users.

Acknowledgement
This study was supported by PUTI grant number NKB-3663/UN2.RST/HKP.05.00/2020 from Universitas Indonesia.

References

AASHTO. (2001).

AASHTO. (2004).

AASHTO. (2011). A Policy On Geometric Design of Highway and Streets. 444 North Capitol Street, NW, Suite 249.

Almatrisa Mustikha Hutami. (2017). Analisa Kinerja Lajur Pendakian Ditinjau Berdasarkan Kecepatan Kendaraan dan Penggunaan Lajur Pendakian yang Melintas pada Tol Cipularang (Cikampek-Purwakarta-Padalarang) KM 97.

Altimeter. (2021). Alat Pengukur Altimeter.

AutoCAD. (2021). AutoCAD Desain Lajur Pendakian. Depok.

BAPPENAS. (2005). BAB I Pendahuluan-Perpustakaan BAPPENAS. Retrieved from Databoks: http://perpustakaan.bappenas.go.id/lontar/file?file=digital/98517-[_Konten_]- c6577.pdf

Bina Marga. (1997). Jalan No. 038/TBM/1997. In Tata Cara Perencanaan Geometriksk Jalan Antar Kota. Jakarta: Dinas PUPR.

BPS Kabupaten Magetan. (2015, November 25). Letak dan Kondisi Geografis Kabupaten Magetan. Retrieved from Databoks: https://magetankab.bps.go.id/statictable/2015/11/25/6/letak-dan-kondisi-geografis-kabupaten-magetan.html

BPS Kabupaten Magetan. (2019). Statistik Daerah Kabupaten Magetan 2019. Magetan: Badan Pusat Statistik Kabupaten Magetan. Retrieved Desember 28, 2020, from https://magetankab.bps.go.id/publication/download.html?nrbvfeve=YzljM2JkYWY1Mj RiYjg1NWU2MDVlYjNh&xzmn=aHR0cHM6Ly9tYWdldGFua2FiLmJwcy5nby5pZC9wdWJ saWNhdGlvbi8yMDE5LzEyLzA0L2M5YzNiZGFmNTI0YmI4NTVlNjA1ZWIzYS9zdGF0aXN0 aWstZGFlcmFoLWthYnVwYXRlbi1tYWdldGFuLTIwM

BPS Kabupaten Magetan. (2020, Mei 5). Badan Pusat Statistik Kabupaten Magetan Jumlah Kendaraan Bermotor Menurut Jenis Kendaraan di Kabupaten Magetan, 2017-2019. Retrieved from Databoks: https://magetankab.bps.go.id/statictable/2020/05/05/570/jumlah-kendaraanbermotor-menurut-jenis-kendaraan-di-kabupaten-magetan-unit-2017-2019.html

Departemen Permukiman dan Prasarana Wilayah. (2004). Pedoman Konstruksi dan Bangunan. Penentuan Klasifikasi Fungsi Jalan di Kawasan Perkotaan, Pd T-18-2004-B, 8.

Dinas PU. (2009). Standar Konstruksi dan Bangunan No. 007/BM/2009. Retrieved from Geometriks Jalan Bebas Hambatan Untuk Jalan Tol No. 007/BM/2009: https://www.slideshare.net/faisal_fafa/standard-geometriksk-jalan-tol

Dirjen Bina Marga. (1997). Tata Cara Perencanaan Geometriksk Antar Kota. Jakarta: Direktorat Jenderal Bina Marga.

Dokumentasi Penulis. (2021). Hasil Dokumentasi Penulis.

Erwin Kusnandar. (2009). Jurnal Jalan dan Jembatan. Pengkinian Manual Kapasitas Jalan Indonesia 1997, 11. Google Earth. (2021).

Google Earth Kabupaten Magetan. Retrieved from https://earth.google.com/web/search/jalan+tol+magetan/@-7.63097608,111.37035966,217.84956096a,193.98915934d,35y,215.4139212h,0t,0r/data=CigiJgokCShIV2tRaTRAESdIV2tRaTTAGbhSNqE0J0RAIT5pD3As207A Google Maps. (2021).

Google Maps Kabupaten Magetan Jawa Timur. Retrieved from https://www.google.com/maps/search/sdn+sukomoro+1+magetan/@- 7.6310015,111.3696318,17.75z

Hakiim Lazuardi. (2010). Pedoman Penggunaan dan Pengenalan Program PTV Vissim. PTV Vissim the Mind of Movement, 21-41.

Haryadi etc al. (2017). Modul Vissim UMY 2017. Retrieved from Modul Pembelajaran Traffic Micro-Simulation Program PTV.Vissim 9: https://www.scribd.com/document/363199498/Modul-Vissim-UMY-2017

Highway England. (2020). Design Manual For Roads And Bridges. CD 109 Highway Link Design Design Manual For Roads And Bridges Revision 1, 105.

Karakteristik Mikro Lalu Lintas. (2010). 21 BAB III Landasan Teori 3.1 Karakteristik Mikro Lalu Lintas. BAB III Landasan Teori, 21.

Kementerian PUPR. (2005). Pelatihan Road Design Engineer (Ahli Teknik Desain Jalan). Modil RDE - 10 : Perencanaan Geometriksk Jalan.

Kementerian PUPR. (2017). Perencanaan Geometriksk Jalan Tingkat Dasar. In Modul 3 Dasar-Dasar Perencanaan Geometriksk Ruas Jalan. Bandung: PUSDIKLAT Jalan, Perumahan, Permukiman, dan Pengembangan Infrastruktur Wilayah.

L. Yang, J.Zheng, Y.Cheng et al. (2019). An Asymmetric Cellular Automata Model For Heterogeneous Traffic Flow On Freeways With A Climbing Lane. Physica A: Statistical Mechanics and Its Applications, 122277. Retrieved from https://doi.org/10.1016/j.physa.2019.122277

Menteri Pekerjaan Umum. (2011). Peraturan Menteri Pekerjaan Umum No. 19/PRT/M/2011. Peraturan Menteri Pekerjaan Umum No. 19/PRT/M/2011 tentang Persyaratan Teknis Jalan dan Kriteria Perencanaan Teknis Jalan.

Pedoman IKJ Direktorat Jenderal Bina Marga. (2012). Panduan Teknis I Rekayasa Keselamatan Jalan. Panduan Teknis I Rekayasa Keselamatan Jalan.

Pemerintah Pusat. (2004). Undang-undang (UU) tentang Jalan. UU RI No.38 Tahun 2004 tentang

Jalan. Pengolahan Penulis. (2021).

Peraturan Menteri. (2018). Perubahan Atas Peraturan Menteri Perhubungan Nomor PM 34 Tahun 2014 tentang Marka Jalan. Jakarta. 56 Universitas Indonesia

PTV Vissim. (2021). State of the Art Traffic Simulation. Jerman. RSNI. (2004).

RSNI Standar Nasional Indonesia T-14-2004. Badan Standardisasi Nasional.

S.Choi, J.Suh, H.Yeo. (2017). Microscopic Analysis of Climbing Lane Performance at Freeway Uphill Section. Transportation Research Procedia, 98-109. Retrieved from http://dx.doi.org/10.1016/j.trpro.2017.03.081

Silvia Sukirman. (1999). Retrieved from Dasar-dasar Perencanaan Geometriksk Jalan: https://www.academia.edu/37821794/Dasar_Dasar_Perencanaan_Geometriksk_Jalan_Silvia_Sukirman_

Survei Lapangan Penulis. (2021). Survei Lapangan Data Penunjang. Magetan.

Unit Laka Lantas Kabupaten Magetan. (2020). Laporan Kecelakaan atau Insiden Selama Bulan Januari-Desember 2020. Magetan: Satuan Lalu Lintas Kabupaten Magetan.

V.Valencia-Alaix, A.Garcia. (2020). Operational Evaluation of Climbing Lanes On Steep Grades and Heavy Trucks. Transportation Research Procedia, 840-849.

V. P. Arpriyanita, T. Tjahjono. (2021). Perancangan Lajur Pendakian di Jalan Provinsi Studi Kasus di Kabupaten Magetan Jawa Timur.

AUTHOR INDEX